THE THEORY OF GROUPS:

An Introduction

THIS BOOK IS PART OF THE
ALLYN AND BACON SERIES IN ADVANCED MATHEMATICS
CONSULTING EDITOR: IRVING KAPLANSKY,
UNIVERSITY OF CHICAGO

JOSEPH J. ROTMAN

University of Illinois

Boston

THE THEORY OF GROUPS

An Introduction

Allyn and Bacon, Inc.

First printing . . . March 1965
Second printing . . . August 1966

QA
171
R67

לזכרר נצח אבי מורי הנכבד

אליהו ב״ר יוסף יונה הלוי

PREFACE

Quand j'ai voulu me restreindre, je suis tombé dans l'obscurité; j'ai préféré passer pour un peu bavard.

H. Poincaré, *Analysis situs,* Journal de l'Ecole Polytechnique, 1895, pp. 1–121.

This text is designed for the student who wants to learn the basic ideas and techniques of the theory of groups. We assume that the reader knows the rudiments of modern algebra, by which we mean that matrices and finite-dimensional vector spaces are friends, while groups, rings, fields, and homomorphisms are only acquaintances. A familiarity with elementary set theory is also assumed, but some appendices are at the back of the book so that the reader may see whether my notation is the same as his.

No claims are made that this is an encyclopedia of elementary group theory. In fact, many important topics, e.g., representation theory, transfer, k-ply transitivity, and topological groups, are not treated. The omission of representation theory, an indispensable tool of any group theorist, may seem to be a particularly serious omission, but I feel that a considerable amount of ring theory must be developed to present this subject properly, and limitations of space prevent such a development here. Moreover, an excellent exposition of representation theory already exists in *Representation Theory of Finite Groups and Associative Algebras*, by C. Curtis and I. Reiner (Wiley, 1962).

The table of contents gives an outline of what has not been omitted. Here are some comments on unusual aspects of each chapter. 1. *Groups and Homomorphisms;* 2. *The Isomorphism Theorems.* Since I believe that categories are useful, I have tried to emphasize homomorphisms as well as groups whenever reasonable. 3. *Permutation Groups.* For reasons given in the text, the simplicity of A_n is proved by referring everything to A_6. 4. *Direct Products.* The basis theorem for finite abelian groups is proved by vector space techniques, and the fundamental theorem is proved by adapting the proof of Ulm's theorem to the finite case. These two proofs complement each other, for the Ulm invariants are dimensions of certain vector spaces associated to a primary abelian group. 5. *The Sylow Theorems.* Sylow subgroups are defined as maximal p-subgroups, so that existence and imbedding are immediate consequences of the definition. 6. *Normal and Subnormal Series.* A brief account of some Galois theory over subfields of the complex numbers is included. A second deviation is that a series is called *normal* if its terms are normal subgroups, *subnormal* if its terms are subnormal subgroups. 7. *Extensions.* S. MacLane's "logarithmic" notation is used: If $G/K \approx Q$, G and K are written additively and Q is written multiplicatively. 8. *Some Simple Groups.* After proving the simplicity of the PSL, two simple, nonisomorphic groups of the same order are exhibited. 9. *Infinite Abelian Groups.* Since injectivity is more intuitive than projectivity, divisible groups are treated before free abelian groups. 10. *Homological Algebra.* The basic properties of Ext_Z are proved by considering factor sets and classes of short exact sequences under Baer sum. 11. *Free Groups and Free Products.* The notion of generators and relations motivates the definition of a free group as a solution to a universal mapping problem. A. J. Weir's proof of the Nielsen-Schreier theorem is given, for it relies on a minimum of cancellation arguments. 12. *The Word Problem.* This chapter is the most unusual section in the book. Aside from the customary license given to an author for his closing chapter, there are several reasons for discussing the word problem: It is an interesting problem related to groups; the recent solution of W. W. Boone and J. L. Britton has a group-theoretical flavor; no other account exists outside the journals.

I am fortunate in having attended lectures on group theory given by I. Kaplansky, S. MacLane, and M. Suzuki. Their influence is evident throughout in many elegant ideas and proofs. I am grateful to W. W. Boone and J. L. Britton for their kind assistance with the material on the word problem. C. R. B. Wright read my original manuscript and made many valuable comments. I wish to thank also my colleagues at the University of Illinois, especially G. Brown, J. Eagon, and H. Paley, for their helpful suggestions. Finally, I thank the National Science Foundation who supported a part of this work.

JOSEPH J. ROTMAN

Urbana, Illinois

CONTENTS

TO THE READER

Exercises in a text generally have two functions: to reinforce the reader's grasp of the material; to provide puzzles whose solution gives a certain pleasure. In this text, the exercises have a third function: to enable the reader to discover important facts, examples, and counterexamples. The serious reader should attempt the exercises as they arise (many are not difficult), for subsequent proofs often depend on them. An asterisk before an exercise, however, indicates that that exercise is not essential to this exposition, but it gives no information about the relative difficulty of the exercise.

Chapter 1

Groups and Homomorphisms

Our study of groups begins with the consideration of a rather general setting.

Definition   If G is a nonempty set, a **binary operation** on G is a function $\mu: G \times G \to G$.

A binary operation assigns to each ordered pair a, b of elements of G a third element $\mu(a,b)$ of G. In practice, μ is thought of as a "multiplication" of elements of G, and instead of $\mu(a,b)$, more suggestive notations used are ab, $a + b$, $a \circ b$, and $a * b$. In this chapter, we shall use the latter notation.

Two remarks must be made here. First, it is quite possible that $a * b$ and $b * a$ are distinct elements of G. Second, the law of substitution—if $a = a'$ and $b = b'$, then $a * b = a' * b'$—is just the statement that μ is a well defined (i.e., single-valued) function.

One cannot develop a theory in this rarefied atmosphere; conditions on the binary operation are needed in order to obtain interesting results. If we are given elements a_1, a_2, a_3 of G (not necessarily distinct), the notation $a_1 * a_2 * a_3$ is ambiguous. Since one can $*$ only two elements of G at a time, there is a choice: form $a_1 * a_2$ first, and now $*$ this new element of G with a_3 to get $(a_1 * a_2) * a_3$; or form $a_1 * (a_2 * a_3)$. In general, these two elements are not the same. For example, if G is the set of all integers (positive, negative, and zero) and if the binary operation is subtraction, i.e., $a * b = a - b$, then almost any choice of integers a, b, c yields an example in which $(a - b) - c \neq a - (b - c)$.

3

Definition   A binary operation $*$ on G is **associative** in case

$$(a * b) * c = a * (b * c)$$

for every three elements a, b, c of G.

Associativity allows one to multiply every ordered triple of elements of G unambiguously; parentheses are unnecessary, and there is no confusion in writing $a * b * c$. If we are confronted by four elements of G or, more generally, by a finite number of elements of G, must we postulate more intricate associativity axioms in order to do without parentheses?

THEOREM 1.1   Let $*$ be an associative binary operation on G. Any two ways of multiplying the elements a_1, a_2, $\cdots$, a_n of G in this order yield the same element of G.

Proof   We prove the theorem by induction on n, where $n \geq 3$. If $n = 3$, the theorem is true, for we are assuming that $*$ is associative.

Let $n > 3$. How does one multiply n elements? Since a binary operation allows multiplication of only two elements at a time, one first chooses a pair of adjacent a's and multiplies them; then, either he multiplies this new element by an a adjacent to it or he chooses two other adjacent a's and multiplies them. With each choice, the total number of factors decreases by one, so that eventually one is left with only two factors. Suppose now that

$$X = (a_1 * \cdots * a_i) * (a_{i+1} * \cdots * a_n)$$

and

$$Y = (a_1 * \cdots * a_j) * (a_{j+1} * \cdots * a_n)$$

are elements of G obtained by two people multiplying the a together, each having made his own choices. The parentheses indicate the final multiplication each has just performed. For notational convenience, we assume that $i \leq j$. Since each of the final factors in X and in Y contains less than n of the a, the inductive hypothesis allows us to rearrange parentheses in them. Therefore, we may assume $i < j$ (or we are done) and write

$$X = (a_1 * \cdots * a_i) * ([a_{i+1} * \cdots * a_j] * [a_{j+1} * \cdots * a_n])$$

and

$$Y = ([a_1 * \cdots * a_i] * [a_{i+1} * \cdots * a_j]) * (a_{j+1} * \cdots * a_n).$$

If we denote $a_1 * \cdots * a_i$ by A, $a_{i+1} * \cdots * a_j$ by B, and $a_{j+1} * \cdots * a_n$ by C, then $X = A * (B * C)$ and $Y = (A * B) * C$. Since A, B, and C are unambiguously defined, by induction, and since $*$ is associative, we have $X = Y$, as we wished. ∎

As a result of this theorem, the notation $a_1 * a_2 * \cdots * a_n$ is unambiguous if $*$ is an associative multiplication.

Definition   A **semigroup** is a set G with an associative binary operation.

A semigroup is a pair, but we shall usually say that G is a semigroup and tacitly assume that $*$ is known. The reader must realize, however, that there are many possible operations on a set G that make it a semigroup. For example, the set of positive integers is a semigroup under either of the binary operations of ordinary addition or ordinary multiplication.

Notation   Let G be a semigroup and let $a \in G$. Let $a^1 = a$; if $n > 1$, then $a^n = a^{n-1} * a$.

COROLLARY 1.2   Let G be a semigroup and let $a \in G$. If m and n are positive integers, $a^m * a^n = a^{m+n}$.

Proof   Both elements arise from a product of $m + n$ factors equal to a; they differ only in the arrangement of parentheses. ∎

The most important semigroups are groups.

Definition   A **group** is a semigroup G such that:

(i)   There is an element e in G with

$$e * a = a \quad \text{for all } a \in G.$$

(ii)   For every $a \in G$, there is a b in G with

$$b * a = e.$$

(Note that the element e in (ii) is the same e appearing in (i).)

LEMMA 1.3   If G is a group and $a \in G$, then $a * a = a$ implies $a = e$.

Proof   There is an element $b \in G$ with $b * a = e$. Now

$$b * (a * a) = b * a = e.$$

On the other hand,

$$(b * a) * a = e * a = a.$$

Therefore, $a = e$. ∎

THEOREM 1.4   In a group G, $a * e = a$ for all $a \in G$, and if $b * a = e$, then $a * b = e$. Furthermore, there is only one element e satisfying (i), and given any $a \in G$, there is only one $b \in G$ satisfying (ii).

Proof   We first show that in this particular case, the order in which we multiply makes no difference.

Suppose $b * a = e$. Then $(a * b) * (a * b) = a * (b * a) * b = a * (e * b) = a * b$. By Lemma 1.3, $a * b = e$.

If $a \in G$, then $e * a = a$. Choose b with $b * a = e$. Then $a * e = a * (b * a) = (a * b) * a = e * a = a$, by our calculation above. Therefore $a * e = a$.

We now prove the uniqueness assertions. Suppose $e_0 * a = a$ for all $a \in G$; in particular, $e_0 * e_0 = e_0$. By the lemma, $e_0 = e$.

Finally, suppose $b * a = e$ and $c * a = e$. Then $a * b = e$ and $c = c * e = c * (a * b) = (c * a) * b = e * b = b$. ∎

As a result of the uniqueness assertions of the theorem, we may now give names to e and to b. We call e the **identity** of G, and if $b * a = e$, we call b the **inverse** of a and denote it a^{-1}.

COROLLARY 1.5   If G is a group and $a \in G$, then

$$(a^{-1})^{-1} = a.$$

Proof $(a^{-1})^{-1}$ is that element $b \in G$ such that $b * a^{-1} = e$. But we have just seen that $a * a^{-1} = e$, so that the uniqueness of the inverse implies that $b = a$. ∎

Definition   Let G be a group and $a \in G$. We define the **powers** of a as follows: If n is a positive integer, then a^n has been described above; define $a^0 = e$; finally, define a^{-n} as $(a^{-1})^n$.

Exercises   1.1   If G is a group and $a, b \in G$, then

$$(a * b)^{-1} = b^{-1} * a^{-1}.$$

1.2   Let G be a group, $a \in G$, and m, n, k any (possibly negative) integers. The following formulas hold:

$$a^m * a^n = a^{m+n};$$
$$(a^m)^n = a^{mn};$$
$$(a^{m+n})^k = a^{mk+nk}.$$

1.3   In a group G, $a * x = b$ and $y * a = b$ each has a unique solution in G, where a and b are given elements of G.

1.4   A semigroup G in which the equations $a * x = b$ and $y * a = b$ have solutions for every a and b in G is a group.

1.5   Let G be a group and let $a \in G$. Define a function $T_a: G \to G$ by $T_a(x) = a * x$; (T_a is called **left translation** by a). Prove that T_a is a one-to-one correspondence.

1.6   Let Z denote the additive group of integers. (We shall adhere to this notation from now on.) What is the identity of Z? If $a \in Z$, what is its inverse? State Corollary 1.5 for Z.

1.7   Let G denote the multiplicative group of positive rationals. What is the identity of G? If $a \in G$, what is its inverse?

1.8   Let n be a positive integer, and let G be the multiplicative group of all nth roots of unity, i.e., all complex numbers of the form $e^{(2\pi i k)/n}$, where $k \in Z$. What is the identity of G? If $a \in G$, what is its inverse? How many elements does G have?

1.9   Let M be the multiplicative group of all 2×2 nonsingular matrices with rational entries. What is the identity of M? If $a \in M$, what is its inverse? Exhibit elements a and b in M such that $a * b \neq b * a$.

1.10   Prove that the following four matrices form a multiplicative group:

$$\begin{bmatrix} 1 & 0 \\ 0 & 1 \end{bmatrix}, \begin{bmatrix} -1 & 0 \\ 0 & 1 \end{bmatrix}, \begin{bmatrix} 1 & 0 \\ 0 & -1 \end{bmatrix}, \begin{bmatrix} -1 & 0 \\ 0 & -1 \end{bmatrix}.$$

1.11   Let X be a nonempty set, and let G be the set of all one-to-one correspondences of X onto itself. If f and g are in G, define $f * g$ to be the composite of f and g:

$$(f * g)(x) = f(g(x)) \qquad \text{for every } x \in X.$$

Prove that G is a group.

When does one "know" a group G? One answer (but not the only answer, as we shall see later) is that all the elements of G are known and all possible products can be computed. This answer can be made to look more sophisticated in the special case when G is finite. Let $a_1, a_2, \cdots, a_n$ be a list with no repetitions of all the elements in G. A **multiplication table** of G is the $n \times n$ matrix whose ijth entry is $a_i * a_j$:

G	a_1	a_2		a_n
a_1	$a_1 * a_1$	$a_1 * a_2$	$\cdots$	$a_1 * a_n$
a_2	$a_2 * a_1$	$a_2 * a_2$	$\cdots$	$a_2 * a_n$
.				
.				
.				
a_n	$a_n * a_1$	$a_n * a_2$	$\cdots$	$a_n * a_n$

Therefore, one "knows" a finite group if he can write a multiplication table for it. (We say "a" multiplication table rather than "the" multiplication table, since the matrix depends on the particular listing of the elements of G.) One also speaks of a multiplication table of an infinite group, but in this case, of course, the matrix is infinite.

Let us now consider two almost trivial examples of groups. Let G be the multiplicative group with elements $\{1, -1\}$; let H be the additive group of integers modulo 2. Compare multiplication tables of these two groups:

G	1	-1
1	1	-1
-1	-1	1

H	$\bar{0}$	$\bar{1}$
$\bar{0}$	$\bar{0}$	$\bar{1}$
$\bar{1}$	$\bar{1}$	$\bar{0}$

It is quite clear that G and H are distinct groups; it is equally clear that there is no significant difference between them. We formalize this idea.

Definition Let $(G,*)$ and $(H,\circ)$ be groups. A **homomorphism** $f: G \rightarrow H$ is a function for which

$$f(a * b) = f(a) \circ f(b) \qquad \text{for all } a, b \in G.$$

An **isomorphism** is a homomorphism that is also a one-to-one correspondence.[1] Two groups G and H are **isomorphic,** denoted $G \approx H$, if there is an isomorphism $f: G \rightarrow H$.

The groups G and H, whose multiplication tables are given above, are isomorphic; define $f: G \rightarrow H$ by $f(1) = \bar{0}$ and $f(-1) = \bar{1}$.

Exercise 1.12 Isomorphic groups have the same number of elements. Prove that the converse is false by showing that Z_4 (the additive group of integers modulo 4) is not isomorphic to the group of four matrices in Exercise 1.10.

Two basic problems occurring in mathematics are: (1) classify all systems of a given kind, e.g., all groups, all vector spaces, all topological spaces; (2) classify all the transformations of one system into another. By a classification of systems, one usually means a scheme that distinguishes essentially different systems, or to say it another way, a scheme that tells when two systems are essentially the same. A classification of transformations is more subtle, and we needn't discuss it further now. As an illustration, consider the collection of all finite-dimensional vector spaces over a field F. In this case, the first problem is answered by the theorem that two such spaces are isomorphic if and only if they have the same dimension. Even the second problem has been answered. The transformations of vector spaces are, of course, the linear transformations, which give rise to similarity classes of matrices, and these are classified by the canonical forms. The same problems arise in group theory: (1) when are two groups isomorphic; (2) how may one describe the homomorphisms from one group to another? In contrast to our

---

[1] Many authors use "isomorphism" to mean "homomorphism and one-to-one"; here, isomorphisms are always onto as well.

illustration, both problems are exceedingly difficult (if not impossible) and are only partially solved.

The reader is advised that homomorphisms are powerful tools in the study of groups, and they should be used as much as possible.

Exercises   1.13   If $f: G \to H$ and $g: H \to K$ are homomorphisms, then so is $g \circ f: G \to K$.

1.14   If $\mathfrak{C}$ is a collection of groups, then the relation $G \approx H$ is an equivalence relation on $\mathfrak{C}$.

1.15   Let $f: G \to H$ be a homomorphism, and let $a \in G$. For every $n \in Z, f(a^n) = f(a)^n$. Note the special cases $n = 0$ and $n = -1$.

1.16   Let G be a group and let X be a set having the same number of elements as G. If $f: G \to X$ is a one-to-one correspondence, there is a unique binary operation that can be defined on X so that X is a group and f is an isomorphism.

1.17   Let G be the multiplicative group of positive reals and let H be the additive group of all reals. Show that log: $G \to H$ is an isomorphism.

1.18   Let G be the additive group of reals and let T be the **circle group**, i.e., the multiplicative group of all complex numbers of absolute value 1. For a fixed real y, prove that $f: G \to T$ defined by $f(x) = e^{iyx}$ is a homomorphism. Which real numbers x are such that $f(x) = 1$? (It can be proved that these f are the only *continuous* homomorphisms from G to T.)

1.19   If G is the multiplicative group of all $n \times n$ nonsingular matrices with entries in a field F, and if F^* is the multiplicative group of nonzero elements of F, then determinant is a homomorphism from G to F^*.

1.20   Let a be a fixed element of a group G. Prove that $f: G \to G$ defined by

$$f(x) = a * x * a^{-1}$$

is an isomorphism. (f is called **conjugation** by a.)

1.21   Let G be the multiplicative group of nth roots of unity, and let H be the additive group of integers modulo n. Prove that $G \approx H$.

1.22   Let G be the additive group of all polynomials in x with coefficients in Z, and let H be the multiplicative group of positive rationals. Prove that $G \approx H$. (*Hint:* Use the fundamental theorem of arithmetic to construct an isomorphism.)

Having solved Exercise 1.22, the reader may wish to reconsider his answer to the question: When does one "know" a group? Surely the reader could construct multiplication tables for the two groups G and H, but it was not obvious at the outset that these groups are essentially the same. As an alternative answer to the question of "knowing," we suggest that one knows a group G when he can determine, given any other group H, whether or not G and H are isomorphic.

Definition   Two elements a and b in a semigroup G **commute** in case $a * b = b * a$. A semigroup is **abelian**[2] (or commutative) in case every two elements in G commute.

Exercises   1.23   Let a_1, a_2, $\cdots$, a_n be elements of an abelian semigroup G. If b_1, b_2, $\cdots$, b_n is a rearrangement of the a_i, then $a_1 * a_2 * \cdots * a_n = b_1 * b_2 * \cdots * b_n$.

1.24   Let a and b lie in a semigroup G. If a and b commute, then $(a * b)^n = a^n * b^n$ for every integer $n > 0$. If G is a group, the equation holds for all $n \in Z$.

1.25   Let G be a group in which the square of every element is the identity. Prove that G is abelian.

1.26   A group G is abelian if and only if the function $f: G \rightarrow G$ defined by $f(x) = x^{-1}$ is a homomorphism.

Definition   A semigroup G is a **cancellation semigroup** in case, for every a, b, $c \in G$, each of the equations $a * b = a * c$ and $b * a = c * a$ implies $b = c$.

Exercises (contd.)   *1.27   Prove that every abelian cancellation semigroup G can be imbedded in a group. (*Hint:* As in the construction of the rationals from the integers, consider all pairs $(a,b) \in G \times G$ under the equivalence relation: $(a,b) \equiv (a',b')$ if $a * b' = a' * b$.)

Mal'cev has exhibited a cancellation semigroup that cannot be imbedded in a group.

*1.28 (*Kaplansky*)   An element x in a ring R has a *left quasi-inverse* in case there is an element $y \in R$ with $x + y - yx = 0$. Prove that a ring R in which every element but one has a left quasi-

---

[2] In honor of N. H. Abel (1802–1829).

inverse is a division ring. (*Hint:* Let R' be the set R with the exceptional element deleted; consider the binary operation on R' defined by $x \circ y = x + y - xy$.)

*1.29   Let G be a finite group and $f: G \to G$ an isomorphism. If f has no fixed points (i.e., $f(x) = x$ implies $x = e$) and if $f^2 = $ identity (i.e., for all $x \in G$, $f(f(x)) = x$), then G is abelian. (*Hint:* Prove that every element in G has the form $x^{-1} * f(x)$.)

Chapter 2

The Isomorphism
Theorems

Subgroups

From now on, we shall usually write ab instead of $a * b$, and 1 will denote the identity element instead of e.

Definition   A nonempty subset S of a group G is a **subgroup** of G in case S is a group under the binary operation of G.

Let G be the additive group of reals and S the multiplicative group of positive rationals. S is a group contained in G, but S is not a subgroup, since the binary operations are not the same. Indeed, a group S contained in G is a subgroup if and only if the inclusion $i: S \to G$ is a homomorphism. It follows from Exercise 1.15 that the identity elements of S and of G are the same.

LEMMA 2.1   Let S be a subset of a group G; S is a subgroup of G if and only if:

(i) $1 \in S$.
(ii) $a \in S$ implies $a^{-1} \in S$.
(iii) $a, b \in S$ implies $ab \in S$.

Proof   The verifications of the axioms are easy. ∎

THEOREM 2.2   Let S be a subset of a group G; S is a subgroup if and only if S is nonempty, and whenever $a, b \in S$, then $ab^{-1} \in S$.

Proof   We use Lemma 2.1.

   (i)   Since S is nonempty, it contains an element a. Hence, $aa^{-1} = 1 \in S$.
   (ii)   If $b \in S$, then $1b^{-1} = b^{-1} \in S$.
   (iii)   If $a, b \in S$, then $a(b^{-1})^{-1} = ab \in S$. ∎

Examples   **1** If G is a group, G itself and $\{1\}$ are subgroups of G; any other subgroup of G is called **proper**.
   2 If $a \in G$, let $[a]$ denote the set of all powers of a. $[a]$ is a subgroup, the **cyclic subgroup generated by** a; a is called a **generator** of $[a]$. A cyclic subgroup may have several different generators, e.g., $[a] = [a^{-1}]$.

Definition   A group G is **cyclic** if $G = [a]$ for some $a \in G$.

We now consider several ways of manufacturing subgroups.

THEOREM 2.3   The intersection of any family of subgroups of G is again a subgroup of G.

Proof   Let $\{S_\alpha\}$ be a family of subgroups of G, and let $S = \cap\, S_\alpha$. Since $1 \in S_\alpha$ for every α, $1 \in S$, and so S is nonempty. Suppose $a, b \in S$. These elements got into S by being in every S_α. Since each S_α is a subgroup, $ab^{-1} \in S_\alpha$ for every α, and so $ab^{-1} \in S$. ∎

THEOREM 2.4   If X is a subset of a group G, there is a smallest subgroup H of G that contains X, i.e., if S is any other subgroup containing X, then $S \supset H$.

Proof   There do exist subgroups of G containing X, e.g., G itself. Let H be the intersection of all the subgroups of G that contain X. By the preceding theorem, H is a subgroup and it clearly contains X. The fact that H is the smallest such subgroup follows from the observation that the intersection is contained in each of the sets being intersected. ∎

Definition   If X is a subset of a group G, the smallest subgroup of G containing X is denoted $[X]$ and is called **the subgroup of G generated by** X. We say that X **generates** $[X]$.

If X is a finite set, then $X = \{a_1, a_2, \cdots, a_n\}$. For notational convenience, we write $[X] = [a_1, a_2, \cdots, a_n]$ instead of $[\{a_1, a_2, \cdots, a_n\}]$.

Exercises   2.1   If X is empty, $[X] = \{1\}$; if X is nonempty, $[X]$ is the set of all finite products of powers of elements in X. In particular, if $X = \{a\}$, $[X] = [a]$ is a cyclic subgroup.

2.2   The set-theoretical union of two subgroups is a subgroup if and only if one is contained in the other. Is this true if we replace "two subgroups" by "three subgroups"?

2.3   If H and K are subgroups of G, we denote $[H \cup K]$ by $H \vee K$. Prove that $H \vee K$ is the smallest subgroup of G containing H and K.

2.4   Let S be a subgroup of G with $S \neq G$. If $G - S$ is the complement of S in G, then $[G - S] = G$.

2.5   The multiplicative group of positive rationals is generated by all rationals of the form $1/p$, where p is prime.

2.6   Let $f: G \to H$ be a homomorphism. Prove that the **image** of $f = \{h \in H: h = f(x)$ for some $x \in G\}$ is a subgroup of H.

Definition   Let S and T be nonempty subsets of a group G.

$$ST = \{st: s \in S \quad \text{and} \quad t \in T\}.$$

In particular, if we write t for $\{t\}$, then

$$St = \{st: s \in S\}.$$

Definition   Let S be a subgroup of G. A **right coset of S in G** is a subset St; (a **left coset** is tS). We say that t is a **representative** of St (and also of tS).

Exercises   2.7   The multiplication of nonempty subsets of G defined above is associative.

2.8   Let S be a subgroup of G. Prove that $St = S$ if and only if $t \in S$.

2.9   If S is a subgroup of G, then $SS = S$.

2.10   If S is a finite nonempty subset of G and $SS = S$, then S is a subgroup of G. Is this true if S is infinite?

2.11   There is a one-to-one correspondence between S and St; conclude that any two right cosets of S have the same number of elements.

A right coset of S in G has many representatives. The next lemma gives a criterion for determining whether two right cosets of S are the same when a representative of each is known.

LEMMA 2.5   Let S be a subgroup of G. Then $Sa = Sb$ if and only if $ab^{-1} \in S$. ($aS = bS$ if and only if $a^{-1}b \in S$.)

Proof   If $Sa = Sb$, then $a \in Sb$ and $a = sb$ for some $s \in S$. Therefore, $ab^{-1} = s$ and $ab^{-1} \in S$. Conversely, if $ab^{-1} = s \in S$, then $a = sb$, so that $Sa = Ssb = Sb$, by Exercise 2.8. ∎

THEOREM 2.6   If S is a subgroup of G, then any two right cosets of S in G are either identical or disjoint.

Proof   We show that if there is an element x in $Sa \cap Sb$, then $Sa = Sb$. Such an element has the form $x = s_1a = s_2b$, where s_1 and s_2 lie in S. Hence $ab^{-1} = s_1^{-1}s_2 \in S$, so that Lemma 2.5 gives $Sa = Sb$. ∎

Theorem 2.6 may be paraphrased to say that a subgroup S induces a partition of the group G (into right cosets). This being true, there must be an equivalence relation on G lurking somewhere in the background.

Exercise   2.12 If S is a subgroup of G, define a relation on G by $a \equiv b$ in case $ab^{-1} \in S$. Prove that this relation is an equivalence relation whose equivalence classes are the right cosets of S. Use this fact to give an alternative proof of Theorem 2.6.

It is interesting to note that each of the three properties of a subgroup listed in Lemma 2.1 yields a corresponding property of the relation $a \equiv b$.

THEOREM 2.7   If S is a subgroup of G, the number of right cosets of S in G equals the number of left cosets of S in G.

Proof   Let R denote the set of all right cosets of S in G, and let L denote the set of all left cosets. We exhibit a one-to-one correspondence $f: R \to L$. If $Sa \in R$, your first guess is to define $f(Sa) = aS$, but this does not work. Your second guess, $f(Sa) = a^{-1}S$, is correct. It must be verified that f is well defined, i.e., if $Sa = Sb$, then $a^{-1}S = b^{-1}S$ (this is why your first guess is wrong). We also leave to the reader the verification that f is a one-to-one correspondence. ∎

Definition   If S is a subgroup of G, the **index of S in G**, denoted $[G:S]$, is the number of right cosets of S in G.

Theorem 2.7 tells us that there is no need to define a "right index" and a "left index," for the number of right cosets is the same as the number of left cosets.

Definition   The **order** of G, denoted $|G|$, is the number of elements in G.

THEOREM 2.8 (*Lagrange*)   If S is a subgroup of a finite group G, then $[G:S] = |G|/|S|$ (so that $|S|$ divides $|G|$).

Proof   The right cosets of S partition G into $[G:S]$ parts, each of which has precisely $|S|$ elements. ∎

COROLLARY 2.9   If $|G| = p$, where p is prime, then G is cyclic.

Proof   Since p is prime, Lagrange's theorem says that G can have no proper subgroups. Choose $a \in G$, $a \neq 1$. Then $[a]$ is a subgroup of G and $[a] \neq \{1\}$, so that $[a] = G$. ∎

Definition   If $a \in G$, the **order** of a is $|[a]|$. (Thus, the order of a is either a positive integer or infinity.)

COROLLARY 2.10   If G is a finite group and $a \in G$, then the order of a divides $|G|$.

Exercises   2.13   Let G be a finite group with subgroups H and K. If $K \subset H \subset G$, then $[G:K] = [G:H][H:K]$.
    2.14   Let S and T be subgroups of a finite group G. Prove that $|S|\,|T| \leq |S \cap T|\,|S \vee T|$.
    2.15   If $a \in G$ has finite order n, then n is the least positive integer

such that $a^n = 1$. If a has infinite order, then $a^n \neq 1$ for all $n \neq 0$.

2.16   If $a^n = 1$, then the order of a divides n.

2.17   If G is a group of order $2n$, then the number of elements in G of order 2 is odd.

2.18   If two elements a and b commute, and if $a^m = 1 = b^n$, then $(ab)^k = 1$, where $k = lcm\{m,n\}$. (The order of ab may be less than k: let $b = a^{-1}$.) Conclude that if a and b have finite order and if a and b commute, then their product ab also has finite order.

2.19   This exercise shows that a product of two elements of finite order may have infinite order; of course this cannot happen in a finite group.

Let G be the multiplicative group of all 2×2 nonsingular matrices with rational entries. Let

$$a = \begin{bmatrix} 0 & -1 \\ 1 & 0 \end{bmatrix} \quad \text{and} \quad b = \begin{bmatrix} 0 & 1 \\ -1 & -1 \end{bmatrix}.$$

Show that $a^4 = 1$ and $b^3 = 1$, but that ab has infinite order.

2.20   Let $G = [a]$ have order n. Prove that a^k is a generator of G if and only if $(k,n) = 1$.

Definition   The **Euler φ-function** is defined as follows: If $h = 1$, then $\varphi(h) = 1$; if $h > 1$, then $\varphi(h)$ is the number of integers k such that $1 \leq k < h$ and $(k,h) = 1$.

Exercises (contd.)   2.21   If $h = p^t$, where p is prime, then

$$\varphi(h) = p^t \left(1 - \frac{1}{p} \right).$$

2.22   Let $(r,s) = 1$. If $x \in G$ has order rs, then $x = yz$, where y has order r, z has order s, and y and z commute; the factors y and z are unique.

2.23   If $h = rs$, where $(r,s) = 1$, then

$$\varphi(rs) = \varphi(r)\varphi(s).$$

2.24   If the distinct prime divisors of h are $p_1, \cdots, p_m$, then

$$\varphi(h) = h \left(1 - \frac{1}{p_1} \right) \cdots \left(1 - \frac{1}{p_m} \right).$$

2.25 Prove that every subgroup of a cyclic group is cyclic. (*Hint:* Use the division algorithm.)

2.26 Prove that two cyclic groups are isomorphic if and only if they have the same order.

2.27 Let $a \in G$ have finite order, and let $f: G \rightarrow H$ be a homomorphism. Prove that the order of $f(a)$ divides the order of a.

2.28 (*Fermat*) Let p be a prime; for any integer n, show that $n^p \equiv n \pmod{p}$. (*Hint:* If Z_p denotes the integers modulo p, then the nonzero elements of Z_p form a multiplicative group of order $p - 1$.)

*2.29 (*H. B. Mann*) Let G be a finite group, and let S and T be nonempty subsets. Prove that either $G = ST$ or $|G| \geq |S| + |T|$.

*2.30 Using the result of Mann, prove that every element in a finite field F is a sum of two squares.

Normal Subgroups and Quotient Groups

There is one kind of subgroup that is especially interesting, for it is intimately related to homomorphisms.

Definition   A subgroup S of G is a **normal subgroup of** G, denoted $S \triangleleft G$, in case $aSa^{-1} \subset S$ for every $a \in G$.

The first properties of normal subgroups are contained in the following exercises.

Exercises   2.31 A subgroup S of G is normal in G if and only if $aSa^{-1} = S$ for every $a \in G$. ✓

2.32 If G is abelian, then every subgroup of G is normal. The converse is false, as the group of quaternions shows (see Exercise 5.23).

2.33 A subgroup S is normal in G if and only if every right coset of S in G is also a left coset of S in G.

2.34 Any subgroup S in G of index 2 is normal.

2.35 If $S \triangleleft G$, $a \in G$ and $s \in S$, then there exists an element $s' \in S$ with $as = s'a$ (this is a partial commutativity).

Definition   Let $x \in G$. A **conjugate** of x is an element of the form axa^{-1}, where $a \in G$.

Exercises (*contd.*)   2.36   A subgroup S of G is normal if and only if whenever $x \in S$, all conjugates of x also lie in S. Conclude that $S \lhd G$ if and only if $f(S) \subset S$ for every conjugation f (see Exercise 1.20).

2.37   Let G be the multiplicative group of all $n \times n$ nonsingular matrices over a field F. Prove that the set of all matrices of determinant 1 is a normal subgroup of G.

2.38   Any intersection of normal subgroups of G is itself a normal subgroup of G. Conclude that if X is any subset of G, there is a smallest normal subgroup of G containing X; this subgroup is called the **normal subgroup of G generated by** X.

2.39   If X is empty, the normal subgroup generated by X is $\{1\}$. If X is nonempty, the normal subgroup generated by X is the subgroup generated by all conjugates of elements in X.

2.40   If H and K are normal subgroups of G, then so is $H \vee K$.

2.41   (**Modular Law**)   Let A, B, and C be normal subgroups of G. If $A \cap C = B \cap C$, $A \vee C = B \vee C$, and $A \subset B$, then $A = B$.

Here is another version of the modular law, which is also called the **Dedekind law**. If A, B, and C are normal subgroups of G and if $A \subset C$, then

$$(A \vee B) \cap C = A \vee (B \cap C).$$

The construction of a **quotient group** in the following theorem is of fundamental importance.

THEOREM 2.11   If $S \lhd G$, then the cosets of S in G form a group, denoted G/S, of order $[G:S]$.

Proof   In order to define a group, we must present a set and a binary operation. The set is the collection of all cosets of S in G; note that since $S \lhd G$, we need not bother with the adjectives "right" and "left." As multiplication, we propose the multiplication of nonempty subsets that we defined earlier. Recall that we proved then (Exercise 2.7) that this multiplication is associative. Now $(Sa)(Sb) = Sa(a^{-1}Sa)b$ (because S is normal) $= S(aa^{-1})Sab = SSab = Sab$ (because S is a subgroup). Thus, we have proved that

$SaSb = Sab$, so that a product of two cosets of S is itself a coset of S. We leave to the reader the proof that the identity is S and that the inverse of Sa is Sa^{-1}, so that we have constructed a group (which is denoted G/S). Finally, the definition of index says that $|G/S| = [G:S]$. ∎

Before giving examples of quotient groups, we make a remark on notation. If $(G,+)$ is an abelian group with subgroup H, a coset of H is a subset $x + H$, and two cosets $x + H$ and $y + H$ are equal if and only if $x - y \in H$.

Examples   3   Let Z be the additive group of integers, and for a fixed integer m, let H be the subgroup consisting of all multiples of m. H is a normal subgroup of Z because Z is abelian.

The elements of Z/H are the cosets $n + H$. There are exactly m cosets, for each coset has a unique representative k, where $0 \leq k < m$. The binary operation in Z/H obeys the rule:

$$(k + H) + (n + H) = (k + n) + H.$$

This group may be more familiar if we observe that $k + H = n + H$ if and only if $k - n \in H$, i.e., $k \equiv n \,(\text{modulo } m)$. By analogy, an arbitrary quotient group G/H is often called G modulo H.

4   Let G be the multiplicative group of all $n \times n$ nonsingular matrices over a field F, and let H be the normal subgroup of all matrices of determinant 1 (see Exercise 2.37). We shall show that $G/H \approx F^*$, the multiplicative group of all nonzero elements in F.

If $a \in G$, then $\det(a) \in F^*$, since a is nonsingular. Define a function $d\colon G/H \to F^*$ by

$$d(Ha) = \det(a).$$

This function is well defined, for if $Hb = Ha$, then $b = ha$ for some $h \in H$; therefore, $\det(h) = 1$ and

$$\det(b) = \det(ha) = \det(h)\det(a) = \det(a);$$

d is a homomorphism, for

$$d(HaHb) = d(Hab) = \det(ab) = \det(a)\det(b) = d(Ha)d(Hb);$$

d is one-to-one, for if $d(Ha) = d(Hb)$, then $\det(a) = \det(b)$. Therefore, $\det(ab^{-1}) = 1$ and $ab^{-1} \in H$, so that $Ha = Hb$. Finally, d is onto, for if $x \in F^*$, then the diagonal matrix a that has x in the upper left corner and 1 elsewhere on the diagonal has determinant x and $d(Ha) = x$. Thus, d is an isomorphism.

The Isomorphism Theorems

There are three theorems that describe the relationship among quotient groups, normal subgroups, and homomorphisms. The reader should be warned that the numbering of these theorems is not canonical, so that one man's first isomorphism theorem may be another man's second. A second remark is that a testimony to the elementary character of these theorems is that analogs of them are true for every type of algebraic system, e.g., groups, rings, and vector spaces.

Definition   Let $f: G \to H$ be a homomorphism. The **kernel** of f is the subset of G:

$$\text{kernel } f = \{x \in G: f(x) = 1\}.$$

THEOREM 2.12 (*First Isomorphism Theorem*)   Let $f: G \to H$ be a homomorphism with kernel K. Then K is a normal subgroup of G and $G/K \approx \text{image } f$.

Proof   Since $f(1) = 1$, K is a nonempty subset of G. K is a subgroup of G, for if $a, b \in K$, then $f(ab^{-1}) = f(a)f(b)^{-1} = 1$, and so $ab^{-1} \in K$. K is normal in G: If $x \in aKa^{-1}$ (where $a \in G$), then $x = aka^{-1}$ for some $k \in K$, and $f(x) = f(a)f(k)f(a)^{-1} = 1$; therefore, $x \in K$ and $aKa^{-1} \subset K$.

The remainder of the proof is patterned after the example of determinants given above. Define $F: G/K \to H$ by

$$F(Ka) = f(a).$$

Now F is well defined, for if $Ka = Kb$, then $ab^{-1} \in K$, $f(ab^{-1}) = 1$, and so $f(a) = f(b)$. F is a homomorphism, for

$$\begin{aligned} F(KaKb) &= F(Kab) = f(ab) \\ &= f(a)f(b) = F(Ka)F(Kb). \end{aligned}$$

F is one-to-one, for if $F(Ka) = F(Kb)$, then $f(a) = f(b)$; therefore, $f(ab^{-1}) = 1$, $ab^{-1} \in K$, and so $Ka = Kb$. (That F is one-to-one is the converse of the statement that F is well defined.) Clearly, the image of F is the image of f. Therefore, F is the desired isomorphism. ▮

Exercises   2.42   Let $f\colon G \to H$ be a homomorphism with kernel K. There exists a homomorphism $g\colon G/K \to H$ such that $f = g\pi$, where $\pi\colon G \to G/K$ is defined by $\pi(x) = Kx$.

2.43   Let $N \lhd G$ and let $f\colon G \to H$ be a homomorphism whose kernel contains N. Then f induces a homomorphism $f_\#\colon G/N \to H$, namely, $f_\#(Na) = f(a)$.

2.44   Let $f\colon G \to H$ be a homomorphism. f is one-to-one if and only if kernel $f = \{1\}$.

2.45   Let $f\colon G \to H$ be a homomorphism, and let S be a subgroup of H. Then $f^{-1}(S)$ is a subgroup of G and contains the kernel of f.

Definition   If $a,\ b \in G$, the **commutator** of a and b is the element $a^{-1}b^{-1}ab$. The **commutator subgroup** of G, denoted G', is the subgroup of G generated by all the commutators in G.

We shall see in Chapter 3 that a product of commutators need not be a commutator. Hence, the *set* of all commutators need not form a subgroup.

Exercises (contd.)   2.46   Prove that G' is a normal subgroup of G. (*Hint:* Use Exercise 2.36.)

2.47   If H is any normal subgroup of G, then G/H is abelian if and only if $G' \subset H$.

2.48   For any group G

$$G' = \{a_1a_2 \cdots a_na_1^{-1}a_2^{-1} \cdots a_n^{-1}\colon a_i \in G \text{ and } n \geq 2\}.$$

(*Hint*[1]: $(aba^{-1}b^{-1})(cdc^{-1}d^{-1})$
$$= a(ba^{-1})b^{-1}c(dc^{-1})d^{-1}a^{-1}(ab^{-1})bc^{-1}(cd^{-1})d.)$$

THEOREM 2.13   Let $K \lhd G$. There is a group H (namely, G/K) and a homomorphism π of G onto H whose kernel is exactly K.

Proof   Define π to be the function that assigns to any element of G its coset of K, i.e., $\pi(a) = Ka$. The proofs of the assertions of the theorem can be painlessly supplied by the reader. ▮

[1] Communicated to me by P. M. Weichsel.

Definition   The map $\pi: G \to G/K$ is called the **natural map** (or the natural homomorphism).

With Theorems 2.12 and 2.13, we have exhibited the relationship between normal subgroups and homomorphisms: Given any homomorphism, there is a normal subgroup (its kernel); given any normal subgroup K, there is a homomorphism (the natural map) having K as its kernel. We point out that different homomorphisms can have the same kernel. For example, let $f: Z \to Z$ be the identity map, and let $g: Z \to Z$ be defined by $g(n) = -n$. The kernel of each of these maps is $\{0\}$, but clearly $f \neq g$.

THEOREM 2.14   If S and T are subgroups of G and if one of them is normal, then $ST = S \vee T = TS$.

Proof   Recall that ST is just the set of products of the form st, where $s \in S$ and $t \in T$; hence, ST and TS are always subsets of $S \vee T$. Thus, we need show only that ST and TS are themselves subgroups in order to show $S \vee T$ is a subset of ST (and of TS). Let us suppose $T \lhd G$. If $s_1 t_1$ and $s_2 t_2 \in ST$, then

$$(s_1 t_1)(s_2 t_2)^{-1} = s_1(t_1 t_2^{-1} s_2^{-1}) = s_1(s_2^{-1} t_3)$$

for some $t_3 \in T$ (this is the partial commutativity from the normality of T), and $s_1(s_2^{-1} t_3) = (s_1 s_2^{-1}) t_3 \in ST$. A similar proof shows that TS is a subgroup. ∎

THEOREM 2.15 (*Second Isomorphism Theorem*)   Let S and T be subgroups of G with T normal. Then $S \cap T$ is normal in S, and $S/(S \cap T) \approx ST/T$.

Remark   The accompanying diagram is a mnemonic for this theorem.

Proof   Let $\pi: G \to G/T$ be the natural map, and let π_0 be the restriction of π to S. Since π_0 is a homomorphism whose kernel is $S \cap T$, Theorem 2.12 tells us that $S \cap T \lhd S$ and that $S/(S \cap T) \approx$ image π_0. But image π_0 is just the collection of all cosets of T having representatives in S; these are precisely the cosets in ST/T. ∎

A corollary of the second isomorphism theorem is a strengthening of the inequality of Exercise 2.14. If one of the subgroups S and T is normal, there is an equality $|S|\,|T| = |S \cap T|\,|S \vee T| = |S \cap T|\,|ST|$. This equation is often called the **product formula.**

THEOREM 2.16 (*Third Isomorphism Theorem*)   Let $K \subset H \subset G$, where both H and K are normal subgroups of G. Then H/K is a normal subgroup of G/K and

$$(G/K)/(H/K) \approx G/H.$$

Proof   Again we let the first isomorphism theorem do the dirty work. Define $f: G/K \to G/H$ by $f(Ka) = Ha$. The reader can check that f is a well defined homomorphism whose kernel is H/K and whose image is G/H. ∎

The Correspondence Theorem

The main theorem of this section could justifiably be called the fourth isomorphism theorem.

Let G and H be sets, and let $f: G \to H$ be a function. The reader is aware that f induces a "forward motion" and a "backward motion" between the subsets of G and the subsets of H. The forward motion assigns to every subset S of G its image $f(S)$ in H; the backward motion assigns to every subset L of H its inverse image $f^{-1}(L)$ in G. Now, if f is onto, these motions define a one-to-one correspondence between the subsets of H and some of the subsets of G. The following theorem is the group-theoretic translation of this observation.

THEOREM 2.17 (*Correspondence Theorem*)   Let $K \lhd G$ and let $\pi: G \to G/K$ be the natural map; π defines a one-to-one correspondence between the set of those subgroups of G containing K and the set of all subgroups of G/K.

If the subgroup of G/K corresponding to $S \subset G$ is denoted S^*, then

   (i) $S^* = S/K = \pi(S)$;
   (ii) $T \subset S$ if and only if $T^* \subset S^*$, and then $[S:T] = [S^*:T^*]$;
   (iii) $T \lhd S$ if and only if $T^* \lhd S^*$, and then $S/T \approx S^*/T^*$.

A mnemonic diagram for this theorem is

$$
\begin{array}{l}
G \xrightarrow{\ \pi\ } G/K \\
S \longleftrightarrow S/K \\
K \longrightarrow \{1\}
\end{array}
$$

Proof   We first show that the correspondence is one-to-one. Suppose S and T are subgroups of G containing K, and that $S/K = T/K$; we must prove that $S = T$. If $s \in S$, then $Ks = Kt$ for some $t \in T$; hence, $ks = k't$ for some $k, k' \in K$. Therefore, $s = k^{-1}k't \in T$, since $K \subset T$, and so $S \subset T$. A symmetric argument proves the reverse inclusion.

We now prove that the correspondence is onto. If A is a subgroup of G/K, we must find a subgroup S of G containing K for which $S/K = A$. By Exercise 2.45, if we define $S = \pi^{-1}(A)$, then S is a subgroup of G that contains K; furthermore, $S/K = \pi(S) = \pi(\pi^{-1}(A)) = A$, since π is onto.

It is obvious that this correspondence preserves inclusions. In order to prove $[S:T] = [S^*:T^*]$, we must show that the set of cosets Ts (where $s \in S$) is in one-to-one correspondence with the set of cosets T^*s^* (where $s^* \in S^*$). Such a correspondence is given by $Ts \leftrightarrow T^*\pi(s)$; the verification is left to the reader.[2]

If $T \lhd S$, then we conclude from the third isomorphism theorem that $T/K \lhd S/K$ and $(S/K)/(T/K) \approx S/T$, i.e., $T^* \lhd S^*$ and $S^*/T^* \approx S/T$. Suppose, conversely, that $T^* \lhd S^*$. Let $\eta: S^* \to S^*/T^*$ be the natural map and let $\pi_0 = \pi|S$. The reader may verify that T is the kernel of $\eta\pi_0: S \to S^*/T^*$, which implies that $T \lhd S$. ∎

---

[2] If all groups are finite, we may prove that $[S:T] = [S^*:T^*]$ as follows:

$$
\begin{aligned}
[S^*:T^*] &= |S^*|/|T^*| = |S/K|/|T/K| \\
&= (|S|/|K|)/(|T|/|K|) \\
&= |S|/|T| = [S:T].
\end{aligned}
$$

Exercises 2.49 Let H be a subgroup of G which contains G', the commutator subgroup of G. Prove that $H \triangleleft G$.

*2.50 (*Zassenhaus*) Let G be a finite group such that, for some fixed integer $n > 1$, $(xy)^n = x^n y^n$, for all $x, y \in G$. Let $G_n = \{z \in G : z^n = 1\}$ and $G^n = \{x^n : x \in G\}$. Show that both G_n and G^n are normal subgroups of G and that $|G^n| = [G : G_n]$. (*Note:* The wise reader lets homomorphisms do the work for him.)

2.51 Let G be a finite group with a normal subgroup H such that $(|H|, [G : H]) = 1$. Show that H is the unique subgroup of G of order $|H|$. (*Hint:* If K is another such subgroup, what happens to K in G/H?)

2.52 If $H \triangleleft G$, need G contain a subgroup isomorphic to G/H?

2.53 Prove that the circle group T is isomorphic to R/Z, where R is the additive group of real numbers. (*Hint:* Use Exercise 1.18.)

2.54 Prove that H is a maximal normal subgraph of G (i.e., there is no normal subgroup strictly between G and H) if and only if G/H has no proper normal subgroups.

Chapter 3

Permutation Groups

Permutations

The reader knows the formula giving the roots of a quadratic polynomial, and he is aware of similar formulas giving the roots of polynomials of degree 3 and degree 4. Many mathematicians put their faith in a faulty induction and tried to find a formula that would give the roots of an arbitrary polynomial of degree 5. In 1824, Abel proved, by studying permutations of the roots of quintic polynomials, that no such formula exists, and this result led Galois to his discovery of the intimate relationships between polynomials and certain groups of permutations of their roots. Influenced by the beauty of the work of Abel and Galois, most nineteenth century mathematicians considered only those groups whose elements are permutations (we shall see presently that this is no restriction at all). We now proceed to develop this point of view.

Definition   If X is a nonempty set, a **permutation** of X is a function $\alpha\colon X \to X$ which is a one-to-one correspondence.

Definition   If X is a nonempty set, the **symmetric group** on X, denoted S_X, is the group whose elements are the permutations of X and whose binary operation is composition of functions.

Of particular interest is the special case when X is finite. If $X = \{1, 2, \cdots, n\}$, we write S_n instead of S_X, and we call S_n the symmetric group of degree n, or the symmetric group on n letters. Note that $|S_n| = n!$.

Exercises   3.1   Write a multiplication table for S_3.

    3.2   Let X and Y be two sets, and let $f: X \to Y$ be a one-to-one correspondence. Prove that $\alpha \to f \circ \alpha \circ f^{-1}$ defines an isomorphism between S_X and S_Y.

    3.3   Suppose that $X \subset Y$, where X is nonempty. Prove that S_X can be imbedded in S_Y, i.e., S_X is isomorphic to a subgroup of S_Y.

Let X denote the set $\{1, 2, \cdots, n\}$. One way of denoting a permutation α of X is by displaying its values:

$$\alpha = \begin{pmatrix} 1 & 2 & \cdots & n \\ \alpha(1) & \alpha(2) & \cdots & \alpha(n) \end{pmatrix}.$$

Thus, $\alpha = \begin{pmatrix} 1 & 2 & 3 \\ 3 & 2 & 1 \end{pmatrix}$ and $\beta = \begin{pmatrix} 1 & 2 & 3 \\ 2 & 3 & 1 \end{pmatrix}$ are permutations of $\{1, 2, 3\}$. Their product is $\alpha\beta = \begin{pmatrix} 1 & 2 & 3 \\ 2 & 1 & 3 \end{pmatrix}$ (we compute this product by first applying β and then α).[1] Note that $\beta\alpha = \begin{pmatrix} 1 & 2 & 3 \\ 1 & 3 & 2 \end{pmatrix}$, so that $\alpha\beta \neq \beta\alpha$. It follows that S_3, and hence any larger symmetric group, is nonabelian.

Cycles

In this section, we shall consider some factorizations of permutations in S_n as products of simpler permutations, called *cycles*.

Definition   Let $x \in X$ and $\alpha \in S_X$; α **fixes** x if $\alpha(x) = x$; otherwise α **moves** x.

Definition   Let $i_1, i_2, \cdots, i_r$ be distinct integers between 1 and n. If $\alpha \in S_n$ fixes the other integers and

$$\alpha(i_1) = i_2, \quad \alpha(i_2) = i_3, \quad \cdots, \quad \alpha(i_{r-1}) = i_r, \quad \alpha(i_r) = i_1,$$

then α is an r-**cycle**. We also say that α is a cycle of **length** r.

    A way to denote an r-cycle α, other than the cumbersome

---

[1] Some authors compute the product $\alpha\beta$ in the reverse order.

two-rowed notation we introduced earlier, is $\alpha = (i_1 \; i_2 \; \cdots \; i_r)$. For example,

$$\begin{pmatrix} 1 & 2 & 3 & 4 \\ 2 & 3 & 4 & 1 \end{pmatrix} = (2 \; 3 \; 4 \; 1),$$

$$\begin{pmatrix} 1 & 2 & 3 & 4 & 5 \\ 5 & 1 & 4 & 2 & 3 \end{pmatrix} = (1 \; 5 \; 3 \; 4 \; 2),$$

and

$$\begin{pmatrix} 1 & 2 & 3 & 4 & 5 \\ 2 & 3 & 1 & 4 & 5 \end{pmatrix} = (2 \; 3 \; 1).$$

All 1-cycles equal the identity permutation, which we thus denote (1).

Exercises   3.4   Prove that $(1 \; 2 \; 3 \; \cdots \; r) = (2 \; 3 \; \cdots \; r \; 1) = (3 \; 4 \; \cdots \; r \; 1 \; 2) = \cdots = (r \; 1 \; 2 \; \cdots \; r - 1)$. Conclude that there are r such notations for this cycle.

   3.5   The order of an r-cycle is r.

   3.6   Exhibit two 2-cycles whose product is a 3-cycle. This example shows that if α and β do not commute, nothing intelligent can be said about the order of $\alpha\beta$ in terms of the orders of the factors.

   3.7   Let α and β be r-cycles in S_X. If there is an $x_0 \in X$ such that (i) both α and β move x_0, and (ii) $\alpha^k(x_0) = \beta^k(x_0)$ for all integers k, then $\alpha = \beta$.

Definition   Two permutations α and β in S_X are **disjoint** in case every x moved by one is fixed by the other. In symbols, if $\alpha(x) \neq x$, then $\beta(x) = x$, and if $\beta(y) \neq y$, then $\alpha(y) = y$. A set of permutations is **disjoint** if each pair of them is disjoint.

Exercises (contd.)   3.8   Let $\alpha = (i_1 \; i_2 \; \cdots \; i_r)$ and $\beta = (j_1 \; j_2 \; \cdots \; j_s)$. Prove that α and β are disjoint if and only if $\{i_1, i_2, \cdots, i_r\} \cap \{j_1, j_2, \cdots, j_s\} = \phi$.

   3.9   If α and β are disjoint, then $\alpha\beta = \beta\alpha$.

   3.10   A permutation $\alpha \in S_n$ is **regular** if it is (1) or if it has no fixed points and is the product of disjoint cycles of the same length. Prove that α is regular if and only if α is a power of an n-cycle.

   3.11   Let $\alpha = \beta_1\beta_2 \cdots \beta_m$, where the β_i are disjoint r_i-cycles. Prove that the order of α is $lcm\{r_1, r_2, \cdots, r_m\}$. Conclude that each r_i divides the order of α. Conclude further that if p is prime, then every power of a p-cycle is a p-cycle, or (1).

3.12   If α is an n-cycle, then α^k is a product of (n,k) disjoint cycles, each of length $n/(n,k)$. (*Hint:* Use Exercises 3.10 and 3.11.)

LEMMA 3.1   If $\alpha \in S_X$, the relation on X defined by

$$x \equiv_\alpha y \qquad \text{if } \alpha^k(x) = y \text{ for some integer } k,$$

is an equivalence relation on X.

Proof   Left to the reader. ∎

Definition   The equivalence classes of X under the relation $x \equiv_\alpha y$ are called the **orbits** of α.

If $x_0 \in X$, the orbit of α containing x_0 is $\{y \in X: y = \alpha^k(x_0)$ for some integer $k\}$; in other words, the orbit consists of all the elements obtained from x_0 by successively applying α (or α^{-1}). In order to provide examples, we shall now translate our earlier definitions into the language of orbits. First, "x_0 is fixed by α" means that x_0 is the sole resident of its orbit under α. Cycles provide a more interesting example. If $\alpha = (i_1 \ i_2 \ \cdots \ i_r)$, then $\alpha(i_1) = i_2$, $\alpha^2(i_1) = i_3$, $\cdots$, $\alpha^{r-1}(i_1) = i_r$, so that a permutation $\neq (1)$ is a cycle if and only if it has just one orbit with more than one element, i.e., just one nontrivial orbit. A cycle is an r-cycle if its nontrivial orbit contains exactly r elements. As a final example, α is a regular permutation (Exercise 3.10) in case all its orbits have the same size.

LEMMA 3.2   If X is a finite set and $\alpha \in S_X$, then there is a partition of X into disjoint subsets $Y_1, Y_2, \cdots, Y_m$ such that, for all $i = 1, 2, \cdots, m$, $\alpha(Y_i) = Y_i$ and $\alpha | Y_i$ is a cycle.

Proof   Let $Y_1, Y_2, \cdots, Y_m$ be the orbits of α. The two properties follow immediately from the definition of $x \equiv_\alpha y$. ∎

THEOREM 3.3   Every permutation $\alpha \neq (1)$ in S_n is the product of disjoint cycles of length ≥ 2; this factorization is unique except for the order in which the cycles are written.

Proof   Let $Y_1, Y_2, \cdots, Y_m$ be the orbits of α; Lemma 3.2 tells us that each $\alpha | Y_i$ is a cycle. If we define $\beta_i \in S_n$ $(i = 1, 2, \cdots, m)$ as that permutation which is α on Y_i and which leaves everything else fixed, then β_i is a cycle in S_n. Further, the β_i are pairwise disjoint and $\alpha = \beta_1 \beta_2 \cdots \beta_m$ (just evaluate both sides). We obtain the desired factorization if we delete all factors β_i equal to the identity.

We now prove the uniqueness assertion. Suppose $\alpha = \beta_1 \beta_2 \cdots \beta_m = \gamma_1 \gamma_2 \cdots \gamma_k$, where each of these is a factorization of α into pairwise disjoint cycles of length ≥ 2. If α moves x, then one of the β and one of the γ must also move x. Since disjoint cycles commute, we may assume for notational convenience that β_1 and γ_1 move x. For any integer t,

$$\beta_1^t(x) = \alpha^t(x) = \gamma_1^t(x).$$

Since, by Exercise 3.7, a cycle is completely determined by the behavior of its powers on any element it moves, $\beta_1 = \gamma_1$. We now cancel these factors, and the proof is completed by an induction on $\max \{m, k\}$. ∎

Exercises   3.13   Write the following permutation as a product of disjoint cycles:

$$\begin{pmatrix} 1 & 2 & 3 & 4 & 5 & 6 & 7 & 8 & 9 \\ 6 & 4 & 7 & 2 & 5 & 1 & 8 & 9 & 3 \end{pmatrix}.$$

3.14   If p is a prime, prove that the only elements of order p in S_n are products of disjoint p-cycles.

Definition   A 2-cycle is also called a **transposition.**

Of all the permutations, surely the transposition, which merely interchanges two points, is the simplest.

THEOREM 3.4   Every $\alpha \in S_n$ is a product of transpositions.

Proof   By Theorem 3.3, it suffices to factor any r-cycle into a product of transpositions. This is done in the following way:

$$(1 \ 2 \ \cdots \ r) = (1 \ r)(1 \ r - 1) \cdots (12). ∎$$

Any permutation can thus be realized as a sequence of interchanges. This factorization, however, is not so nice as the factorization into disjoint cycles. First of all, the transpositions occurring need not commute; e.g., $(123) = (13)(12) \neq (12)(13)$. Second, the factors are not uniquely determined; e.g., $(123) = (13)(12) = (23)(13) = (13)(42)(12)(14) = (13)(42)(12)(14)(23)(23)$. Is there any uniqueness in such a factorization? We shall prove that the number of factors is always even or always odd.

Consider the polynomial in n variables:

$$g(x_1, x_2, \cdots, x_n) = \prod_{j > i} (x_j - x_i).$$

Notice that the condition $j > i$ implies that every pair of distinct integers between 1 and n occurs as subscripts in exactly one factor of g. If $\alpha \in S_n$, we form a new polynomial in the n variables:

$$\alpha g = \prod_{j > i} (x_{\alpha(j)} - x_{\alpha(i)}).$$

Since α is a permutation, every pair of distinct integers between 1 and n occurs in exactly one factor of αg. Therefore, except for signs, the factors of g and of αg are identical. Hence, $\alpha g = \pm g$.

Definition   A permutation $\alpha \in S_n$ is **even** if $\alpha g = g$; α is **odd** if $\alpha g = -g$.

If α, $\beta \in S_n$, then $(\alpha\beta)g = \alpha(\beta g)$, for both are equal to $\prod_{j > i} (x_{\alpha\beta(j)} - x_{\alpha\beta(i)})$. It follows that if both α and β are even or if both α and β are odd, then $\alpha\beta$ is even, while if one factor is even and the other odd, then $\alpha\beta$ is odd.

Definition   The **alternating group** of degree n, denoted A_n, is the set of all even permutations in S_n.

Define a function $\varphi: S_n \to G$, where G is the multiplicative group $\{1, -1\}$, by $\varphi(\alpha) = 1$ if α is even and $\varphi(\alpha) = -1$ if α is odd. Our preceding remarks prove that φ is a homomorphism. Given a homomorphism, we ask the canonical questions: What is kernel φ; what is image φ?

THEOREM 3.5 A_n is a normal subgroup of S_n of order $\frac{1}{2}n!$.

Proof   It follows from the definitions of A_n and the homomorphism φ that $A_n = $ kernel φ. We claim that image $\varphi = \{1,-1\}$, i.e., that φ is onto. In order to prove this, it suffices to exhibit an odd permutation. The transposition $\tau = (1\ \ 2)$ is odd, for the only factor in $g(x_1, x_2, \cdots, x_n)$ that changes sign is $x_2 - x_1$. By the first isomorphism theorem, $A_n \lhd S_n$ and $S_n/A_n \approx \{1,-1\}$. Therefore, $|A_n| = \frac{1}{2}n!$. ∎

THEOREM 3.6 $\alpha \in S_n$ is even if and only if α is a product of an even number of transpositions; $\alpha \in S_n$ is odd if and only if α is a product of an odd number of transpositions.

Proof   We first prove that every transposition $\tau = (i\,j)$ is odd. This could be proved by actually considering the action of τ on $g(x_1, x_2, \cdots, x_n)$, but that would be tedious. Suppose, instead, that $(i\,j)$ is even, i.e., $(i\,j) \in A_n$. Since $A_n \lhd S_n$, every conjugate of $(i\,j)$ is also in A_n. But $(1\ 2)$ is a conjugate of $(i\,j)$: if $\gamma = (i\ 1)(j\ 2)$, then $\gamma(i\,j)\gamma^{-1} = (i\ 1)(j\ 2)(i\,j)(j\ 2)(i\ 1) = (1\ 2)$, contradicting the fact that $(1\ 2)$ is odd.[2]

Suppose $\alpha \in S_n$ and $\alpha = \tau_1\tau_2 \cdots \tau_m$, where each τ_i is a transposition. Then $\varphi(\alpha) = \varphi(\tau_1\tau_2 \cdots \tau_m) = \varphi(\tau_1)\varphi(\tau_2) \cdots \varphi(\tau_m) = (-1)^m$. Now α is even if and only if $\varphi(\alpha) = 1$, and α is odd if and only if $\varphi(\alpha) = -1$. Therefore, α is even if and only if m is even, and α is odd if and only if m is odd. ∎

COROLLARY 3.7   If $\alpha \in S_n$, the number of factors occurring in any factorization of α into transpositions is always even or always odd.

Proof   A permutation cannot be both even and odd. ∎

Exercises   3.15 An $n \times n$ **permutation matrix** is a matrix obtained from the $n \times n$ identity matrix E by permuting its columns. If P_n is the set of all $n \times n$ permutation matrices, prove that P_n is a multiplicative group and that $\theta: S_n \to P_n$ is an isomorphism, where $\theta(\alpha)$ is the matrix obtained from E by permuting its columns accord-

---

[2] This computation is a special case of a theorem we shall soon prove and which tells precisely when two permutations are conjugate in S_n.

ing to α. Prove that α is even (or odd) if and only if det $\theta(\alpha)$ is 1 (or -1).

3.16   An r-cycle is even if and only if r is odd.

3.17   If $n > 2$, then A_n is generated by the 3-cycles.

3.18   If a subgroup G of S_n contains an odd permutation, then $|G|$ is even and exactly half the elements of G are odd permutations.

3.19   Imbed S_n as a subgroup in A_{n+2}.

3.20   Prove that S_n can be generated by (12), (13), $\cdots$, (1n); prove that S_n can also be generated by (1 2) and (12 $\cdots$ n).

Conjugates

In this section we study conjugates and conjugacy classes, first for arbitrary groups and then for the special case of symmetric groups.

We begin by defining another equivalence relation.

Definition   If G is a group, the relation "x is a conjugate of y in G" is an equivalence relation on G; the equivalence classes are called **conjugacy classes.**

As an example, if G is the multiplicative group of all $n \times n$ nonsingular matrices over a field F, then two matrices lie in the same conjugacy class if and only if they are similar.

Now x and y lie in the same conjugacy class if there is an element $a \in G$ with $y = axa^{-1}$. There is thus an isomorphism $f \colon G \to G$ (namely, conjugation by a) with $y = f(x)$. It follows that all elements in the same conjugacy class have the same order. An amusing consequence is that, for any two elements a and b in G, ab and ba have the same order.

An element $x \in G$ is the sole resident of its conjugacy class if $x = axa^{-1}$ for all $a \in G$, i.e., x commutes with every element in G. In an abelian group, therefore, conjugacy classes are not of much interest.

Definition   The **center** of G, denoted $Z(G)$, is the set of all $x \in G$ that commute with every element in G.

Exercises 3.21 $Z(G)$ is a normal, abelian subgroup of G.
3.22 If G is a nonabelian group, then $G/Z(G)$ is not cyclic.
3.23 A subgroup S of G is a normal subgroup of G if and only if S is a (set theoretical) union of conjugacy classes of G.
*3.24 Let G be a group containing an element of finite order $n > 1$ and which contains exactly two conjugacy classes. Prove that G is a cyclic group of order 2.

It is very useful to count the number of elements in a conjugacy class. To this end, we introduce the following subgroup.

Definition If $x \in G$, the **centralizer** of x in G, denoted $C_G(x)$, is the set of all $a \in G$ that commute with x.

It is immediate that $C_G(x)$ is a subgroup of G. When the meaning is clear from the context, we shall abbreviate $C_G(x)$ by $C(x)$.

THEOREM 3.8 The number of conjugates of x in G is $[G: C_G(x)]$, and hence this number is a divisor of $|G|$ when G is finite.

Proof If a and b are elements of G, then the following statements are equivalent:

$axa^{-1} = bxb^{-1}$;
$a^{-1}b$ commutes with x;
$a^{-1}b \in C(x)$;
a and b lie in the same left coset of $C(x)$.

The function ψ, defined by $\psi(axa^{-1}) = aC(x)$, is thus a one-to-one correspondence between the set of distinct conjugates of x and the left cosets of $C(x)$. ∎

We return to symmetric groups, and we ask when two permutations are conjugate in S_n.

LEMMA 3.9 If α and β are in S_n, then $\alpha\beta\alpha^{-1}$ is the permutation having the same cycle structure as β and which is obtained by applying α to the symbols in β.

Example If $\beta = (13)(247)$ and $\alpha = (256)(143)$, then $\alpha\beta\alpha^{-1} = (\alpha 1\ \alpha 3)(\alpha 2\ \alpha 4\ \alpha 7) = (41)(537)$.

Proof   Let $\beta = \gamma_1\gamma_2 \cdots (\cdots i\,j \cdots) \cdots \gamma_t$ be a factorization of β into disjoint cycles. In order to prove that two permutations are equal, we must show that they have the same effect on each symbol. We have pictured β so that $\beta(i) = j$. Suppose $\alpha(i) = k$ and $\alpha(j) = m$. The instructions in the lemma say that we should send k into m. On the other hand, $\alpha\beta\alpha^{-1}$ sends $k \to i \to j \to m$, so that both permutations have the same effect, and hence are equal. ∎

THEOREM 3.10 α and β in S_n are conjugate in S_n if and only if they have the same cycle structure.

Proof   Our lemma shows that conjugate permutations have the same cycle structure.

Conversely, let α and β have the same cycle structure. Define $\gamma \in S_n$ as follows: Place α over β so that the cycles of the same length correspond; let γ: top $\to$ bottom. By the lemma, $\gamma\alpha\gamma^{-1} = \beta$, so that α and β are conjugate. ∎

For example, if
$$\alpha = (231)(45)(6)$$
and
$$\beta = (162)(34)(5),$$

then $\gamma\alpha\gamma^{-1} = \beta$, where

$$\gamma = \begin{pmatrix} 1\,2\,3\,4\,5\,6 \\ 2\,1\,6\,3\,4\,5 \end{pmatrix} = (1\ 2)(3\ 4\ 5\ 6).$$

If $1 < k \leq n$, then there are $(1/k)[n(n-1) \cdots (n-k+1)]$ distinct k-cycles in S_n. This formula may be used to compute the number of permutations α in S_n of a given cycle structure if one is careful about the case when several factors of α have the same length. For example, the number of permutations in S_4 of the form $(1\ 2)(3\ 4)$ is

$$\frac{1}{2}\left(\frac{4 \times 3}{2} \times \frac{2 \times 1}{2}\right),$$

the factor ½ occurring in order that we not count $(ab)(cd) = (cd)(ab)$ twice.

Let us now examine S_4 in some detail, using the accompanying table.

Cycle Structure	Number of Them	Order	Parity
(1)	1	1	Even
(12)	$6 = (4 \times 3)/2$	2	Odd
(123)	$8 = (4 \times 3 \times 2)/3$	3	Even
(1234)	$6 = 4!/4$	4	Odd
(12)(34)	$3 = \dfrac{1}{2}\left(\dfrac{4 \times 3}{2} \times \dfrac{2 \times 1}{2}\right)$	2	Even
	$24 = 4!$		

Thus, the 12 elements of A_4 are eight 3-cycles, three products of disjoint transpositions, and the identity. These elements are: (123), (132), (234), (243), (341), (314), (412), (421), (14)(23), (12)(34), (13)(24), and the identity (1).

We now show that the converse of Lagrange's theorem is false.

THEOREM 3.11 A_4 is a group of order 12 having no subgroup of order 6.

Proof   If H is such a subgroup, then $[A_4 : H] = 2$, so that H is a normal subgroup. Thus, if $\alpha \in H$, H contains all conjugates of α by *even* permutations.

Since 8 of the 12 elements of A_4 are 3-cycles, H must contain a 3-cycle α. How many conjugates does α have in H? By Theorem 3.10, α has 8 conjugates in S_4, so that the centralizer of α in S_4 has index 8 and order $24/8 = 3$. There are thus only 3 permutations in S_4 (a fortiori, in the smaller A_4) that commute with α; these must be α, α^{-1}, and (1). Since these all lie in A_4, the centralizer of α in A_4 has order 3 and hence has index $12/3 = 4$. Therefore, α has 4 conjugates in A_4, and all lie in H, since H is normal.

Now H must contain an element β of order 2, for if it contained a fifth 3-cycle, it would also contain its 4 conjugates, and there would be more than 6 elements in H. Since β is even, $\beta = (ab)(cd)$. We have discovered 6 elements in H: 4 3-cycles, β, and (1), and this is our quota. But we can exhibit another element in H! Since $H \lhd A_4$, $\gamma\beta\gamma^{-1} \in H$, where $\gamma = (acb)$; but $\gamma\beta\gamma^{-1} = (ca)(bd) \neq \beta$. This contradiction completes the proof. ∎

It is now easy to give an example showing that the product formula may fail when neither subgroup is normal. Let S and T be cyclic subgroups of A_4 of orders 2 and 3 respectively. Then $|S|\,|T| = 6$, but $|S \cap T|\,|S \vee T| = |S \vee T| = 12$, since A_4 has no subgroup of order 6.

Exercises   3.25   Prove that A_4 is the only subgroup of S_4 having order 12.

3.26   Let G be a finite group with subgroup H of index 2. If $x \in H$ has m conjugates in G, then x has either m or $m/2$ conjugates in H.

*3.27 (*Carmichael*)   Let G be the subgroup of S_{16} generated by the following eight elements:

$$(ac)(bd); \quad (eg)(fh);$$
$$(ik)(jl); \quad (mo)(np);$$
$$(ac)(eg)(ik); \quad (ab)(cd)(mo);$$
$$(ef)(gh)(mn)(op); \quad (ij)(kl).$$

Prove that G' is generated by the first four elements listed above, and that $|G'| = 16$. Moreover,

$$\alpha = (ik)(jl)(mo)(np) \in G',$$

but α is not a commutator.

The Simplicity of A_n

Definition   A group is **simple** if it contains no proper normal subgroups.

Exercises   3.28   If $H \triangleleft G$, prove that G/H is simple if and only if H is a maximal normal subgroup of G, i.e., there is no normal subgroup N with $H \subsetneq N \subsetneq G$. (*Hint:* Use the correspondence theorem, Theorem 2.17.)

3.29   Prove that an abelian group is simple if and only if it is finite and of prime order.

3.30 (*Schur*)   Let $f: G \to H$ be a non-trivial homomorphism, i.e., f does not send every element into 1. If G is simple, then f is one-to-one.

Our immediate goal is to provide the reader with some examples of simple groups. The classification of all finite simple groups is still (at this writing) an unsolved problem, but there are many simple groups known other than the ones we shall exhibit.

We shall prove that if $n \neq 4$, then A_n is simple. If we examine the small A_n, we see that A_1, A_2, and A_3 are simple, for they have orders 1, 1, and 3, respectively. We have just examined A_4. Now

$$V = \{(1), (12)(34), (13)(24), (14)(23)\}$$

is easily seen to be a subgroup of A_4 (which is called the **Klein 4-group**). Since V contains all the permutations in S_4 of a given cycle structure, V is a normal subgroup of S_4, a fortiori, $V \lhd A_4$. Therefore, A_4 is not simple. Let us now examine S_5 and A_5.

S_5			
Cycle Structure	Number of Them	Order	Parity
(1)	1	1	Even
(12)	$10 = (5 \times 4)/2$	2	Odd
(123)	$20 = (5 \times 4 \times 3)/3$	3	Even
(1234)	$30 = (5 \times 4 \times 3 \times 2)/4$	4	Odd
(12345)	$24 = 5!/5$	5	Even
(12)(34)	$15 = \dfrac{1}{2}\left(\dfrac{5 \times 4}{2} \times \dfrac{3 \times 2}{2}\right)$	2	Even
(123)(45)	$20 = \dfrac{5 \times 4 \times 3}{3} \times \dfrac{2 \times 1}{2}$	6	Odd
	$120 = 5!$		

A_5			
Cycle Structure	Number of Them	Order	Parity
(1)	1	1	Even
(123)	20	3	Even
(12345)	24	5	Even
(12)(34)	15	2	Even
	60		

LEMMA 3.12 A_5 is simple.

Proof   (i)   All 3-cycles are conjugate in A_5. (We know this is true in S_5, but now we are only allowed to conjugate by even permutations.)

In S_5 a 3-cycle α has 20 conjugates (for our table shows that there are 20 3-cycles). Hence, $C_S(\alpha)$ has index 20 and order 6. We can exhibit these 6 elements that commute with α: If, for example, $\alpha = (1\ 2\ 3)$, then the elements of $C_S(\alpha)$ are (1), (123), (132), (45), (123)(45), (132)(45). Now only the first three of these are even, so that $C_A(\alpha)$ has order 3 and hence index 20 in A_5. Therefore, α has 20 conjugates in A_5, so that all 3-cycles are conjugate in A_5.

(ii)   All products of disjoint transpositions are conjugate in A_5.

If, for example, $\alpha = (12)(34)$, then our table shows that α has 15 conjugates in S_5. By Exercise 3.26, α has either 15 or 15/2 conjugates in A_5, and the latter is clearly impossible.

(iii)   There are two conjugacy classes of 5-cycles in A_5, each of which has 12 elements.

In S_5, $\alpha = (12345)$ has 24 conjugates, so that $C_S(\alpha)$ has 5 elements, and these must be the powers of α. Therefore, $|C_A(\alpha)| = 5$, and so the number of conjugates in A_5 is $60/5 = 12$.

We have now surveyed all the conjugacy classes occurring in A_5. If H is a normal subgroup of $A_5 \neq \{1\}$, then H is a union of conjugacy classes of A_5. The order of H is thus a sum of certain of the numbers 1, 20, 15, 12, 12. Since H contains (1), it is easily checked that one never gets a proper divisor of 60. Therefore, $|H| = 60$ and $H = A_5$; it follows that A_5 is simple. ∎

LEMMA 3.13   Let $H \lhd A_n$, where $n \geq 5$. If H contains a 3-cycle, then $H = A_n$.

Proof   We shall first show that (123) and (ijk) are conjugate in A_n (and thus that all 3-cycles are conjugate in A_n). If these cycles are not disjoint, at most 5 symbols are moved by them. Let $A^* \subset A_n$ be the alternating group on these symbols; (if the cycles move less than 5 symbols, just supplement them to get 5 symbols). As in part (i) of Lemma 3.12, (123) and (ijk) are conjugate in A^*; a fortiori, they are conjugate in A_n. If the cycles are disjoint, then we have just seen that (123) is conjugate to (i23) and (i23) is conjugate to (ijk); therefore, (123) is conjugate to (ijk).

Since H is normal in A_n, it must contain all 3-cycles once it contains one of them. But A_n is generated by the 3-cycles; therefore, $H = A_n$. ∎

LEMMA 3.14 A_6 is simple.

Proof   Let $H \neq \{1\}$ be a normal subgroup of A_6, and let $\alpha \in H$ be distinct from (1). Suppose $\alpha(i) = i$ for some i. If

$$F(i) = \{\beta \in A_6 : \beta(i) = i\},$$

then $F(i) \approx A_5$ and $\alpha \in H \cap F(i)$. Since A_5 is simple and $H \cap F(i)$ is normal in $F(i)$ (second isomorphism theorem), $H \cap F(i) = F(i)$, i.e., $F(i) \subset H$. Therefore, H contains a 3-cycle, and so $H = A_6$, by Lemma 3.13.

We may now assume that no α in H (other than (1)) fixes an i, $1 \le i \le 6$. By considering the cycle structures of permutations in S_6, the reader may see that the only even permutations α that fix nothing have cycle structure (12)(3456) or (123)(456). In S_6, the first of these has 90 conjugates and the second has 40 conjugates. Since $[S_6 : A_6] = 2$, the conjugacy classes of these elements in A_6 (hence in its normal subgroup H) have sizes 90 or 45 and 40 or 20 (Exercise 3.26). Since H is a union of conjugacy classes, its order is obtained by adding certain of the numbers 1, 20, 20, 45, 45. Noting that H must contain (1), the reader may verify that no such sum is a divisor of 360. This last case is thus impossible, and so A_6 is simple. ∎

THEOREM 3.15   If $n \neq 4$, A_n is a simple group.

Proof   We have already seen that the theorem is true for $n \le 6$. Suppose now that $n > 6$ and H is a normal subgroup of A_n; let $\alpha \in H$ be distinct from (1). There exists a 3-cycle β that does not commute with α. Since $H \lhd A_n$, $\alpha\beta\alpha^{-1}\beta^{-1} \in H$ (and this commutator $\neq$ (1)). But $(\alpha\beta\alpha^{-1})\beta^{-1}$ is a product of two 3-cycles, and so it moves at most 6 symbols $\{i_1, \cdots, i_6\}$. Let

$$F = \{\gamma \in A_n : \gamma \text{ fixes all } j \neq i_1, \cdots, i_6\}.$$

Then $F \approx A_6$ and $H \cap F \neq \{(1)\}$. Since A_6 is simple, $F \subset H$; therefore, H contains a 3-cycle, and so $H = A_n$. Therefore, A_n is simple. ∎

A defense of this proof is in order, for much shorter proofs exist in the literature (e.g., in Vol. I of van der Waerden's book, *Modern Algebra*). First, the key role of the 3-cycles makes 6 a more natural starting point than 5. Second, it is important that the reader become familiar with permutation groups and with the notions of conjugacy and centralizer. I feel that the proof above is best suited for these several purposes.

Exercises   3.31   If $n \neq 4$, A_n is the only proper normal subgroup of S_n.

3.32   Consider the chain of subgroups:

$$S_4 \supset A_4 \supset V \supset W \supset \{(1)\},$$

where $W = [(12)(34)]$. We have already seen that V (the 4-group) is normal in A_4. Show that W is normal in V, but that W is not normal in A_4. Conclude that normality need not be transitive.

3.33   A group G is called **centerless** if $Z(G) = \{1\}$. Prove that S_n is centerless if $n \geq 3$, and that A_n is centerless for $n \geq 4$.

3.34   Give an example of a group G with more than one element such that $G = G'$ (G' is the commutator subgroup of G).

*3.35   The following is an example of an infinite simple group. Let X be the set of positive integers, and let S be the group of all permutations of X; let F be the subgroup of S consisting of all α that move only finitely many elements of X.

The subgroup of F generated by all 3-cycles, denoted A_∞, is the **infinite alternating group.** Prove that A_∞ is an infinite simple group. (*Hint:* Use the proof of Theorem 3.15.)

Some Representation Theorems

A very useful technique in studying a group G is to represent it in terms of something familiar and concrete. If the elements of a group happen to be permutations or matrices, we may be able to obtain extra information by considering cycle structures or traces. In this section, we give some elementary theorems on representations, i.e., on homomorphisms into familiar groups.

The following theorem shows that the study of groups of permutations is no less general than the study of arbitrary groups.

THEOREM 3.16 (Cayley) Every group G is isomorphic to a subgroup of S_G. In particular, every finite group of order n is isomorphic to a subgroup of S_n.

Proof For each $a \in G$, define $T_a: G \to G$ by $T_a(x) = ax$ (T_a is left translation by a). In Exercise 1.5, we saw that T_a is a one-to-one correspondence, so that $T_a \in S_G$. The function τ sending a into T_a is thus a function from G to S_G.

We claim that τ is one-to-one and that τ is a homomorphism. If $a \neq b$ are elements of G, then $T_a(1) = a \neq b = T_b(1)$, so that $T_a \neq T_b$ and $\tau(a) \neq \tau(b)$; therefore, τ is one-to-one. Finally, consider $\tau(ab) = T_{ab}$ and $\tau(a)\tau(b) = T_a T_b$. In order to show that these permutations are the same, we must show that they assign the same value to each $x \in G$. But $T_{ab}(x) = (ab)x$, and $T_a T_b(x) = T_a(bx) = a(bx)$, and these are the same by associativity. ∎

It follows from Cayley's theorem and Exercise 3.20 that every finite group can be imbedded in a group that can be generated by two elements.

Exercise 3.36 If G is a finite group, each T_a in the above proof is a regular permutation. (*Hint:* The orbits of T_a are the right cosets of $[a]$ in G.) For this reason, the homomorphism τ is called the (left) **regular representation** of G.

COROLLARY 3.17 Let G be a finite group of order n, and let F be a field. G is isomorphic to a subgroup of the multiplicative group $M_n(F)$ of all $n \times n$ nonsingular matrices over F.

Proof By Cayley's theorem, there is an imbedding $\tau: G \to S_n$. By Exercise 3.15, there is an isomorphism $\theta: S_n \to P_n$, the multiplicative group of $n \times n$ permutation matrices. Since the entries of a permutation matrix are only 0 and 1, we may consider P_n as a subgroup of $M_n(F)$. ∎

THEOREM 3.18   Let B be a subgroup of index n in a group G. There is a homomorphism $\rho: G \to S_n$ whose kernel is contained in B. Indeed, kernel $\rho = \bigcap_{x \in G} xBx^{-1}$.

Proof   Let $X = \{g_1B, \cdots, g_nB\}$ be the family of all left cosets of B in G. If $a \in G$, we may define a function $\rho(a): X \to X$ by: $\rho(a)$ sends each g_iB into ag_iB. It is easy to check that each $\rho(a)$ is a permutation and that $\rho: G \to S_X \approx S_n$, defined by $a \to \rho(a)$, is a homomorphism.

If $a \in$ kernel ρ, then $\rho(a)$ is the identity permutation, i.e., $ag_iB = g_iB$ for all i. There are thus elements b_i, b_i' in B with $ag_ib_i = g_ib_i'$ for all i. Therefore,

$$a = g_ib_i'b_i^{-1}g_i^{-1} \in g_iBg_i^{-1} \qquad \text{for all } i,$$

and so

$$a \in \bigcap_i g_iBg_i^{-1}.$$

Since every subgroup $xBx^{-1} = g_iBg_i^{-1}$ for some i, it follows that kernel $\rho \subset \bigcap_{x \in G} xBx^{-1}$. The reverse inclusion is easy to prove and is left to the reader. ∎

It follows immediately that $\bigcap_{x \in G} xBx^{-1}$ is a normal subgroup of G, but this follows easily from the definitions.

COROLLARY 3.19   If an infinite group G contains a proper subgroup B of finite index, then G contains a proper normal subgroup of finite index.

Proof   Let B have index n. By Theorem 3.18, there is a homomorphism $\rho: G \to S_n$ whose kernel K is contained in B. Therefore, $K \lhd G$, and since G/K is isomorphic to a subgroup of the finite group S_n, K has finite index in G. ∎

COROLLARY 3.20   A simple group G containing a proper subgroup B of index n can be imbedded in S_n.

Proof   By Theorem 3.18, there is a homomorphism $\rho: G \to S_n$ whose kernel K is contained in B. Since G is simple, $K = \{1\}$ or

$K = G$; since B is proper, $K \subset B \neq G$. Therefore, $K = \{1\}$ and ρ is one-to-one. ∎

Corollary 3.20 provides a substantial improvement over Cayley's theorem, at least for simple groups. For example, if $G \approx A_5$, then Cayley's theorem asserts that G can be imbedded in S_{60}. On the other hand, G contains a subgroup B of order 12 (isomorphic to A_4) and hence of index 5; therefore, Corollary 3.20 asserts that G can be imbedded in S_5.

Counting Orbits

Let G be a group of permutations acting on a set X, i.e., G is a subgroup of S_X. Two elements x and y in X are **G-equivalent** in case there is some $t \in G$ with $t(x) = y$.

Definition The G-equivalence classes of X are called the **orbits** of G.

If $G = [\alpha]$, where α is a permutation, then this notion of equivalence and orbit is precisely our earlier one. If G is not cyclic, we have a generalization of our previous definition, which allows us to translate several earlier definitions into the language of orbits. By the Cayley theorem, any subgroup S of G is a group of permutations on G: If $s \in S$, s acts on G by left translation. The orbits of S are just the right cosets of S in G, as the reader should verify.

A second example is provided by conjugations. If we denote the set of all conjugations of G by $I(G)$, then it is easily checked that $I(G)$ is a group of permutations on G. In this case, the orbits are just the conjugacy classes of G.

THEOREM 3.21 Let X be a finite set, and let G be a group of permutations on X. If N is the number of orbits of G, then

$$N = \frac{1}{|G|} \sum_{t \in G} F(t),$$

where $F(t)$ is the number of x in X that are fixed by t.

Proof If $x \in X$, then the set of all $t \in G$ that fix x forms a subgroup H_x of G (called the **stabilizer** of x). We claim that there are exactly $r = [G:H_x]$ elements $y \in X$ that are G-equivalent to x. Let $t_1H_x, \cdots, t_rH_x$ be the distinct left cosets of H_x in G. If $t \in t_iH_x$, then $t(x) = t_i(x)$, but if $i \neq j$, then $t_i(x) \neq t_j(x)$ lest $t_i^{-1}t_j$ fix x. The size of the orbit of x is thus $r = [G:H_x]$, as we claimed. It follows that if y and x are in the same orbit, then $|H_y| = |G|/r = |H_x|$.[4]

In the sum $\sum_{t \in G} F(t)$, each element $x \in X$ is counted $|H_x|$ times. Therefore, the elements constituting the orbit of x are collectively counted $[G:H_x]|H_x| = |G|$ times. Each orbit thus contributes $|G|$ to the sum, so that $\sum_{t \in G} F(t) = N|G|$. ∎

COROLLARY 3.22   Let X be a finite set and let G be a group of permutations on X. The size of every orbit of G divides $|G|$.

Proof   We saw in the proof of the theorem that the size of the orbit containing x is $[G:H_x]$, where H_x is the stabilizer of x. ∎

Exercises   3.37   Use Theorem 3.21 to prove Lagrange's theorem.
   3.38   In the case of $I(G)$ acting on G, prove that the stabilizer of x is $C_G(x)$, the centralizer of x in G.

It is clear that we get more information about a permutation group G if we know it lies in a small S_n rather than in a larger one. One indication that the imbedding of G in S_n is best (i.e., that n is as small as possible) is that G is "dense" in S_n in the sense of the following definition.

Definition   A permutation group G on X is **transitive** in case, for each x and $y \in X$, there is a $t \in G$ with $t(x) = y$.

(One also speaks of degrees of transitivity ("k-ply transitivity") which mean that a group is even more densely imbedded in a symmetric group.)

Exercise   3.39   Let G be finite and let $n < |G|$. G is isomorphic to a transitive subgroup of S_n if and only if G contains a subgroup H

---

[4] In fact, one can prove that H_x and H_y are isomorphic: If $t(y) = x$, then $H_y = t^{-1}H_xt$.

of index n such that neither H nor any proper subgroup of H is normal in G. (*Hint:* For sufficiency, use Theorem 3.18; for necessity, take for H the stabilizer of any symbol.)

Theorem 3.21 was used by G. Polya to solve some interesting combinatorial problems in chemistry; we illustrate his technique here. Given q distinct colors, how many striped neckties are there having n stripes (of equal width)? Clearly, the two neckties below are the same.

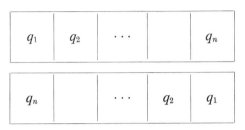

If, then, X is the set of all ordered sets of n colored boxes, then the cyclic group $G = \{1, t\}$ operates on X, where t is the permutation

$$t = \begin{pmatrix} 1 & 2 & \cdots & n \\ n & n-1 & \cdots & 1 \end{pmatrix},$$

and a necktie is just an orbit of G. In order to apply Theorem 3.21, we need only compute $F(1)$ and $F(t)$. There are q^n elements in X and each is fixed by the identity; hence $F(1) = q^n$. To compute $F(t)$, we first observe that since t has order 2, t is a product of disjoint transpositions. In fact, t is a product of k disjoint transpositions, where $k = \left[\dfrac{n+1}{2}\right]$: If $n = 2k$, then $t = (1\ n)(2\ n-1) \cdots (k\ k+1)$; if $n = 2k + 1$, then $t = (1\ n)(2\ n-1) \cdots (k\ k+2)$. An ordered set of $n = 2k$ colored boxes is thus fixed by t if and only if $q_1 = q_n$, $q_2 = q_{n-1}, \cdots, q_k = q_{k+1}$; there is a similar statement if $n = 2k + 1$. We conclude that

$$F(t) = q^k = q^{[(n+1)/2]}.$$

The number of neckties is thus

$$\tfrac{1}{2}(q^n + q^{[(n+1)/2]}).$$

Exercises   *3.40   If there are q colors available, prove that there are

$$\tfrac{1}{4}(q^{n^2} + 2q^{[(n^2+3)/4]} + q^{[(n^2+1)]/2})$$

distinct $n \times n$ colored tablecloths. (*Hint:* The group is a cyclic group of order 4 consisting of rotations of 0°, 90°, 180°, and 270°. The generator of the group is a permutation of n^2 ordered colored boxes and it is a product of disjoint 4-cycles.)

*3.41   If there are q colors available, prove that there are

$$\frac{1}{n} \sum_{d|n} \varphi\left(\frac{n}{d}\right) q^d$$

colored roulette wheels having n compartments. In this formula, φ is the Euler φ-function, and the summation ranges over all divisors d of n. (*Hint:* The group is a cyclic group of order n operating by rotating by multiples of $(360/n)°$. Using Exercise 3.12 for $\alpha = (1\ 2 \cdots n)$, show that there are

$$\frac{1}{n} \sum_{0 \le k < n} q^{(n,k)}$$

roulette wheels. The desired formula arises from this one by collecting terms having the same exponent.)

We recommend the book by Burnside (see Bibliography) to the reader who wishes to study these ideas further. The book of H. Wielandt, *Finite Permutation Groups*, Academic Press, 1964, is also highly recommended.

Chapter 4

Finite Direct Products

Direct Products

Definition If H and K are groups, the **(external)** **direct product** of H and K, denoted $H \times K$, is the set of all ordered pairs (h,k), where $h \in H$ and $k \in K$, with the binary operation

$$(h,k)(h',k') = (hh',kk').$$

It is easy to check that $H \times K$ is a group containing isomorphic copies of H and K, namely, $H \times \{1\}$ and $\{1\} \times K$.

Exercises 4.1 The operation of direct product is commutative: For any groups H and K, $H \times K \approx K \times H$.

4.2 The operation of direct product is associative: For any three groups H_1, H_2, H_3, $(H_1 \times H_2) \times H_3 \approx H_1 \times (H_2 \times H_3)$. Conclude that the notations $H_1 \times H_2 \times \cdots \times H_m$ and $\prod_{i=1}^{m} H_i$ are unambiguous.

4.3 $H \times \{1\}$ and $\{1\} \times K$ are normal subgroups of $H \times K$; these two subgroups generate $H \times K$ and their intersection is $\{(1,1)\}$.

4.4 The elements $(h,1)$ and $(1,k)$ commute. Conclude that if $(h,k)^n = (1,1)$, then $h^n = 1$ and $k^n = 1$.

4.5 Prove that $Z\left(\prod_{i=1} H_i\right) = \prod_{i=1} Z(H_i)$. Conclude that a direct product of groups is abelian if and only if each factor is abelian.

*4.6 Let G be an abelian group, and let $f: H \to G$ and $g: K \to G$ be homomorphisms. Prove that there exists a unique homomorphism $F: H \times K \rightarrow G$ that extends both f and g, i.e., $F(h,1) = f(h)$ and $F(1,k) = g(k)$. Show that this is false if G is not abelian.

Notation   If n is a positive integer, then $\sigma(n)$ will denote the cyclic group of order n.

Such a notation is legitimate, for we have already proven in Exercise 2.26 that any two cyclic groups of order n are isomorphic.

Exercises (contd.)   4.7 If $(m,n) = 1$, then $\sigma(mn) \approx \sigma(m) \times \sigma(n)$.

4.8   If p is prime, prove that $\sigma(p^2) \not\approx \sigma(p) \times \sigma(p)$.

We now adopt another point of view. It is easy to multiply two polynomials together; it is harder to factor a given polynomial. We have just seen how to "multiply" two groups together; can we "factor" a given group?

THEOREM 4.1   Let G be a group with normal subgroups H and K; if $H \cap K = \{1\}$ and $HK = G$, then $G \approx H \times K$.

Proof   Let $a \in G$. Since $HK = G$, $a = hk$ for some $h \in H$ and $k \in K$, and we claim that h and k are uniquely determined by a. If $a = h_1k_1$, then $hk = h_1k_1$ and $h^{-1}h_1 = kk_1^{-1}$. This element is simultaneously in H and K, i.e., in $H \cap K = \{1\}$; hence, $h = h_1$ and $k = k_1$.

Define $f: G \rightarrow H \times K$ by $f(a) = (h,k)$, where $a = hk$. Is f a homomorphism? If $a = hk$ and $a' = h'k'$, then $aa' = hkh'k'$ which is not in the proper form for evaluating f. Were it true that $kh' = h'k$, however, then we would be done. Indeed, we prove that for any $h \in H$ and $k \in K$, $hk = kh$. Consider the commutator $h^{-1}k^{-1}hk$. Now $(h^{-1}k^{-1}h)k \in K$, since K is normal, and $h^{-1}(k^{-1}hk) \in H$, since H is normal. Therefore, this commutator is in $H \cap K = \{1\}$, and so $hk = kh$. We let the reader prove that f is a one-to-one correspondence. ∎

We pause to give an example that shows that all of the hypotheses in Theorem 4.1 are necessary. Let $G = S_3$, $H = A_3$ and $K = [(12)]$. It is easy to check that $H \cap K = \{1\}$ and that $HK = G$. Note that H is normal, but that K is not. Were $S_3 = H \times K$, then $S_3 \approx \sigma(3) \times \sigma(2)$ which is abelian, a contradiction.

THEOREM 4.2 Let $G = H \times K$, and let $H_1 \lhd H$ and $K_1 \lhd K$. Then $H_1 \times K_1 \lhd G$ and $G/(H_1 \times K_1) \approx (H/H_1) \times (K/K_1)$.

Proof Let $\pi\colon H \to H/H_1$ and $\rho\colon K \to K/K_1$ be the natural maps. Define $F\colon G \to (H/H_1) \times (K/K_1)$ by $F(h,k) = (\pi h, \rho k)$. The kernel of F is $H_1 \times K_1$ and the image of F is $(H/H_1) \times (K/K_1)$. $\blacksquare$

COROLLARY 4.3 If $G = H \times K$, then $G/(H \times \{1\}) \approx K$.

The elements of an external direct product are ordered pairs, a rather restrictive condition. We say that a group G is the **(internal) direct product** of H and K if H and K are normal subgroups of G with $H \cap K = \{1\}$ and $H \vee K = HK = G$. The emphasis here is that the factors themselves, not merely isomorphic copies of them, lie in G. (If $G = H \times K$ is an external direct product, then it is also the internal direct product of $H \times \{1\}$ and $\{1\} \times K$, but it is not the internal direct product of H and K.) The two versions of direct product, of course, yield isomorphic groups. In the future, we shall not distinguish between external and internal, using "direct product" without an adjective. In almost all cases, however, our point of view is internal.

Exercises 4.9 We denote by 0 the trivial homomorphism that sends every element into the identity. If G is an additive abelian group, prove that $G \approx H \times K$ if and only if there exist homomorphisms

$$H \underset{q}{\overset{i}{\rightleftarrows}} G \underset{j}{\overset{p}{\rightleftarrows}} K$$

with $q \circ i = 1\colon H$ (the identity function on H), $p \circ j = 1\colon K$, $p \circ i = 0$, $q \circ j = 0$, and $j \circ q(x) + i \circ p(x) = x$ for all $x \in G$.

4.10 Let G be a group with normal subgroups H and K. $G \approx H \times K$ if and only if each $a \in G$ has a unique expression $a = hk$, where $h \in H$ and $k \in K$.

4.11 If G is a group with normal subgroups $H_1, \cdots, H_m$, then $G \approx \prod_{i=1}^{m} H_i$ if and only if $G = \left[\bigcup_{i=1}^{m} H_i \right]$, and for all j, $H_j \cap \left[\bigcup_{i \neq j} H_i \right] = \{1\}$.

4.12. Let $N \lhd G = H \times K$. Prove that either N is abelian or N intersects one of the factors H or K nontrivially.

4.13   Give an example of a group $H \times K$ that contains a nontrivial normal subgroup N such that $N \cap H = \{1\}$ and $N \cap K = \{1\}$. Conclude that if $N \lhd H \times K$, then $N \neq (N \cap H) \times (N \cap K)$ is possible.

The Basis Theorem

For the next three sections, we shall deal exclusively with abelian groups. As is the usual custom, we now shift from the multiplicative notation to the additive notation. The following dictionary should prove useful.

$$
\begin{array}{ccc}
ab & \cdots\cdots\cdots & a + b \\
a^{-1} & \cdots\cdots\cdots & -a \\
1 & \cdots\cdots\cdots & 0 \\
a^n & \cdots\cdots\cdots & na \\
ab^{-1} & \cdots\cdots\cdots & a - b \\
HK & \cdots\cdots\cdots & H + K \\
Ha & \cdots\cdots\cdots & a + H \\
\text{direct product} & \cdots\cdots\cdots & \text{direct sum} \\
H \times K & \cdots\cdots\cdots & H \oplus K \\
\displaystyle\prod_{i=1}^{m} H_i & \cdots\cdots\cdots & \displaystyle\sum_{i=1}^{m} H_i
\end{array}
$$

If $G = H \times K$, H is called a **direct factor** of G; in additive notation, H is a **direct summand** of G.

Two remarks that hold for abelian groups greatly simplify our study:

1. If $a, b \in G$ and $n \in Z$, then $n(a + b) = na + nb$.
2. If H is a nonempty subset of G, then $[H]$ is the set of all (finite) linear combinations of elements of H with coefficients in Z.

Definition   Let p be a prime. A group G is **p-primary** (or is a **p-group**) in case every element in G has order a power of p.

If one is working wholly in the context of abelian groups, he uses the term *p-primary*; otherwise, the usage of *p-group* is preferred.

THEOREM 4.4 (*Primary Decomposition*)   Every finite abelian group G is a direct sum of p-primary groups.

Proof   For any prime p, let G_p be the set of all elements in G whose order is a power of p. Now $0 \in G_p$, and since G is abelian, G_p is a subgroup of G. We claim that $G = \sum G_p$, where the indices range over all primes p dividing $|G|$; we use the criterion of Exercise 4.11.

(i)   Let $x \in G$, $x \neq 0$, and let the order of x be n. By the fundamental theorem of arithmetic (see Appendix V), $n = p_1^{e_1} p_2^{e_2} \cdots p_k^{e_k}$, where the p_i are distinct primes and the exponents $e_i \geq 1$. Set $n_i = n/p_i^{e_i}$, and observe that $(n_1, n_2, \cdots, n_k) = 1$ [1] (for what prime could be a common divisor of the n_i?). Therefore, there exist integers m_i such that $\sum m_i n_i = 1$; hence, $\sum (m_i n_i x) = x$. Note that $p_i^{e_i}(m_i n_i x) = m_i n x = 0$, so that $m_i n_i x \in G_{p_i}$. We conclude that the collection of G_p generates G.

(ii)   Suppose $x \in G_p \cap \left[\bigcup_{q \neq p} G_q \right]$. On the one hand, $p^e x = 0$ for some e; on the other hand, $x = \sum x_q$, where $q^{e_q} x_q = 0$ for exponents e_q. If we set $t = \Pi q^{e_q}$, then $tx = 0$. Clearly, $(p^e, t) = 1$, so that there are integers a and b with $ap^e + bt = 1$. Therefore, $x = ap^e x + btx = 0$. ∎

Definition   The subgroups G_p of G are called the **primary components** of G.

We plan to show that every finite abelian group is a direct sum of cyclic groups. Theorem 4.4 allows us to consider, without loss of generality, the special case of finite p-primary abelian groups.

Exercise   4.14   Let G be a p-primary abelian group, and let $y_1, \cdots, y_t$ be elements of G for which

$$[y_1, \cdots, y_t] = [y_1] \oplus \cdots \oplus [y_t].$$

---

[1] A *common divisor* of a set of integers $\{n_1, \cdots, n_k\}$ is a nonzero integer c that divides each n_i; the *greatest common divisor* (gcd), denoted $(n_1, \cdots, n_k)$, is a positive common divisor that is divisible by every common divisor. It may be shown, in a manner analogous to the special case of a set of two integers, that the gcd exists and is a linear combination of $n_1, \cdots, n_k$. (See Appendix V.)

(a) If $z_1, \cdots, z_t$ are elements of G with $pz_i = y_i$, for all i, then $[z_1, \cdots, z_t] = [z_1] \oplus \cdots \oplus [z_t]$.

(b) If $k_1, \cdots, k_t$ are integers, then

$$[k_1 y_1, \cdots, k_t y_t] = [k_1 y_1] \oplus \cdots \oplus [k_t y_t].$$

Definition   Let G be an abelian group and m a positive integer.

$$mG = \{mx : x \in G\}.$$

It is immediate that mG is a subgroup of G. In fact, mG is the image of the homomorphism $f : G \to G$ defined by $f(x) = mx$.

LEMMA 4.5   An abelian group G with $pG = \{0\}$ is a vector space over Z_p, and it is a direct sum of cyclic groups when G is finite.

Proof   Let $\bar{k}$ denote the residue class of the integer k in Z_p. Define a scalar multiplication on G by

$$\bar{k}x = kx, \quad \text{where } x \in G.$$

This operation is well defined, for if $k \equiv k' \bmod(p)$, then $k - k' = mp$ for some integer m, so that

$$(k - k')x = mpx = 0;$$

hence,

$$kx = k'x.$$

It is easily checked that G is a vector space over Z_p, and as such has a basis $\{x_1, x_2, \cdots, x_t\}$ when G is finite. We let the reader prove, using Exercise 4.11, that G is the direct sum of the $[x_i]$. ∎

We exploit the relationship between direct sums and independence in the coming proof.

THEOREM 4.6 (Basis Theorem)   Every finite abelian group G is a direct sum of primary cyclic groups.

Proof   By Theorem 4.4, we may assume that G is p-primary. We perform an induction on m, where m is an integer such that $p^m G = \{0\}$. If $m = 1$, the theorem is just Lemma 4.5.

Suppose that $p^{m+1}G = \{0\}$. If $H = pG$, then $p^m H = \{0\}$. By induction,

$$H = pG = \sum [y_i].$$

Since $y_i \in pG$, there are elements $z_i \in G$ with $pz_i = y_i$. If L is the subgroup of G generated by the z_i, then

$$L = \sum [z_i],$$

as Exercise 4.14(a) shows.

We claim that L is a direct summand of G, and so we must produce a complementary subgroup M of G such that $L \oplus M = G$.

If $G[p] = \{x \in G : px = 0\}$, then $p(G[p]) = \{0\}$, so that $G[p]$ is a vector space over Z_p, by Lemma 4.5. If k_i is the order of y_i, then $k_i z_i$ has order p, and so

$$k_i z_i \in G[p].$$

By Exercise 4.14(b), the set of $k_i z_i$ is an independent subset of the vector space $G[p]$. Therefore, we can extend this set to a basis of $G[p]$, i.e., there are elements $\{x_1, x_2, \cdots, x_s\}$ such that

$$\{\text{the } k_i z_i, x_1, x_2, \cdots, x_s\}$$

is a basis of $G[p]$. Let $M = [x_1, x_2, \cdots, x_s]$. Observe that, as in the proof of Lemma 4.5,

$$M = \sum [x_j].$$

We now show that $G = L \oplus M$, which will complete the proof.

(i) $L \cap M = \{0\}$. If $x \in L \cap M$, then $x = \sum b_i z_i = \sum a_j x_j$. Now $px = 0$ (since $x \in M$), so that $\sum pb_i z_i = 0$, which implies

$$0 = pb_i z_i = b_i y_i, \qquad \text{for all } i.$$

Hence, $b_i = b_i' k_i$ for some integers b_i' by Exercise 2.16. Therefore,

$$0 = \sum b_i' k_i z_i - \sum a_j x_j,$$

so that independence implies each term is 0; thus, $x = 0$.

(ii) $G = L + M$. Let $x \in G$. Now

$$px = \sum c_i y_i = \sum pc_i z_i,$$

so that

$$p(x - \sum c_i z_i) = 0,$$

and
$$x - \sum c_i z_i \in G[p].$$
Therefore,
$$x - \sum c_i z_i = \sum a_j x_j + \sum b_i k_i z_i,$$
i.e.,
$$x = \sum (c_i + b_i k_i) z_i + \sum a_j x_j \in L + M. \blacksquare$$

Exercises   4.15   Let G be a finite abelian group of order n. If m divides n, show that G contains a subgroup of order m. (Compare with Theorem 3.11.)

4.16   A finite abelian p-primary group is generated by its elements of largest order.

4.17   Let F be a finite field and let G be the multiplicative group consisting of its nonzero elements. Prove that G is cyclic. (*Hint:* Suppose G is not cyclic; use Theorem 4.6 and the theorem that a polynomial of degree k over F has at most k roots in F.)

4.18   If $G = \sum_{i=1}^{n} H_i$, then $mG = \sum_{i=1}^{n} mH_i$.

4.19   If $G = \sum_{i=1}^{n} H_i$, then $G[p] = \sum_{i=1}^{n} (H_i[p])$.

4.20   Let H be a finite abelian group with $pH = \{0\}$ for some prime p. (H is called an **elementary** abelian group.) Prove that any two decompositions of H into a direct sum of cyclic groups have the same number of summands. Denote this number $d(H)$. (The astute reader will note that $d(H)$ is the dimension of H considered as a vector space over Z_p.)

The Fundamental Theorem of Finite Abelian Groups

We now have quite a bit of information about finite abelian groups, but we still have not answered the basic question: If G and H are finite abelian groups, when are they isomorphic? Since both G and H are direct sums of cyclic groups, your first guess is that $G \approx H$ if they have the same number of summands of each kind. There are two things wrong with this guess. First of all, since, e.g., $\sigma(6) \approx$

$\sigma(3) \oplus \sigma(2)$, we had better require that G and H have the same number of *primary* summands of each kind. Our second objection is much more serious. How can we count summands at all; to do so would require a unique factorization theorem analogous to the fundamental theorem of arithmetic, where the analog of a prime number is a primary cyclic group. Such an analog does exist; it is called the fundamental theorem of finite abelian groups, and it is this theorem we now discuss.

Let G be a finite p-primary abelian group, and let $G = \sum \sigma_i$, where each σ_i is a cyclic subgroup of G. We seek a way to count the number of σ_i that have order precisely p^n (n fixed). Now $p^n G = \sum p^n \sigma_i$ (Exercise 4.18), so that multiplying by p^n erases all the summands of order $\leq p^n$. Similarly, multiplying by p^{n+1} erases all summands of order $\leq p^{n+1}$. Since $p^n G / p^{n+1} G$ is a group in which every nonzero element has order p, Exercise 4.20 allows us to count its cyclic summands. One might reasonably expect that this number is, in fact, the number of summands of G of order p^{n+1}. Let's look. Suppose $G = \sigma(p) + \sigma(p^3)$. We calculate that $p^0 G = G$; $pG = p\sigma(p^3)$; $p^2 G = p^2 \sigma(p^3)$; $p^3 G = \{0\}$. Hence (notation as in Exercise 4.20), $d(p^0 G / pG) = 2$; $d(pG/p^2 G) = 1$; $d(p^2 G / p^3 G) = 1$, $d(p^3 G / p^4 G) = 0$, etc. We get some numbers, but it is not what we expected. (It is not difficult to see that $d(p^n G / p^{n+1} G)$ is the number of cyclic summands of order $\geq p^{n+1}$.)

Let us be more clever. How can we distinguish between those elements in $p^n G$ coming from σ_i of order p^{n+1} and those elements in $p^n G$ coming from σ_i of larger order? Let a_i be a generator of σ_i. If $|\sigma_i| = p^{n+1}$, then $p^n a_i$ has order p; if $|\sigma_i| > p^{n+1}$, then $p^n a_i$ does not have order p. This elementary observation suggests that we amend our original idea by replacing $p^n G$ by $p^n G \cap G[p]$; i.e., we shall be interested only in elements of order p.

Notation   If G is a finite p-primary abelian group, and if $n \geq 0$ is an integer, then

$$U(n,G) = d\left(\frac{p^n G \cap G[p]}{p^{n+1} G \cap G[p]}\right).$$

Experimenting with $G = \sigma(p) \oplus \sigma(p^3)$ gives the following data: $U(0,G) = 1$; $U(1,G) = 0$; $U(2,G) = 1$; all other U are 0. This is much more satisfactory; in this example, $U(n,G)$ is the number of cyclic summands of G of order p^{n+1}.

THEOREM 4.7   Let G be a finite p-primary abelian group. Any two decompositions of G into a direct sum of cyclic groups have the same number of summands of each order. In fact, the number of cyclic summands of order p^{n+1} is $U(n,G)$.

Proof   Let $G = \sum \sigma_i$, where each σ_i is a cyclic subgroup of G. We claim that the number of σ_i of order p^{n+1} is $U(n,G)$. In order to prove this, we adopt the following notation:

$$G = \sum \sigma(p) \oplus \sum \sigma(p^2) \oplus \cdots \oplus \sum \sigma(p^t),$$

where we have just collected like terms; we allow the case $\sum \sigma(p^k) = \{0\}$ if there are no summands of order p^k. Now, by Exercise 4.19,

$$G[p] = \sum \sigma(p) \oplus \sum p\sigma(p^2) \oplus \cdots \oplus \sum p^{t-1}\sigma(p^t),$$

while

$$p^nG = \sum p^n\sigma(p^{n+1}) \oplus \cdots \oplus \sum p^n\sigma(p^t) \qquad (n \leq t).$$

Hence, for all $n < t$,

$$p^nG \cap G[p] = \sum p^n\sigma(p^{n+1}) \oplus \sum p^{n+1}\sigma(p^{n+2}) \oplus \cdots \oplus \sum p^{t-1}\sigma(p^t),$$

so that we finally obtain, by Corollary 4.3,

$$p^nG \cap G[p]/p^{n+1}G \cap G[p] \approx \sum p^n\sigma(p^{n+1}).$$

Therefore, $U(n,G)$ is the number of summands σ_i of order p^{n+1}. Now the important observation is that the number $U(n,G)$ is defined solely in terms of G; $U(n,G)$ does not in any way depend on the particular decomposition of G into a direct sum of cyclic groups! Thus, the number of σ_i of order p^n is the same for any two decompositions of G. ∎

THEOREM 4.8   Let G and H be finite p-primary abelian groups. Then $G \approx H$ if and only if $U(n,G) = U(n,H)$ for all $n \geq 0$.

Proof   Suppose $f: G \to H$ is an isomorphism. Now $G = \sum \sigma_i$, where each σ_i is cyclic. By Theorem 4.7, $U(n,G)$ is the number of σ_i of order p^{n+1}. Now

$$H = f(G) = \sum f(\sigma_i),$$

and $f(\sigma_i) \approx \sigma_i$ for all i. For each n, there are thus $U(n,G)$ summands $f(\sigma_i)$ of H of order p^{n+1}. But, by Theorem 4.7, this number is $U(n,H)$. Therefore, $U(n,G) = U(n,H)$ for all $n \geq 0$.
The converse is left to the reader. ∎

We have only to delete the adjective "p-primary" in Theorems 4.7 and 4.8 to finish our discussion. The hard work has already been done, and the following three statements (whose proofs may be supplied by the reader) complete the picture.

LEMMA 4.9   Let G and H be finite abelian groups, and let $f\colon G \to H$ be a homomorphism. For each p,

$$f(G_p) \subset H_p.$$

THEOREM 4.10   Let G and H be finite abelian groups; $G \approx H$ if and only if $G_p \approx H_p$ for all primes p.

THEOREM 4.11 (*Fundamental Theorem of Finite Abelian Groups*)   Let G be a finite abelian group. Any two decompositions of G into direct sums of primary cyclic groups have the same number of summands of each order.

Exercises   4.21   Let G and H be finite abelian groups. If $G \oplus G \approx H \oplus H$, prove that $G \approx H$.
4.22   Suppose A, B, and C are finite abelian groups. If $A \oplus B \approx A \oplus C$, then $B \approx C$.
4.23   How many nonisomorphic abelian groups are there of order 360?
4.24   Let H be a subgroup of a finite abelian group G. Prove that G contains a subgroup isomorphic to G/H.
4.25   If G is an elementary abelian group, there exist subgroups H_i of G such that
  (i) $H_i \cap H_j = \{0\}$ if $i \neq j$;
  (ii) $G = \bigcup H_i$ (set-theoretical union).
(*Hint:* Every vector space is the union of lines passing through the origin.)
*4.26   If G is a finite p-primary group, then

$$U(n,G) = d(p^n G/p^{n+1}G) - d(p^{n+1}G/p^{n+2}G).$$

Modules and Matrices

We digress from our study of groups to apply Theorems 4.6 and 4.11 to linear algebra; we shall prove the existence and uniqueness of the rational canonical form of a square matrix over an arbitrary field F. At this stage, this project is one of translation, so that we need only introduce a new vocabulary. Our exposition is complete, but since we are assuming that the reader is comfortable with linear algebra, our pace is not leisurely.

Definition   Let R be a commutative ring with unit. An **ideal** I in R is a nonempty subset of R such that
   (i) $a, b \in I$ imply $a - b \in R$.
   (ii) $a \in I$ and $r \in R$ imply that $ra \in I$.
An important example of an ideal is the set of all multiples of a fixed $r_0 \in R$ by elements of R; this ideal is denoted (r_0) and is called the **principal ideal generated by** r_0. Thus,

$$(r_0) = \{x \in R: x = rr_0 \quad \text{for some } r \in R\}.$$

Definition   A **principal ideal domain** is a domain in which every ideal is a principal ideal. (A **domain** is a commutative ring with unit that has no divisors of zero.)

Examples   **1**   In Z, condition (ii) follows from (i); since every subgroup of Z is cyclic, every ideal in Z is principal.
   2   If F is any field, then the only ideals in F are $\{0\}$ and F itself; since $\{0\} = (0)$ and $F = (1)$, F is a principal ideal domain.
   3   Let F be a field and let $F[x]$ be the ring of polynomials in x with coefficients in F. The reader may prove that any nonzero ideal I in $F[x]$ consists precisely of all the multiples (by polynomials) of the monic polynomial of least degree which is in I.

For the remainder of this discussion, R will denote any of the three examples given above. (Indeed, our discussion is valid when R is any principal ideal domain, but we do not need the extra generality.)

Definition An abelian group V is an R-**module** in case a "scalar multiplication" is defined, i.e., there is a function $R \times V \to V$ (whose values we write in multiplicative notation) that satisfies:

(i) $(rs)\alpha = r(s\alpha)$;
(ii) $(r + s)\alpha = r\alpha + s\alpha$;
(iii) $r(\alpha + \beta) = r\alpha + r\beta$;
(iv) $1\alpha = \alpha$

for every $\alpha, \beta \in V$ and $r, s \in R$.

Thus, an R-module is just like a vector space except that we allow the scalars to be in R.

Examples **4** If $R = Z$, an R-module is an abelian group, for the axioms (i) to (iv) are always true for scalars in Z.

5 If $R = F$, an R-module is a vector space over F.

6 Let V be a vector space over F, and let $T: V \to V$ be a linear transformation. We make V into an $F[x]$-module that we denote V^T by defining

$$(a_0 + a_1x + a_2x^2 + \cdots + a_nx^n)\alpha$$
$$= a_0\alpha + a_1T\alpha + a_2T^2\alpha + \cdots + a_nT^n\alpha.$$

The reader should check that we have defined a scalar multiplication.

We present our vocabulary list now, after which we shall discuss some of its entries.

abelian group	R-module
prime	irreducible element
order of an element	order ideal of an element
finite order	nonzero order ideal
finite group	finitely generated module in which every element has finite order
order a power of p	order ideal generated by a power of an irreducible element
subgroup	submodule
cyclic subgroup	cyclic submodule

An element $u \in R$ is a **unit** in case $uv = 1$ for some $v \in R$. In Z, the only units are ± 1; in F any nonzero element is a unit; in $F[x]$, the nonzero constants are the units.

A nonzero element $r \in R$ is **irreducible** in case r is not a unit and in every factorization $r = ab$, either a or b is a unit. In Z, the irreducibles are the primes (positive and negative); F has no irreducibles; in $F[x]$, the irreducibles are the irreducible polynomials. (We are reminding the reader that $F[x]$ is a unique factorization domain, i.e., that the fundamental theorem of arithmetic is valid there.)

Let $\alpha \in V$, where V is an R-module. The **order ideal of** $\alpha = \{r \in R: r\alpha = 0\}$. It is quickly verified that the order ideal is an ideal. Because R is a principal ideal domain, this order ideal consists of all the multiples of a fixed element in R. In Z, we choose this fixed element to be positive (and we get the usual definition of order); in $F[x]$, we choose this fixed element to be the monic polynomial of smallest degree in the ideal. We say that $\alpha \in V$ has **finite order** if its order ideal is nonzero.

An R-module V is **finitely generated** in case it contains a finite number of elements $\alpha_1, \alpha_2, \cdots, \alpha_k$ such that any element in V is a linear combination of these α with coefficients in R. In particular, an R-module V is **cyclic** if it is generated by just one of its elements, i.e., there is an element $\alpha_0 \in V$ such that any element $\alpha \in V$ has the form $\alpha = r\alpha_0$ for some $r \in R$.

Finally, a subset W of the R-module V is a **submodule** of V in case it is a subgroup of V which is closed under scalar multiplication, i.e., if $\alpha \in W$ and $r \in R$, then $r\alpha \in W$.

Exercises   4.27 R itself is an R-module. Prove that the submodules of R are its ideals.

4.28   Let G be a finitely generated abelian group in which every element has finite order; prove that G is finite. (**Burnside's problem** asks whether every finitely generated group (not necessarily abelian!) in which every element has finite order is a finite group. Novikov announced, in 1959, that the answer is "no." The first published counterexample appeared in 1964, and is due to Golod and Šafarevič.)

THEOREM 4.12   Let R be a principal ideal domain, and let V be a finitely generated R-module in which every element has finite order. Then V is a direct sum of primary cyclic submodules.

Proof   If V is generated by $\alpha_1, \cdots, \alpha_k$, there are nonzero elements $s_i \in R$ with $s_i \alpha_i = 0$. The element $r = \Pi \, s_i$ is nonzero and $rV = \{0\}$. Since every principal ideal domain is a unique factorization domain (Appendix V), there is a factorization $r = p_1^{e_1} \cdots p_k^{e_k}$, where each p_i is irreducible. Now if $r_i = r/p_i^{e_i}$, then the gcd $(r_1, \cdots, r_k) = 1$ (for what irreducible element could divide each r_i?). There are thus elements $a_i \in R$ with $\sum a_i r_i = 1$ (Appendix V), and the reader may now translate the proof of the primary decomposition (Theorem 4.4).

In order to adapt the proofs of Lemma 4.5 and Theorem 4.6 to modules, we need an analog of the field Z_p. (The reader who is unfamiliar with quotient rings must wait until Chapter 8 (where they are defined and examined) before he can complete this proof.) If r is an irreducible element in R, then $R/(r)$ is a field. Furthermore, if V is a primary R-module such that $rV = \{0\}$, then V is a vector space over $R/(r)$; this is proved in exactly the same way as Lemma 4.5. The generalization of the basis theorem is now just translation. ∎

Let us now consider our special example of an $F[x]$-module V^T, where V is a vector space and $T \colon V \to V$ is a linear transformation. Here is our last vocabulary list.

module...............	V^T
generator of the........ order ideal of α	monic polynomial $m(x)$ of least degree such that $m(T)\alpha = 0$
submodule............	**invariant subspace** (a subspace W with $T(W) \subset W$)

If V is a finite-dimensional vector space over F, it is immediate that V^T is a finitely generated $F[x]$-module. Also, the Cayley-Hamilton theorem tells us that every element in V^T has finite order. These two observations are the hypotheses needed to apply Theorem 4.12.

COROLLARY 4.13   Let V be a finite-dimensional vector space over F, and let $T \colon V \to V$ be a linear transformation. Then V^T is a direct sum of primary cyclic invariant subspaces.

Exercises   4.29 A subspace W of V is a cyclic invariant subspace if and only if there is a vector $\alpha \in W$ such that the set $\{\alpha, T\alpha, T^2\alpha, \cdots, T^{k-1}\alpha\}$ is a basis of W (for some $k \geq 1$).

4.30 If W has a basis of the form

$$\{\alpha, T\alpha, T^2\alpha, \cdots, T^{k-1}\alpha\},$$

then adjoining $T^k\alpha$ to this set makes it dependent, and there is an equation

$$T^k\alpha = \sum_{i=0}^{k-1} b_i T^i \alpha.$$

Prove that the order ideal of α is generated by the polynomial

$$x^k - b_{k-1}x^{k-1} - \cdots - b_0.$$

We remind the reader of the correspondence between linear transformations on V and matrices. Let V be m-dimensional, and let $\{\epsilon_1, \epsilon_2, \cdots, \epsilon_m\}$ be an ordered basis of V. If $T: V \to V$, then, for each i, $T\epsilon_i$ is a linear combination of the ϵ_j:

$$T\epsilon_i = \sum a_{ji}\epsilon_j.$$

The matrix of T relative to the original basis of the ϵ_j is $A = (a_{ji})$. Therefore, the coordinates of $T\epsilon_1$ form the first *column* of A, the coordinates of $T\epsilon_2$ form the second column of A, and so forth.

Definition   Let $c(x) = x^k - b_{k-1}x^{k-1} - \cdots - b_0$. The **companion matrix of** $c(x)$ is the $k \times k$ matrix

$$\begin{bmatrix} 0 & 0 & 0 & \cdots & 0 & b_0 \\ 1 & 0 & 0 & \cdots & 0 & b_1 \\ 0 & 1 & 0 & \cdots & 0 & b_2 \\ 0 & 0 & 1 & \cdots & 0 & b_3 \\ \cdot & \cdot & \cdot & & \cdot & \cdot \\ \cdot & \cdot & \cdot & & \cdot & \cdot \\ \cdot & \cdot & \cdot & & \cdot & \cdot \\ 0 & 0 & 0 & \cdots & 1 & b_{k-1} \end{bmatrix}$$

Exercise   4.31   Let $T: V \to V$, and let W be a cyclic invariant subspace of V. If $\{\alpha, T\alpha, T^2\alpha, \cdots, T^{k-1}\alpha\}$ is a basis of W, the matrix of T on W is the $k \times k$ companion matrix of $c(x)$, where $c(x)$ generates the order ideal of α.

Definition   The companion matrix of $f(x)$ is **primary** if $f(x)$ is a power of an irreducible polynomial.

Definition   Let A be a $k \times k$ matrix and let B be an $m \times m$ matrix. The **direct sum** of A and B is the $(k + m) \times (k + m)$ matrix

$$\begin{bmatrix} A & 0 \\ 0 & B \end{bmatrix}.$$

The analogous definition for the direct sum of a finite number of matrices may be supplied by the reader. Note that the direct sum of A and B is similar to the direct sum of B and A.

THEOREM 4.14   Every $n \times n$ matrix A over a field F is similar to a direct sum of primary companion matrices.

Proof   Let V be an n-dimensional vector space over F; choose some ordered basis of V. The matrix A now defines a linear transformation $T: V \rightarrow V$, for its columns tell us how to transform the chosen basis of V. Given this T, we can make V into an $F[x]$-module V^T. By Corollary 4.13, V^T is a direct sum of primary cyclic invariant subspaces W_i; let α_i be a generator of W_i. By Exercise 4.29, a new basis of V is

$$\{\alpha_1, T\alpha_1, T^2\alpha_1, \cdots ; \alpha_2, T\alpha_2, T^2\alpha_2, \cdots ; \cdots ; \alpha_m, T\alpha_m, T^2\alpha_m, \cdots \}.$$

The matrix B of T with respect to this new basis is a direct sum of primary companion matrices, by Exercise 4.31. Finally, A and B are similar, for they represent the same linear transformation relative to different bases of V. ∎

A direct sum of primary companion matrices is called a **rational canonical form**; Theorem 4.14 tells us that every $n \times n$ matrix over a field F is similar to a rational canonical form. A rational canonical form completely determines its constituent companion matrices; the companion matrices, in turn, completely determine their characteristic polynomials. These polynomials are called the **elementary divisors** of A. It is known that the product of the elementary divisors is the characteristic polynomial of A.

In Chapter 8, we shall study certain groups whose elements are nonsingular matrices. Since the order of an element is the same as the order of any of its conjugates, we can compute the order of a matrix by computing the order of its canonical form. Unfortunately, it is difficult to compute powers of companion matrices. If the field

F is a large one, however, there is another canonical form we can use, and the powers of this form are easily calculated.

Definition   A $k \times k$ **Jordan block** is a $k \times k$ matrix of the form

$$\begin{bmatrix} a & 0 & 0 & \cdots & 0 & 0 \\ 1 & a & 0 & \cdots & 0 & 0 \\ 0 & 1 & a & \cdots & 0 & 0 \\ 0 & 0 & 1 & \cdots & 0 & 0 \\ \cdot & \cdot & \cdot & & \cdot & \cdot \\ \cdot & \cdot & \cdot & & \cdot & \cdot \\ \cdot & \cdot & \cdot & \cdots & a & 0 \\ 0 & 0 & 0 & \cdots & 1 & a \end{bmatrix}$$

(A 1×1 Jordan block is a 1×1 matrix (a).)

Exercises   4.32   Prove that for every positive integer k,

$$\begin{bmatrix} b & 0 \\ 1 & b \end{bmatrix}^k = \begin{bmatrix} b^k & 0 \\ kb^{k-1} & b^k \end{bmatrix}.$$

4.33   Prove that for every integer $k \geq 2$,

$$\begin{bmatrix} a & 0 & 0 \\ 1 & a & 0 \\ 0 & 1 & a \end{bmatrix}^k = \begin{bmatrix} a^k & 0 & 0 \\ ka^{k-1} & a^k & 0 \\ s(k)a^{k-2} & ka^{k-1} & a^k \end{bmatrix}$$

where $s(1) = 0$ and $s(k + 1) = 1 + 2 + \cdots + k$.

4.34   Let $T: W \to W$, and let $\{\alpha, T\alpha, \cdots, T^{k-1}\alpha\}$ be a basis of W, so that the matrix of T is the companion matrix of some polynomial $f(x)$. Suppose $f(x) = (x - a)^k$. If

$$\beta_0 = \alpha, \beta_1 = (T - aE)\alpha, \cdots, \beta_{k-1} = (T - aE)^{k-1}\alpha,$$

prove that $\{\beta_0, \beta_1, \cdots, \beta_{k-1}\}$ is a basis of W. (E is the identity transformation.)

THEOREM 4.15   Let A be an $n \times n$ matrix over F, where F is a field that contains all the characteristic roots of A. Then A is similar to a direct sum of Jordan blocks.

Proof   By Theorem 4.14, it suffices to prove that a primary companion matrix C is similar to a Jordan block. Let $f(x)$ be the polynomial corresponding to C. Our hypothesis on F tells us that $f(x) = (x - a)^k$ for some $a \in F$. Now C determines a transformation $T: W \to W$, where W is a vector space with a basis of the form $\{\alpha, T\alpha, \cdots, T^{k-1}\alpha\}$. Let us compute the matrix of T relative to the basis $\{\beta_0, \beta_1, \cdots, \beta_{k-1}\}$ of W that we examined in Exercise 4.34.

Now, if $j + 1 < k$,

$$
\begin{aligned}
T\beta_j &= T(T - aE)^j\alpha \\
&= (T - aE)^j T\alpha \\
&= (T - aE)^j[(T - aE) + aE]\alpha \\
&= (T - aE)^{j+1}\alpha + (T - aE)^j a\alpha \\
&= \beta_{j+1} + a\beta_j.
\end{aligned}
$$

If $j + 1 = k$, then $(T - aE)^{j+1} = (T - aE)^k = 0$, by the Cayley-Hamilton theorem. Therefore, $T\beta_{k-1} = a\beta_{k-1}$.

The matrix of T is thus a Jordan block J, and so C and J are similar. ∎

A direct sum of Jordan blocks is a **Jordan canonical form**; Theorem 4.15 says that if F contains enough elements, a square matrix is similar to a Jordan canonical form. For example, if F is the complex numbers (or any algebraically closed field), then every square matrix is similar to a Jordan canonical form.

The uniqueness of the various canonical forms will follow from a translation of the fundamental theorem of finite abelian groups (Theorem 4.11).

Definition   If V and W are R-modules, a function $f: V \to W$ is an **R-homomorphism** in case

$$
\begin{aligned}
f(v + v') &= f(v) + f(v'), \\
f(rv) &= rf(v)
\end{aligned}
$$

for all $v, v' \in V$ and all $r \in R$.

Examples   **7** If $R = Z$, then V and W are merely abelian groups. Every homomorphism $f: V \to W$ is a Z-homomorphism, for $f(mv) = mf(v)$ for every integer m.

8 If R is a field, V and W are vector spaces and R-homomorphisms are linear transformations.

9 If $R = F[x]$, then an R-homomorphism $f: V \to W$ has the property that

$$f(\varphi(x)v) = \varphi(x)f(v)$$

for every polynomial $\varphi(x) \in F[x]$.

THEOREM 4.16 (*Fundamental Theorem for Modules*)
Let R be a principal ideal domain and let V be a finitely generated R-module in which every element has finite order. Any two decompositions of V as direct sums of primary cyclic modules have the same number of summands of each order.

Proof   Translation of the fundamental theorem for groups. ∎

In order to apply this fundamental theorem to matrices, we continue our examination of $F[x]$-modules.

LEMMA 4.17   Let V and W be vector spaces over F, and let $T: V \to V$ and $S: W \to W$ be linear transformations. A function $f: V^T \to W^S$ is an $F[x]$-homomorphism if and only if:
  (i) f is a linear transformation of the vector spaces V and W;
  (ii) $f(T(v)) = S(f(v))$.

Proof   If f is an $F[x]$-homomorphism, then $f(\varphi(x)v) = \varphi(x)f(v)$ for all $v \in V$ and all polynomials $\varphi(x) \in F[x]$. In particular, if $\varphi(x)$ is a constant polynomial, then we see that f is a linear transformation; if $\varphi(x) = x$, then $f(xv) = xf(v)$. But the definition of scalar multiplication in V^T is $xv = T(v)$ and the definition of scalar multiplication in W^S is $xf(v) = S(f(v))$.
  For the converse, we are told that

$$f(\varphi(x)v) = \varphi(x)f(v)$$

for all the polynomials $\varphi(x) = $ constant and for the polynomial $\varphi(x) = x$. It follows easily that the equation holds for all polynomials $\varphi(x)$. ∎

Definition   An R-homomorphism $f: V \to W$ is an R-**isomorphism** in case it is a one-to-one correspondence. In this case, we say that V and W are R-**isomorphic.**

THEOREM 4.18   If A and B are $n \times n$ matrices over a field F, then A is similar to B if and only if the corresponding $F[x]$-modules they determine are $F[x]$-isomorphic.

Proof   Let V be a vector space over F with basis $\{\alpha_1, \cdots, \alpha_n\}$, and let T and S be the linear transformations on V defined by A and B, respectively. We let V^T denote V made into an $F[x]$-module by $x\alpha = T\alpha$, and we let V^S denote V made into an $F[x]$-module by $x\alpha = S\alpha$.

If A is similar to B, there is a nonsingular matrix P with $PAP^{-1} = B$, and P defines a linear transformation $f \colon V \to V$. We claim that f is even an $F[x]$-isomorphism between V^T and V^S. By Lemma 4.17, it suffices to prove that $f(T(v)) = S(f(v))$ for all $v \in V$, i.e., $fT = Sf$. In terms of matrices, this is the given equation $PA = BP$.

Suppose, conversely, that $f \colon V^T \to V^S$ is an $F[x]$-isomorphism. By Lemma 4.17, $Sf = fT$, or since f is an isomorphism, $S = fTf^{-1}$. If P is the matrix corresponding to the linear transformation $f \colon V \to V$, then $B = PAP^{-1}$, i.e., A and B are similar. ∎

THEOREM 4.19   Let A and B be $n \times n$ matrices over a field F. A and B are similar if and only if they have the same elementary divisors.

Proof   By the preceding theorem, it suffices to determine when the modules corresponding to A and to B are $F[x]$-isomorphic. By the fundamental theorem (module version), two modules are isomorphic if and only if primary cyclic direct summands occur with equal frequency in direct sum decompositions of the modules. But a cyclic module is determined by its order ideal (just as a cyclic group is determined by its order), and an order ideal is determined by the monic polynomial that generates it. These polynomials are precisely the elementary divisors. ∎

COROLLARY 4.20   A rational canonical form associated with an $n \times n$ matrix A is unique within a permutation of its companion matrices.

Proof   If $\varphi_1(x), \cdots, \varphi_k(x)$ are the elementary divisors of a matrix A, then any rational canonical form for A is a direct sum of companion matrices $C_1, \cdots, C_k$, where C_i is the companion matrix of $\varphi_i(x)$. Therefore, the only rational canonical forms determined by A are those obtained from these C_i in some ordering. ∎

Exercises   4.35   Prove that a Jordan canonical form associated with an $n \times n$ matrix A is unique within a permutation of its Jordan blocks.

4.36   If b and b' are nonzero elements of a field F, then $\begin{bmatrix} a & b \\ 0 & c \end{bmatrix}$ and $\begin{bmatrix} a & b' \\ 0 & c \end{bmatrix}$ are similar.

The Remak-Krull-Schmidt Theorem

If a nonabelian group G is a direct product of normal subgroups, each of which cannot be factored further, is this factorization unique? The affirmative answer for a large class of groups (which contains all finite groups) is the main result of this section. Since we shall consider nonabelian groups, we return to the multiplicative notation.

Definition   A group G is **indecomposable** if $G \neq \{1\}$, and if $G \approx H \times K$, then either H or $K = \{1\}$.

Exercises   4.37   Which of the following groups are indecomposable?

(a) Z; (b) the additive group of rationals; (c) S_n; (d) $\sigma(21)$; (e) the multiplicative group of positive rationals; (f) $\sigma(p^n)$, where p is prime.

4.38   Give necessary and sufficient conditions that a finite abelian group be indecomposable.

Definition   A homomorphism $f: G \to G$ is called an **endomorphism** of G; an isomorphism $f: G \to G$ is called an **automorphism** of G.

There are certain endomorphisms of G that arise quite naturally in the consideration of direct products, as we saw in Exercise 4.9.

Definition   Let $G = H_1 \times H_2 \times \cdots \times H_m$. The homomorphisms $\epsilon_i: G \to H_i$ defined by $\epsilon_i(h_1 h_2 \cdots h_m) = h_i$ are called **projections**.

Exercises   4.39   Every projection ϵ_i is **idempotent,** i.e., $\epsilon_i \circ \epsilon_i = \epsilon_i$.
    4.40   An endomorphism α of G is **normal** in case $a^{-1}\alpha(x)a = \alpha(a^{-1}xa)$ for every a and x in G. Prove that every projection ϵ_i is normal.
    4.41   The composite of normal endomorphisms is a normal endomorphism.
    4.42   If $\alpha: G \to G$ is a normal endomorphism and $H \lhd G$, then $\alpha(H) \lhd G$.

We now introduce a new way of combining endomorphisms; unfortunately, the new function we get is not always a homomorphism.

Definition   If α and β are endomorphisms of G, then $\alpha + \beta: G \to G$ is the function defined by

$$(\alpha + \beta)(x) = \alpha(x)\beta(x)$$

for every $x \in G$.

Exercises   4.43   If G is abelian and α and β are endomorphisms of G, then $\alpha + \beta$ is also an endomorphism of G.
    4.44   Let α and β be endomorphisms of S_3 defined as follows: α is conjugation by (123) and β is conjugation by (132). Show that $\alpha + \beta$ is not an endomorphism of S_3.
    4.45   If $G = H_1 \times H_2 \times \cdots \times H_n$ has corresponding projections $\epsilon_1, \epsilon_2, \cdots, \epsilon_n$, then the "sum" of any k distinct ϵ_i is a normal endomorphism of G. Furthermore,

$$\epsilon_1 + \epsilon_2 + \cdots + \epsilon_n = 1:G.$$

We now consider a condition on a group G that will ensure that it is a direct product of indecomposable groups (for there do exist groups without this property).

Definition   A group G has the ACC (**ascending chain condition**) in case every increasing chain of normal subgroups of G

$$A_1 \subset A_2 \subset \cdots \subset A_n \subset A_{n+1} \subset \cdots$$

stops, i.e., there is an integer t for which $A_t = A_{t+1} = A_{t+2} = \cdots$.
    A group G has the DCC (**descending chain condition**) in case every decreasing chain of normal subgroups of G

$$B_1 \supset B_2 \supset \cdots \supset B_n \supset B_{n+1} \supset \cdots$$

stops.

G **has both chain conditions** if it has both chain conditions!

Every finite group has both chain conditions; Z has the ACC but not the DCC; in Chapter 9, we shall study a group $\sigma(p^\infty)$ that has the DCC but not the ACC.

LEMMA 4.21   If *G* has either chain condition, then *G* is a direct product of a finite number of indecomposable groups.

Proof   Let us say that a group is *good* in case it satisfies the conclusion of Lemma 4.21; otherwise, it is *bad*. If *B* and *C* are good, then so is $B \times C$. Thus, if a group is bad, it has a proper bad direct factor.

Suppose now that *G* is bad. Let $G = A_0$. Assume inductively that there exist $A_0, A_1, \cdots, A_n$ such that for each $i = 1, 2, \cdots, n$, A_i is bad and A_i is a proper direct factor of A_{i-1}. Since A_n is bad, it has a proper bad direct factor A_{n+1}. By induction, we obtain a properly decreasing infinite chain $A_0 > A_1 > \cdots$ of normal subgroups of $G = A_0$. If *G* has the DCC, we have reached a contradiction. Suppose that *G* has the ACC. The direct complements of the A_i can be chosen to form a strictly increasing chain of normal subgroups of *G*, and we have reached a contradiction in this case as well. ∎

LEMMA 4.22   Let *G* have both chain conditions, and let α be a normal endomorphism of *G*. Then α is one-to-one if and only if α is onto. (Thus, either property ensures that α is an automorphism.)

Proof   Suppose α is one-to-one, and $g \notin \alpha(G)$. We prove, by induction, that $\alpha^n(g) \notin \alpha^{n+1}(G)$. If it were, then there would be an element $h \in G$ with $\alpha^n(g) = a^{n+1}(h)$, so that $\alpha(\alpha^{n-1}(g)) = \alpha(\alpha^n(h))$. Since α is one-to-one, $\alpha^{n-1}(g) = \alpha^n(h) \in \alpha^n(G)$, which contradicts the inductive hypothesis. Thus, we have a strictly descending chain of subgroups

$$G \supset \alpha(G) \supset \alpha^2(G) \supset \cdots .$$

Since α is normal, each $\alpha^n(G)$ is a normal subgroup of *G*, and so the DCC is violated. Therefore, α is onto.

Suppose α is onto. Let $A_n =$ kernel α^n; each A_n is a normal subgroup of G because α^n is a homomorphism; (the normality of α is here irrelevant). Thus, we have the ascending chain of normal subgroups:

$$\{1\} = A_0 \subset A_1 \subset A_2 \subset \cdots.$$

Since G satisfies the ACC, this chain stops; let t be the smallest integer for which $A_t = A_{t+1} = \cdots$. We claim that $t = 0$, which will prove our theorem. If $t \geq 1$, there is an $x \in A_t$ with $x \notin A_{t-1}$, i.e., $\alpha^t(x) = 1$, but $\alpha^{t-1}(x) \neq 1$. Since α is onto, there is an element $g \in G$ with $\alpha(g) = x$. Hence, $1 = \alpha^t(x) = \alpha^{t+1}(g)$, so that $g \in A_{t+1} = A_t$. Therefore, $\alpha^t(g) = 1$; but $\alpha^t(g) = \alpha^{t-1}(\alpha(g)) = \alpha^{t-1}(x)$, so that $\alpha^{t-1}(x) = 1$, a contradiction. Thus α is one-to-one. ∎

Definition   An endomorphism α of G is **nilpotent** if there is a positive integer k such that $\alpha^k = 0$, where 0 denotes the trivial endomorphism that sends every element of G into the identity.

THEOREM 4.23 (*Fitting's Lemma*)   Let G have both chain conditions and let α be a normal endomorphism of G. Then $G = K \times H$, where H and K are each invariant under α, $\alpha|K$ is nilpotent, and $\alpha|H$ is onto.

Proof   Let $K_n =$ kernel α^n and $H_n =$ image α^n. As we observed above, there are two chains of normal subgroups:

$$G \supset H_1 \supset H_2 \supset \cdots \quad \text{and} \quad \{1\} \subset K_1 \subset K_2 \subset \cdots.$$

Since G has both chain conditions, each of these chains stops, the H_n after r steps and the K_n after s steps. Let t be the larger of r and s, so that $K_t = K_{t+1} = \cdots$ and $H_t = H_{t+1} = \cdots$; define $H = H_t$ and $K = K_t$. It is easy to check that H and K are each invariant under α.

Suppose $x \in H \cap K$. Now $x \in H$ implies $\alpha^t(g) = x$ for some $g \in G$; $x \in K$ implies $\alpha^t(x) = 1$. Therefore, $\alpha^{2t}(g) = \alpha^t(x) = 1$, so that $g \in K_{2t} = K_t$. Hence, $\alpha^t(g) = 1$ and $x = 1$.

Let $g \in G$. Then $\alpha^t(g) \in H_t = H_{2t}$, so there is an $x \in G$ with $\alpha^{2t}(x) = \alpha^t(g)$. Applying α^t to $g\alpha^t(x^{-1})$ gives 1, so that $g\alpha^t(x^{-1}) \in K_t = K$. Hence, $g = [g\alpha^t(x^{-1})]\alpha^t(x) \in KH$, so that $G = K \times H$.

Now $\alpha(H) = \alpha(H_t) = \alpha(\alpha^t(G)) = \alpha^{t+1}(G) = H_{t+1} = H_t = H$, so that $\alpha|H$ is onto. Finally, let $x \in K$; then $\alpha^t(x) \in K \cap H = \{1\}$ so that $\alpha|K$ is nilpotent. ∎

COROLLARY 4.24   Let G be an indecomposable group having both chain conditions. Any normal endomorphism α of G is either nilpotent or an automorphism.

Proof   By Theorem 4.23, $G = K \times H$ with $\alpha|K$ nilpotent and $\alpha|H$ onto. Since G is indecomposable, either $G = K$ or $G = H$. In the first case, α is nilpotent; in the second case, α is onto and hence is an automorphism, by Lemma 4.22. ∎

COROLLARY 4.25   Let $G \neq \{1\}$ be an indecomposable group having both chain conditions, and let α_1 and α_2 be normal, nilpotent endomorphisms of G. If $\alpha_1 + \alpha_2$ is also an endomorphism of G, then it is nilpotent.

Proof   If $\alpha_1 + \alpha_2$ is an endomorphism of G, it is immediately seen to be normal, so that, by Corollary 4.24, it is either nilpotent or an automorphism. Suppose $\alpha_1 + \alpha_2$ is an automorphism, and let γ be its inverse; γ is easily seen to be normal. Set $\lambda_1 = \alpha_1\gamma$ and $\lambda_2 = \alpha_2\gamma$, so that $1: G = \lambda_1 + \lambda_2$, i.e., $\lambda_1(x)\lambda_2(x) = x$ for all $x \in G$. In particular, $\lambda_1(x^{-1})\lambda_2(x^{-1}) = x^{-1}$. If we take the inverse of both sides, we see that $\lambda_2(x)\lambda_1(x) = x$, and so $\lambda_1 + \lambda_2 = \lambda_2 + \lambda_1$. Now the equation $\lambda_1(\lambda_1 + \lambda_2) = (\lambda_1 + \lambda_2)\lambda_1$ implies that $\lambda_1\lambda_2 = \lambda_2\lambda_1$. It follows that the set of all endomorphisms of G obtained from λ_1 and λ_2 by sums and products forms a commutative ring with unit. Hence, the binomial theorem applies: for any integer $m > 0$,

$$(\lambda_1 + \lambda_2)^m = \lambda_1^m + \binom{m}{1}\lambda_1^{m-1}\lambda_2 + \binom{m}{2}\lambda_1^{m-2}\lambda_2^2 + \cdots + \lambda_2^m.$$

Since α_1 and α_2 are nilpotent, λ_1 and λ_2 are nilpotent (they cannot be automorphisms since they have nontrivial kernels). Therefore, there are positive integers r and s with $\lambda_1^r = 0$ and $\lambda_2^s = 0$. If we take m large enough ($m = r + s - 1$ will do), then we obtain $(\lambda_1 + \lambda_2)^m = 0$. Since $\lambda_1 + \lambda_2 = 1:G$, $1:G = 0$, contradicting our assumption that $G \neq \{1\}$. ∎

It may be shown by induction that if $\alpha_1, \alpha_2, \cdots, \alpha_n$ is a set of normal nilpotent endomorphisms such that every sum of distinct α is an endomorphism, then $\alpha_1 + \alpha_2 + \cdots + \alpha_n$ is nilpotent.

THEOREM 4.26 (*Remak-Krull-Schmidt*)[2]   Let G be a group having both chain conditions. If

$$G = H_1 \times H_2 \times \cdots \times H_s$$

and

$$G = K_1 \times K_2 \times \cdots \times K_t$$

are two decompositions of G into indecomposable groups, then $s = t$, and given any r between 1 and s, there is a reindexing so that $H_i \approx K_i$ for all i, and

$$G = H_1 \times \cdots \times H_r \times K_{r+1} \times \cdots \times K_t.$$

Remark   Our conclusion is stronger than saying that the factors appearing in the two factorizations are determined up to isomorphism; we can even replace factors in one decomposition with factors of the other.

Proof   We shall give the proof for the case $r = 1$, leaving the rest of the proof for the reader to finish by induction. Given the first decomposition, we must find a renumbering of the K so that $H_i \approx K_i$ for all i, and such that

$$G = H_1 \times K_2 \times \cdots \times K_t.$$

Let $\epsilon_1, \epsilon_2, \cdots, \epsilon_s$ be the projections on the H and let $\eta_1, \eta_2, \cdots, \eta_t$ be the projections on the K. Now if $x \in H_1$,

$$\epsilon_1(x) = \epsilon_1 \left(\sum_1^t \eta_j \right) x = \sum \epsilon_1 \eta_j(x).$$

Since every partial sum of $\sum \epsilon_1 \eta_j$ gives a normal endomorphism of H_1, the remark after Corollary 4.25 implies that if $\lambda\colon H_1 \to G$ is the inclusion, not every $\epsilon_1 \eta_j \lambda$ is nilpotent. By Corollary 4.24, one of these maps must be an automorphism of H_1; we renumber so that $\epsilon_1 \eta_1 \lambda$ is an automorphism.

We shall now show that $\eta_1 \lambda\colon H_1 \to K_1$ is an isomorphism. It follows from set theory that $\eta_1 \lambda$ is one-to-one. In order to show that $\eta_1 \lambda$ is onto, consider $I = \eta_1(H_1) \subset K_1$ and $N = \{ x \in K_1 \colon \epsilon_1(x) = 1 \}$. We claim that $K_1 = I \times N$. Note that I is normal in K_1, by Exercise

---

[2] This theorem was first given by Wedderburn, and it has since been polished and generalized by Remak, Krull, Schmidt, Fitting, Ore, Kurosch, Azumaya, Jónsson, Atiyah, and others.

4.42, and N is normal in K_1 by the second isomorphism theorem. If $z \in I \cap N$, then $z = \eta_1(h)$ and $\epsilon_1(z) = 1$; therefore, $\epsilon_1\eta_1\lambda(h) = 1$ and $h = 1$, since $\epsilon_1\eta_1\lambda$ is one-to-one. Thus, $z = \eta_1(h) = 1$ and $I \cap N = \{1\}$. Suppose $y \in K_1$. Now $\epsilon_1(y) \in H_1$, so that, since $\epsilon_1\eta_1\lambda$ is onto, $\epsilon_1(y) = \epsilon_1\eta_1\lambda(v)$ for some $v \in H_1$. It follows that $y = [v\eta_1(v)^{-1}]\eta_1(v) \in NI$; hence, $K_1 = I \times N$. But K_1 is indecomposable. Since $I = $ image $\eta_1\lambda \neq \{1\}$, N is trivial. Therefore, $K_1 = I$ and $\eta_1\lambda$ is onto and hence is an isomorphism. Furthermore, $\epsilon_1|K_1: K_1 \to H_1$ is also an isomorphism, for $\epsilon_1|K_1 = (\epsilon_1\eta_1\lambda)(\eta_1\lambda)^{-1}$.

Now η_1 sends $K_2 \times \cdots \times K_t$ into 1, but η_1 induces an isomorphism on H_1. Therefore,

$$H_1 \cap (K_2 \times \cdots \times K_t) = \{1\}.$$

If we define $G^* = [H_1, K_2 \times \cdots \times K_t]$, then

$$G^* = H_1 \times K_2 \times \cdots \times K_t.$$

If $x \in G$, then $x = k_1 k_2 \cdots k_t$, where each $k_j \in K_j$. Since $\epsilon_1|K_1$ is an isomorphism, the map $\theta: G \to G$ defined by $\theta(x) = \epsilon_1(k_1)k_2 \cdots k_t$ is one-to-one and has image G^*. By Lemma 4.22, θ must be onto, and so $G^* = G$. Finally,

$$K_2 \times \cdots \times K_t \approx G/H_1 \approx H_2 \times \cdots \times H_s,$$

so that the remainder of the theorem follows by induction on max $\{s,t\}$. ∎

Exercises   **4.46**   Use the Remak-Krull-Schmidt theorem to prove the fundamental theorem of finite abelian groups (Theorem 4.11).

4.47   If $K \lhd G$ and if both K and G/K have both chain conditions, prove that G has both chain conditions. Conclude that if K and H each have both chain conditions, so does $K \times H$. (*Hint:* Use the Dedekind law, Exercise 2.41.)

4.48   Let G have both chain conditions; if there is a group H with $G \times G \approx H \times H$, then $G \approx H$.

4.49   Let G have both chain conditions. If $G \approx A \times B$ and $G \approx A \times C$, then $B \approx C$.

4.50   Let G be the multiplicative group of positive rationals. Prove that $G \times Z \times Z \approx G \times Z$, but that $Z \times Z \napprox Z$; conclude that the "cancellation law" is not universally valid.

The Remak-Krull-Schmidt theorem holds for algebraic systems other than groups with both chain conditions; in particular, it holds for R-modules having both chain conditions (where the phrase "normal subgroup" is replaced by "submodule" in the definitions of ACC and DCC). The proof of the Remak-Krull-Schmidt theorem given above is also a proof for R-modules if one further replaces "homomorphism" by "R-homomorphism," and "normal endomorphism" by "R-endomorphism." As an illustration of the value of this translation, we state Fitting's lemma for vector spaces (i.e., R-modules, where R is a field).

FITTING'S LEMMA   If V is a finite-dimensional vector space, and $T: V \to V$ is a linear transformation, then $V = W_1 \oplus W_2$, where W_1 and W_2 are invariant under T, $T|W_1$ is nonsingular, and $T|W_2$ is nilpotent.

The matrix version of Fitting's lemma thus says: Every $n \times n$ matrix over a field F is similar to a matrix of the form

$$\begin{bmatrix} A & 0 \\ 0 & B \end{bmatrix},$$

where A is nilpotent and B is nonsingular.

The proofs of generalizations of the Remak-Krull-Schmidt theorem to more general situations (e.g., to lattices) are easily accessible in the literature; cf. A. G. Kurosh, *Theory of Groups*, Vol. II (see Bibliography).

Chapter 5

The Sylow Theorems

p-Groups

We recall the following definition from the preceding chapter.

Definition If p is a prime, a group G is a **p-group** in case every element $x \in G$ has order some power of p.

We begin with a characterization of finite p-groups.

LEMMA 5.1 If G is a finite abelian group whose order is divisible by a prime p, then G contains an element of order p.[1]

Proof Let $x \in G$ be distinct from 1. If the order of x is pm, then the reader can easily check that x^m is an element in G of order p.

Suppose that x has order t, where $(p,t) = 1$. Since G is abelian, $[x]$ is a normal subgroup and $G/[x]$ is an abelian group of order $|G|/t$. Since $|G|/t$ is divisible by p and is less than $|G|$, an induction on $|G|$ provides an element $\bar{y} \in G/[x]$ of order p. Hence, if $y \in G$ goes into $\bar{y}$ under the natural map, the order of y is a multiple of p (Exercise 2.27). We have returned to the first case. ∎

THEOREM 5.2 (*Cauchy*) If G is a finite group whose order is divisible by a prime p, then G contains an element of order p.

---

[1] This lemma follows immediately from the basis theorem (Theorem 4.6) but we give an argument from first principles so that its elementary character is not disguised.

Proof   If $x \in G$, the number of conjugates of x is $[G:C(x)]$, where $C(x)$ is the centralizer of x in G. Now if $x \notin Z(G)$, then $|C(x)| < |G|$, so that if p divides $|C(x)|$, we are done, by induction. Therefore, we may assume that p does not divide $|C(x)|$ for all $x \notin Z(G)$; better, since $|G| = [G:C(x)]|C(x)|$, we may assume that p does divide $[G:C(x)]$ for all $x \notin Z(G)$ (it is here we use the fact that p is prime).

We partition G into its conjugacy classes and count:

(*) $|G| = |Z(G)| + \sum [G:C(x)],$

where the summation ranges over a complete set of nonconjugate x not in $Z(G)$. Now p divides both $|G|$ and $\sum [G:C(x)]$, so that p divides $|Z(G)|$. Since $Z(G)$ is an abelian group, it contains an element of order p, by Lemma 5.1. ∎

The equation (*) is called the **class equation.**

COROLLARY 5.3   A finite group G is a p-group if and only if $|G|$ is a power of p.

Proof   Suppose there is a prime $q \neq p$ dividing $|G|$. By Cauchy's theorem, there is an element $a \in G$ of order q, contradicting the fact that G is a p-group.

The converse follows immediately from Lagrange's theorem (Theorem 2.8). ∎

THEOREM 5.4   If G is a finite p-group with more than one element, then the center of G, $Z(G)$, has more than one element.

Proof   Partitioning G into its conjugacy classes gives the class equation:

$$|G| = |Z(G)| + h_1 + \cdots + h_m,$$

where the h are the sizes of the distinct conjugacy classes of noncentral elements of G. Suppose $a \in G$ is not in $Z(G)$; then $C(a)$ is a proper subgroup of G, and so, by Corollary 5.3, $[G:C(a)]$ is a power of p. Thus, p divides each of the h, so that p divides $|Z(G)|$. ∎

COROLLARY 5.5   Any group G of order p^2 (p a prime) is abelian.

Proof   Suppose G is not abelian, i.e., $G \neq Z(G)$. Then $Z(G)$ has order p (for this order cannot be 1). Therefore, $G/Z(G)$ has order p and so is cyclic, contradicting Exercise 3.22. ▮

Exercises   5.1   Let $H \lhd G$. If both H and G/H are p-groups, then G is a p-group.
5.2   Let $|G| = p^k$, where p is prime. If $0 \leq n \leq k$, prove that G contains a normal subgroup of order p^n.
5.3   Let G be a finite p-group and let $\{1\} \neq H \lhd G$. Prove that $H \cap Z(G) \neq \{1\}$.

The Sylow Theorems

The major results in this section are basic for understanding the structure of a finite group. We shall prove the existence of largest possible p-subgroups of a finite group G. Now several such subgroups may exist, and we can count the number of them (within a congruence). On the other hand, these subgroups are unique in the sense that any two are isomorphic via a conjugation of G.

Definition   Let p be a prime. A subgroup P of G is a **p-sylow**[2] **subgroup** of G if it is a maximal p-subgroup of G.

Thus, if P is a p-sylow subgroup of G, and if Q is a p-subgroup of G such that $Q \supset P$, then $P = Q$. Observe that every p-subgroup of G is contained in a p-sylow subgroup of G. (If G is infinite, this statement may be proved using Zorn's lemma, Appendix IV.)
We have seen the utility of the notion of conjugate and centralizer of an element; we now consider the analogs of these notions for a subgroup.

Definition   Let H be a subgroup of G. A subgroup S of G is a **conjugate** of H in case there is an element $a \in G$ with $S = aHa^{-1}$.

Observe that conjugate subgroups are isomorphic.

[2] After L. Sylow (1832–1918).

Definition   Let H be a subgroup of G. The **normalizer of H in G**, denoted $N_G(H)$, is the set

$$N_G(H) = \{a \in G: aHa^{-1} \subseteq H\}.$$

When the meaning is clear from the context, we shall abbreviate $N_G(H)$ by $N(H)$.

Exercises   5.4   If H is a subgroup of G, $N_G(H)$ is a subgroup of G containing H, and it is the largest such subgroup in which H is normal.

5.5   Let $I(G)$ denote the group of all conjugations of G, and let X denote the set of all subgroups of G. Prove that $I(G)$ is a group of permutations on X, and if $H \in X$, the orbit of H is the set of all subgroups conjugate to H.

5.6   Prove that the stabilizer of a subgroup H (under the action of $I(G)$) is $\{f_a \in I(G): a \in N_G(H)\}$.

5.7   The number of distinct conjugates of H in G is $[G: N(H)]$, and so this number divides $|G|$ if G is finite.

*5.8   Let G be a finite group with proper subgroup H. Prove that G is not the set-theoretical union of all the conjugates of H. Give an example in which H is not normal and this union is a subgroup.

5.9   Every conjugate of a p-sylow subgroup of G is itself a p-sylow subgroup of G. Conclude that if, for some fixed prime p, G has only one p-sylow subgroup P, then P is normal in G.

5.10   Find the 2-sylow and 3-sylow subgroups of S_3, S_4, and S_5.

LEMMA 5.6   Let P be a p-sylow subgroup of G. Then $N(P)/P$ has no elements $\neq 1$ whose order is a power of p.

Proof   Suppose $\bar{x} \in N(P)/P$ has order a power of p. If S^* is the subgroup of $N(P)/P$ generated by $\bar{x}$, then S^* is a p-group. By the correspondence theorem (Theorem 2.17), there is a subgroup S of G containing P such that $S/P \approx S^*$. By Exercise 5.1, S is a p-group containing P, so that the maximality of P implies $S = P$. Therefore, $S^* = \{1\}$ and $\bar{x} = 1$. ∎

LEMMA 5.7   Let P be a p-sylow subgroup of G, and let $a \in G$ have order a power of p. If $aPa^{-1} = P$, then $a \in P$.

Proof   Clearly, $a \in N(P)$. If $\pi \colon N(P) \to N(P)/P$ is the natural map, then $\pi(a)$ has order a power of p (since a has). By Lemma 5.6, $\pi(a) = 1$, i.e., $a \in \ker \pi = P$. ∎

We need the following fact about orbits.

LEMMA 5.8   Let P be a p-group and let $\alpha \colon P \to S_n$ be a homomorphism. The size of each orbit of $\alpha(P)$ is a power of p (which may be $p^0 = 1$); (of course we are considering $\alpha(P)$ as a permutation group on n letters).

Proof   Since P is a p-group, $\alpha(P)$ is a finite p-group and so has order a power of p. By Corollary 3.22, the size of each orbit divides $|\alpha(P)|$. ∎

We are ready to prove the main theorems of this chapter.

THEOREM 5.9 (Sylow)   Let G be a finite group with p-sylow subgroup P. All p-sylow subgroups of G are conjugate to P, and the number of these subgroups is $\equiv 1 \pmod{p}$, and is a divisor of $|G|$.

Proof   The basic idea is the realization (Exercise 5.9) that conjugation by any element of G sends a p-sylow subgroup into a p-sylow subgroup.

Let X be the set of all the conjugates of P; say,

$$X = \{P_1, P_2, \cdots, P_r\}$$

(where our notation sets $P = P_1$). For any $a \in G$, we define $\alpha_a \colon X \to X$ by

$$\alpha_a(P_i) = aP_i a^{-1}.$$

Now each α_a is one-to-one, for if $aP_i a^{-1} = aP_j a^{-1}$, then $P_i = P_j$. Since any function on a finite set that is one-to-one must be onto, each α_a is a permutation of X. Even more is true: The function $\alpha \colon G \to S_X$ given by $a \to \alpha_a$ is a homomorphism:

$$\alpha_a \alpha_b(P_i) = \alpha_a(bP_i b^{-1}) = abP_i b^{-1} a^{-1} = (ab)P_i (ab)^{-1} = \alpha_{ab}(P_i),$$

so that $\alpha_a \alpha_b = \alpha_{ab}$.

Restrict the map α to a homomorphism $P \to S_X$. By Lemma 5.8, the size of each orbit of $\alpha(P)$ is a power of p. Now what does it mean to say that one of these sizes is 1? There would be an i with $\alpha_a(P_i) = P_i$ for all α_a, i.e., $aP_i a^{-1} = P_i$ for all $a \in P$. By Lemma 5.7, for all $a \in P = P_1$, $a \in P_i$, so that $P \subset P_i$. Since P is a p-sylow subgroup, we must have $P = P_i$. Conclusion: Each orbit has size an "honest" power of p save $\{P_1\}$, which has size 1. Therefore, $r \equiv 1 \pmod{p}$.

Suppose now that Q is a p-sylow subgroup of G which is not a conjugate of P, i.e., Q is not a P_i for any i. Restrict the map α to a homomorphism of $Q \to S_X$. Again Lemma 5.8 tells us that the size of each orbit of $\alpha(Q)$ is a power of p, and again we ask if any of these have size 1. The same argument as before shows that if there were such an orbit $\{P_i\}$, then $Q = P_i$, and this is contrary to the choice of Q. But now every orbit has size an honest power of p, so that p divides r, i.e., $r \equiv 0 \pmod{p}$. This contradicts our previous congruence, so that no such Q can exist. Therefore, every p-sylow subgroup of G is conjugate to P.

Finally, the number of conjugates of P is the index of its normalizer, and so it is a divisor of $|G|$. ∎

THEOREM 5.10 (*Sylow*)   Let G be a finite group of order $p^k m$, where $(p,m) = 1$. Every p-sylow subgroup P of G has order p^k.

Proof   We first prove that $[G:P]$ is prime to p. Since $[G:P] = [G:N(P)][N(P):P]$, it suffices to prove that each of these factors is prime to p. Now $[G:N(P)]$ is just the number of conjugates of P, which we have just seen is $\equiv 1 \pmod{p}$. Also, $[N(P):P] = |N(P)/P|$, and $N(P)/P$ has no elements of order p; by Cauchy's theorem (Theorem 5.2), $|N(P)/P|$ is prime to p. It follows that $[G:P]$ is prime to p.

By Lagrange's theorem, $|P| = p^n$ for $n \leq k$, so that $|G|/|P| = mp^{k-n}$. But $|G|/|P| = [G:P]$ is prime to p, so that $k = n$. ∎

COROLLARY 5.11   Let G be a finite group and let p be a prime. If p^n divides $|G|$, then G contains a subgroup of order p^n.

Proof   If P is a p-sylow subgroup of G, then p^n divides $|P|$, by the preceding theorem. By Exercise 5.2, P (hence G) contains a subgroup of order p^n. ∎

We have now seen how much of the converse of Lagrange's theorem can be salvaged. If m divides $|G|$ and m is a power of a prime, then G contains a subgroup of order m; if m has two distinct prime factors, however, we have exhibited a group G, namely A_4, such that m divides $|G|$ and such that G contains no subgroup of order m.

Exercises   5.11   Let G be a finite group with a p-sylow subgroup P, and let $N = N_G(P)$. Prove that any subgroup of G that contains N (inclusion not necessarily proper) is equal to its own normalizer.

     5.12   Let G be a finite group, and suppose that, for every prime p, every p-sylow subgroup of G is normal. Prove that G is the direct product of its sylow subgroups. (Compare with Theorem 4.4.)

     *5.13   Let G be a finite group with normal subgroup H, and let P be a p-sylow subgroup of G. Prove that $H \cap P$ is a p-sylow subgroup of H, and that HP/H is a p-sylow subgroup of G/H. (*Hint:* Compare orders.)

Some Applications of the Sylow Theorems

We shall now illustrate the power of the Sylow theorems by classifying the groups of small order.

Definition   The **dihedral group** D_n is a group of order $2n$ generated by two elements s and t, which satisfy the relations

$$s^n = 1, \quad t^2 = 1, \quad \text{and} \quad tst = s^{-1}.$$

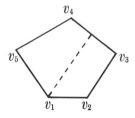

Exercises   5.14   Let A be a regular polygon with vertices $v_1, v_2, \cdots, v_n$, and let G be the set of all rigid motions of A that send vertices into vertices. In particular, let S be a clockwise rotation sending each vertex into the adjacent one, and let T be a reflection of A about the line joining v_1 with the center of A. As usual, multiply in G by first performing one motion and then the other. Prove that $G \approx D_n$.

5.15   What is the center of D_n? (*Hint:* First show that every element in D_n has a factorization $s^i t^j$.)

5.16   Let G be a finite group with p-sylow subgroup P. If $P \lhd G$, is P a direct factor of G?

5.17   Let G be a finite group with normal subgroups H and K. If $G/H \approx G/K$, is $H \approx K$?

THEOREM 5.12   Let p be an odd prime. Any group G of order $2p$ is either cyclic or dihedral.

Proof   By Cauchy's theorem, G contains an element s of order p and an element t of order 2. If $H = [s]$, then $H \lhd G$, since it has index 2. Therefore, $tst = s^i$ for some i. Now $s = t^2 s t^2 = t(tst)t = ts^i t = s^{i^2}$. Hence, $i^2 \equiv 1 \pmod p$, so that, since p is prime, $i \equiv \pm 1 \pmod p$. Thus, $tst = s$ or $tst = s^{-1}$. In the first case, s and t commute, G is abelian, and so $G \approx \sigma(p) \oplus \sigma(2) \approx \sigma(2p)$. In the second case, we have $G \approx D_p$. ∎

THEOREM 5.13   Let $|G| = pq$, where $p > q$ are primes. Then either G is cyclic or G is generated by two elements a and b satisfying the following relations:

$$b^p = 1; \quad a^q = 1; \quad a^{-1}ba = b^r,$$

where $r \not\equiv 1 \pmod p$ but $r^q \equiv 1 \pmod p$.

The second possibility can occur only if q divides $p - 1$.

Proof G contains an element b of order p; let $S = [b]$. Since S is a p-sylow subgroup of G, the number of its conjugates is $1 + up$ for some $u \geq 0$. But $1 + up = [G: N(S)]$ which divides $|G| = pq$. Since $(1 + up, p) = 1$, $1 + up$ divides q. Since $q < p$, $u = 0$, and $S \lhd G$.

Now G contains an element a of order q; let $T = [a]$. T is a q-sylow subgroup of G, so that $[G: N(T)] = 1 + kq$ for some $k \geq 0$. As above, $1 + kq$ divides p, so that either $k = 0$ or q divides $p - 1$. If

$k = 0$, $T \lhd G$ so that $G \approx S \times T$, by Exercise 5.12. Hence, $G \approx \sigma(p) \times \sigma(q) \approx \sigma(pq)$.

We now assume that T is not normal (and so q divides $p - 1$). Since S is normal, $a^{-1}ba = b^r$; furthermore, we may assume $r \not\equiv 1$ (mod p) lest we return to the abelian case. By induction on j, the reader may prove that $a^{-j}ba^j = b^{r^i}$. In particular, if $j = q$, we have $b = b^{r^q}$ so that $r^q \equiv 1 \pmod p$. ∎

COROLLARY 5.14   Let $|G| = pq$, where $p > q$ are primes. If q does not divide $p - 1$, then G is cyclic.

Definition[3]   The **quaternions**, denoted Q, is a group of order 8 having two generators a and b that satisfy the relations

$$a^4 = 1; \quad b^2 = a^2; \quad b^{-1}ab = a^{-1}.$$

Exercises   5.18   Prove that A_5 contains no subgroup of order 15.

5.19   Let G be the multiplicative group of all 2×2 nonsingular complex matrices, and let H be the subgroup of G generated by

$$A = \begin{bmatrix} 0 & i \\ i & 0 \end{bmatrix} \quad \text{and} \quad B = \begin{bmatrix} 0 & 1 \\ -1 & 0 \end{bmatrix}.$$

Prove that $H \approx Q$.

5.20   Consider the set $\{\pm 1, \pm i, \pm j, \pm k\}$ with the multiplication rules: $i^2 = j^2 = k^2 = -1$; $ij = k$; $jk = i$; $ki = j$; $ji = -k$; $kj = -i$; $ik = -j$; and the usual rules for multiplying by ± 1. Prove that we have described a group isomorphic to Q.

5.21   What is the center of Q?

5.22   Prove that $Q/Z(Q)$ is abelian.

5.23   Show that every subgroup of Q is normal. (A group G in which every subgroup is normal is called **hamiltonian**. A finite non-abelian hamiltonian group is isomorphic to $Q \times A \times B$, where A is an abelian group in which every element has odd order, and B is a (necessarily abelian) group in which every element has order 2.)

---

[3] In this definition, as in the definition of D_n, we describe a group by generators and relations. At this point, it is a fair question to ask whether there *is* any group fitting this description; (this question will be answered when we deal with free groups). Therefore, it is necessary here to exhibit particular groups (motions, matrices, etc.) that do satisfy the conditions.

5.24   Prove that Q is not isomorphic to D_4. (*Hint:* Count elements of order 2.)

THEOREM 5.15 Q and D_4 are the only nonabelian groups of order 8.

Proof   If G is a nonabelian group of order 8, then G has no element of order 8 and not every element of G has order 2 (Exercise 1.25). Thus, G contains an element a of order 4. Suppose $b \in G$ and $b \notin [a]$. Since $[a] \lhd G$ (it has index 2) and $G/[a] \approx \sigma(2)$, we must have $b^2 \in [a]$. If $b^2 = a$ or $b^2 = a^3$, then b has order 8, a contradiction. Hence,

$$b^2 = a^2 \quad \text{or} \quad b^2 = 1.$$

Furthermore, since $[a]$ is normal, $b^{-1}ab \in [a]$. Thus,

$$b^{-1}ab = a \quad \text{or} \quad b^{-1}ab = a^3$$

(because a^2 has order 2). The first case is ruled out, for then a and b commute and G is abelian. The following possibilities remain:

(i) $a^4 = 1$, $b^2 = a^2$, and $b^{-1}ab = a^3$.
(ii) $a^4 = 1$, $b^2 = 1$, and $b^{-1}ab = a^3$.

Since $a^3 = a^{-1}$, (i) describes the quaternions Q, and (ii) describes the dihedral group D_4. ∎

THEOREM 5.16   Every group G of order 12 that is not isomorphic to A_4 contains an element of order 6.

Proof   If B is a 3-sylow subgroup of G, then $B = [b]$, where b has order 3. Since B has index 4, Theorem 3.18 gives a homomorphism $\pi: G \to S_4$ whose kernel K is a subgroup of B. Now B has no proper subgroups, so that $K = \{1\}$ or $K = B$. If $K = \{1\}$, then π is one-to-one and G is isomorphic to a subgroup of S_4 of order 12, i.e., to A_4. Since $G \approx A_4$, $K = B$, and so B is normal in G. It follows from Exercise 5.9 that B is the unique 3-sylow subgroup of G. Therefore, there are only two elements in G of order 3, namely, b and b^2.

Let $C(b)$ be the centralizer of b in G. Now $[G: C(b)] = 1$ or 2, for a conjugate of b must have order 3. Therefore $|C(b)| = 12$ or 6; in either case, $C(b)$ contains an element a of order 2. Since a commutes with b, the element ab has order 6. ∎

COROLLARY 5.17   If G has order 12 and $G \not\approx A_4$, then G has a normal 3-sylow subgroup.

Exercises   5.25   Exhibit all the proper subgroups of S_4; there are allegedly 28 of them.

5.26   Prove that $D_3 \approx S_3$.

5.27   Prove that $D_6 \approx S_3 \times \sigma(2)$.

5.28   Prove that there are only two nonabelian groups of order 12 that contain a subgroup of order 6; one of these is D_6; the other shall be denoted T, and it has generators a and b satisfying the relations $a^6 = 1$ and $b^2 = a^3 = (ab)^2$. (We shall examine the group T more carefully in Chapter 7.)

5.29   If G is a nonabelian group of order p^3, where p is a prime, then $Z(G) = G'$, the commutator subgroup of G.

5.30   Let p be an odd prime. Prove that there are at most two nonabelian groups of order p^3: One has generators a and b satisfying the relations $a^{p^2} = 1$, $b^p = 1$, and $b^{-1}ab = a^{1+p}$; the other has generators a, b, and c satisfying the relations $c = a^{-1}b^{-1}ab$, $ca = ac$, and $cb = bc$. (Observe that every element in this second group has order p, so that the generalization of Exercise 1.25 to odd primes is false.)

5.31   Let G be a finite group, and let P be a p-sylow subgroup of G. If H is a normal subgroup of G containing P, then $P \lhd H$ implies $P \lhd G$.

5.32   If G is a nonabelian group of square-free order (more generally, if every sylow subgroup of G is cyclic), it is known that G is not simple. Use this fact to prove that if $|G| = p_1 p_2 \cdots p_t$, where $p_1 < p_2 < \cdots < p_t$ are primes, then G contains a normal p_t-sylow subgroup.

5.33   Prove that there are no nonabelian simple groups of order less than 60.

5.34   Prove that any simple group G of order 60 is isomorphic to A_5. (*Hint:* Show that a 2-sylow subgroup of G has exactly 5 conjugates.) In Chapter 8, we shall exhibit two nonisomorphic finite simple groups having the same order.

Definition   A **generalized quaternion group,** Q_n (for $n \geq 3$), is a group of order 2^n having generators a and b and relations:

$$a^{2^{n-2}} = b^2 = (ab)^2.$$

Exercises (contd.)   5.35   Let G be a group of order 2^n, which is generated by elements a and b. If

$$a^{2^{n-1}} = 1, \quad bab^{-1} = a^{-1}, \quad \text{and} \quad b^2 = a^{2^{n-2}},$$

then $G \approx Q_n$.
   *5.36   Give a group-theoretical proof of Wilson's theorem: If p is a prime, then $(p - 1)! \equiv -1 \bmod(p)$. (*Hint:* Count elements of order p in S_p.)

TABLE OF GROUPS OF SMALL ORDER

Order	Number of Distinct Groups	Groups G	
2	1	$\sigma(2)$	
3	1	$\sigma(3)$	
4	2	$\sigma(4), \sigma(2) \oplus \sigma(2)$	(Theorem 5.5)
5	1	$\sigma(5)$	
6	2	$\sigma(6), S_3$	(Theorem 5.12)
7	1	$\sigma(7)$	
8	5	$\sigma(8), \sigma(4) \oplus \sigma(2),$ $\sigma(2) \oplus \sigma(2) \oplus \sigma(2),$ Q, and D_4	(Theorem 5.15)
9	2	$\sigma(9), \sigma(3) \oplus \sigma(3)$	(Theorem 5.5)
10	2	$\sigma(10), D_5$	(Theorem 5.12)
11	1	$\sigma(11)$	
12	5	$\sigma(12), \sigma(2) \oplus \sigma(6),$ $\sigma(2) \times S_3, A_4, T$	(Theorem 5.16 and Exercise 5.28)
13	1	$\sigma(13)$	
14	2	$\sigma(14), D_7$	(Theorem 5.12)
15	1	$\sigma(15)$	(Corollary 5.14)

There are 14 nonisomorphic groups of order 16 (and 51 of order 32), so that we end our list here. We might add that no one knows a formula giving the number of nonisomorphic groups of order n, for every n.

Chapter 6

Normal and
Subnormal Series

Some Galois Theory

We begin this chapter with a brief history of the study of polynomials. It was well known to mathematicians of the Middle Ages, even to the Babylonians, that the roots of a quadratic polynomial

$$x^2 + bx + c$$

are given by the formula

$$x = \tfrac{1}{2}[-b \pm (b^2 - 4c)^{1/2}].$$

Now every cubic polynomial

$$x^3 + ax^2 + bx + c$$

can be transformed [by sending x into $x - (a/3)$] into a cubic of the form

$$x^3 + qx + r.$$

In 1515, Scipio del Ferro[1] obtained the formula for these roots:

$$x = \left\{ -\frac{r}{2} + \left(\frac{r^2}{4} + \frac{q^3}{27} \right)^{1/2} \right\}^{1/3} + \left\{ -\frac{r}{2} - \left(\frac{r^2}{4} + \frac{q^3}{27} \right)^{1/2} \right\}^{1/3},$$

where the cube roots are chosen so that their product is $-(q/3)$. In 1545, L. Ferrari found a similar formula for the roots of the general quartic polynomial. Abel's proof (1824) of the nonexistence of a

---

[1] This solution is often attributed to Tartaglia, and sometimes to Cardan. Our historical source crediting Scipio del Ferro is Bourbaki.

FRENCH

similar formula for the roots of the general quintic polynomial thus ended 280 years of searching for a generalization of the work of Scipio del Ferro and Ferrari.
    Let

$$f(x) = a_0 + a_1 x + \cdots + a_n x^n$$

be a polynomial over the complex numbers C; $f(x) \in C[x]$. We say that there is a **formula** for a root r of $f(x)$ in case r can be obtained from $a_0, a_1, \cdots, a_n$ by the operations of addition, subtraction, multiplication, division, multiplication by rationals, and extraction of roots. We shall now discuss fields in order to express this idea in a more convenient way.

Definition   Let F be a subfield of C and let $\alpha \in C$. $F(\alpha)$, the field obtained by **adjoining** α to F, is the set of all quotients $f(\alpha)/g(\alpha)$, where $f(\alpha)$ and $g(\alpha)$ are polynomials in α with coefficients in F, and $g(\alpha) \neq 0$.

    It is easy to check that $F(\alpha)$ is a subfield of C containing F and α; indeed, it is the smallest such subfield. Note that $F(\alpha) = F$ if and only if $\alpha \in F$.
    The process of adjoining a number to F may be iterated: If $\alpha_1, \alpha_2, \cdots, \alpha_n$ are in C, we define $F(\alpha_1, \alpha_2, \cdots, \alpha_n) = K(\alpha_n)$, where $K = F(\alpha_1, \alpha_2, \cdots, \alpha_{n-1})$.

Exercises   6.1   Every subfield of C contains the rational numbers, Q.
    6.2   Let F be a subfield of C, and let $\{\alpha_1, \alpha_2, \cdots, \alpha_n\} \subset C$. Prove that $F(\alpha_1, \cdots, \alpha_n) = F(\alpha_{\pi(1)}, \cdots, \alpha_{\pi(n)})$, where π is a permutation of $\{1, 2, \cdots, n\}$.

    If F is any field, a polynomial $f(x) \in F[x]$ of degree n has at most n roots in F. If $F = C$, the fundamental theorem of algebra says that there are complex numbers $\alpha_1, \alpha_2, \cdots, \alpha_n$ (not necessarily distinct) such that

$$f(x) = (x - \alpha_1)(x - \alpha_2) \cdots (x - \alpha_n).$$

Definition   Let F be a subfield of C, and let $f(x) \in F[x]$. The **root field** of $f(x)$ **over** F, $R(f,F)$, is the field $F(\alpha_1, \alpha_2, \cdots, \alpha_n)$, where $\{\alpha_1, \alpha_2, \cdots, \alpha_n\}$ is the set of all roots of $f(x)$.

Note that $R(f,F)$ does depend on F. For example, one way of stating the fundamental theorem of algebra is that $R(f,C) = C$. The reader must remember that $R(f,F)$ is the field obtained from F by adjoining all roots of $f(x)$.

Definition   Let $f(x) \in F[x]$ and $R = R(f,F)$; $f(x)$ is **solvable by radicals** in case there are fields

$$F = K_0 \subset K_1 \subset \cdots \subset K_t = R$$

where each K_{i+1} is obtained from K_i by adjoining a root of an element in K_i.

When we say that there is a formula for the roots of $f(x)$, we really mean that $f(x)$ is solvable by radicals. Let us illustrate this by considering the quadratic formula and the cubic formula.

If $f(x) = x^2 + bx + c$, set $F = Q(b,c)$, where Q is the rationals; observe that $b^2 - 4c \in F$. Let $\alpha = (b^2 - 4c)^{1/2}$, and set $K_1 = F(\alpha)$. The quadratic formula says that K_1 is the root field of $f(x)$ over F.

If $f(x) = x^3 + qx + r$, set $F = Q(q,r)$; observe that $\dfrac{r^2}{4} + \dfrac{q^3}{27} \in F$.

Let

$$\alpha = \left(\frac{r^2}{4} + \frac{q^3}{27}\right)^{1/2},$$

and set $K_1 = F(\alpha)$. Observe further that $-\dfrac{r}{2} + \alpha \in K_1$. Let

$$\beta = \left(-\frac{r}{2} + \alpha\right)^{1/3},$$

and set $K_2 = K_1(\beta)$. Note that $\gamma = -q/3\beta$ is a cube root of $-\dfrac{r}{2} - \alpha$, so that Scipio del Ferro's formula shows that K_2 is the root field of $f(x)$ over F.

Definition   If K is a field, an **automorphism** of K is a one-to-one correspondence $\lambda: K \to K$ such that

$$\lambda(x + y) = \lambda(x) + \lambda(y)$$

and

$$\lambda(xy) = \lambda(x)\lambda(y)$$

for every x and y in K. If F is a subfield of K, we say that λ **fixes** F in case $\lambda(a) = a$ for every $a \in F$.

LEMMA 6.1   Let F be a subfield of K. The set of all automorphisms of K that fix F forms a group (in which the binary operation is composition of functions).

Proof   The reader may verify that if λ and μ are automorphisms of K that fix F, then so is $\lambda\mu^{-1}$. ∎

Definition   Let $f(x) \in F[x]$ and let $R = R(f,F)$. The **Galois group of** $f(x)$ **over** F, denoted $G(R/F)$, is the group of all automorphisms of R fixing F.

THEOREM 6.2   Let $f(x) \in F[x]$ have exactly k distinct roots $\alpha_1, \alpha_2, \cdots, \alpha_k$, and let $R = F(\alpha_1, \alpha_2, \cdots, \alpha_k)$ be the root field of $f(x)$ over F. Every $\lambda \in G(R/F)$ determines a permutation of $\{\alpha_1, \alpha_2, \cdots, \alpha_k\}$; conversely, λ is completely determined by this permutation.

Proof   Suppose $f(x) = a_0 + a_1 x + \cdots + a_n x^n$, where each $a_i \in F$. If $\beta \in R$, $f(\beta) = a_0 + a_1\beta + \cdots + a_n\beta^n \in R$, and

$$\lambda(f(\beta)) = a_0 + a_1\lambda(\beta) + \cdots + a_n\lambda(\beta)^n = f(\lambda(\beta)),$$

since λ fixes F. In particular, if β is a root of $f(x)$, so is $\lambda(\beta)$. Therefore, λ shuffles the α among themselves; λ is a permutation of the α because λ is a one-to-one correspondence.

The definition of adjoining numbers to a field implies that an automorphism μ of R which fixes F is determined once we know $\mu(\alpha_i)$ for $i = 1, 2, \cdots, k$. This last remark may be proved by induction on k. ∎

COROLLARY 6.3   If $f(x) \in F[x]$ has exactly k distinct roots, then $G(R/F)$ is isomorphic to a subgroup of S_k, (where R is the root field of $f(x)$ over F).

Proof   If $\alpha_1, \alpha_2, \cdots, \alpha_k$ are the distinct roots of $f(x)$, then the function

$$\lambda \to \begin{pmatrix} \alpha_1 & \alpha_2 & \cdots & \alpha_k \\ \lambda(\alpha_1) & \lambda(\alpha_2) & \cdots & \lambda(\alpha_k) \end{pmatrix}$$

is a homomorphism of the Galois group into S_k which is one-to-one. ∎

We shall now present some field theory in order to establish a connection between the solvability of a polynomial by radicals and its Galois group.

Let K be a field with subfield F. Clearly, K satisfies the axioms for a vector space over F. *For the remainder of this chapter, all fields will be assumed to be subfields of the complex numbers C.*

Definition   A number $\alpha \in C$ is **algebraic over** F in case $F(\alpha)$ is a finite-dimensional vector space over F (otherwise α is **transcendental over** F).

Exercises   6.3   Prove that $\alpha \in C$ is algebraic over F if and only if there is an irreducible polynomial $p(x) \in F[x]$ having α as a root.

6.4   Let $p(x) = a_0 + a_1x + \cdots + a_nx^n$ be an irreducible polynomial over F of degree n. If α is a root of $p(x)$, prove that $\{1, \alpha, \alpha^2, \cdots, \alpha^{n-1}\}$ is a basis of $F(\alpha)$ viewed as a vector space over F. Conclude that if $[F(\alpha):F]$ denotes the dimension of $F(\alpha)$ over F, then $[F(\alpha):F] = n$.

6.5   Let $p(x) \in F[x]$, and let $p'(x)$ denote its derivative. Prove that $p(x)$ has repeated roots [i.e., is divisible by $(x - \alpha)^2$ for some α] if and only if $p(x)$ and $p'(x)$ have a nonconstant common divisor.

6.6   If $p(x) \in F[x]$ is irreducible over F, then all its roots are distinct.

6.7   Let $F \subset K \subset R$ be fields, where $[K:F]$ and $[R:K]$ are finite. Then

$$[R:F] = [R:K][K:F].$$

(*Hint:* If $\{\alpha_1, \cdots, \alpha_r\}$ is a basis of K over F and $\{\beta_1, \cdots, \beta_s\}$ is a basis of R over K, then the set of rs elements of the form $\alpha_i\beta_j$ is a basis of R over F.)

6.8   Suppose $R \supset F$ and $[R:F]$ is finite. Prove that every $\alpha \in R$ is algebraic over F.

LEMMA 6.4   Let $f(x) \in F[x]$, and let $R = R(f,F)$. Any automorphism $\lambda: F \to F$ can be extended to an automorphism $\lambda^*: R \to R$ (i.e., λ^* agrees with λ on F).

$$R \xrightarrow{\lambda^*} R$$
$$\big| \qquad \big|$$
$$F \xrightarrow{\lambda} F$$

Proof We perform an induction on $[R:F] = d$. If $d = 1$, then $R = F$ and there is nothing to prove. If $d > 1$, then $R \neq F$, so that there is some root α of $f(x)$ not lying in F (of course $\alpha \in R$, by the definition of root field). Now α is a root of some irreducible factor $p(x)$ of $f(x)$. Moreover, if k is the degree of $p(x)$, $k > 1$, since $\alpha \notin F$. By Exercise 6.4, $\{1, \alpha, \alpha^2, \cdots, \alpha^{k-1}\}$ is a basis of $F(\alpha)$ over F. Therefore, we may extend λ to $\lambda_1: F(\alpha) \to F(\alpha)$ by defining:

$$\lambda_1(a_0 + a_1\alpha + \cdots + a_{k-1}\alpha^{k-1})$$
$$= \lambda(a_0) + \lambda(a_1)\alpha + \cdots + \lambda(a_{k-1})\alpha^{k-1}.$$

The reader may check that λ_1 is an automorphism of $F(\alpha)$. Now, by Exercise 6.7, $[R:F(\alpha)] = d/k < d$. Furthermore, since R arises from $F(\alpha)$ by adjoining all the roots of $f(x)$, R is also the root field of $f(x)$ over $F(\alpha)$. With all the inductive assumptions being verified, λ_1, a fortiori λ, can be extended to an automorphism λ^* of R. ∎

The following property provides a useful characterization of root fields.

Definition Let R be a field containing F, with $[R:F]$ finite. R is **normal over** F in case every irreducible $p(x) \in F[x]$ that has one root in R has all its roots in R.

Here is an example of a nonnormal field R over F. Let F be the rationals, and let α be the real cube root of 2. Now α is a root of the irreducible polynomial $x^3 - 2$, so that if $R = F(\alpha)$, then $[R:F] = 3$, and so is finite. On the other hand, R is not normal over F, since $x^3 - 2$ is irreducible downstairs, has one root upstairs, but does not have all its roots upstairs (everything in R is real, whereas the other roots of $x^3 - 2$ are not real).

THEOREM 6.5 Suppose $[R:F]$ is finite. R is normal over F if and only if R is the root field of some polynomial over F.

Proof If $[R:F] > 1$, there is an element $\alpha \in R$ that is not in F. By Exercise 6.8, α is algebraic over F, and so it is a root of an irreducible $p_1(x)$ in $F[x]$. Since R is normal over F, R contains the root field of $p_1(x)$, R_1. If $R = R_1$, we are done. If $R \neq R_1$, there is an element $\beta \in R$ that is not in R_1. As above, β is a root of an irreducible $p_2(x)$ in $F[x]$, and so R contains the root field of $p_1(x)p_2(x)$, R_2. Since $[R:F] > [R:R_1] > [R:R_2]$, this process must stop with $R = R_i$, for some i.

Suppose R is the root field of $f(x)$ over F; suppose further that there is an irreducible $p(x) \in F[x]$ with one root α in R and another root $\beta \notin R$. There is an isomorphism $\lambda: F(\alpha) \to F(\beta)$ fixing F and such that $\lambda(\alpha) = \beta$ (use the bases $\{1, \alpha, \alpha^2, \cdots, \alpha^{n-1}\}$ of $F(\alpha)$ and $\{1, \beta, \beta^2, \cdots, \beta^{n-1}\}$ of $F(\beta)$ given in Exercise 6.4). Let the roots of $f(x)$ be $\gamma_1, \gamma_2, \cdots, \gamma_k$. Now R is the root field of $f(x)$ over $F(\alpha)$ and $R(\beta)$ is the root field of $f(x)$ over $F(\beta)$, for

$$R = F(\alpha)(\gamma_1, \gamma_2, \cdots, \gamma_k) = F(\gamma_1, \cdots, \gamma_k)$$

and

$$R(\beta) = F(\gamma_1, \cdots, \gamma_k)(\beta) = F(\beta)(\gamma_1, \cdots, \gamma_k).$$

By Lemma 6.4, the isomorphism λ given above extends to an isomorphism $\lambda^*: R \to R(\beta)$. In particular, λ^* also fixes F, so that λ^* is an isomorphism of R and $R(\beta)$ considered as vector spaces over F. Therefore, these spaces have the same dimension: $[R:F] = [R(\beta):F]$. Since

$$[R(\beta):F] = [R(\beta):R][R:F],$$

$[R(\beta):R] = 1$, i.e., $R(\beta) = R$, i.e., $\beta \in R$. This contradiction proves that R is normal over F. ∎

Exercises   6.9   Using Lemma 6.4 (and its proof), show that if $p(x) \in F[x]$ is irreducible with root field R, then the set X of all points fixed by every $\lambda \in G(R/F)$ is precisely F. (The definition of $G(R/F)$ merely asserts that $F \subset X$.)

6.10   Let $F \subset K \subset R$, where R and K are each normal over F. Let λ be an automorphism of R fixing F; prove that $\lambda|K$ is an automorphism of K fixing F.

LEMMA 6.6   Let $F \subset K \subset R$, where R and K are each normal over F. Then $G(R/K) \lhd G(R/F)$ and

$$G(R/F)/G(R/K) \approx G(K/F).$$

Proof   Define $\Phi\colon G(R/F) \to G(K/F)$ by

$$\Phi(\lambda) = \lambda|K.$$

By Exercise 6.10, Φ is a well defined function, and Φ is easily seen to be a homomorphism. The kernel of Φ is the set of all homomorphisms of R that fix K, i.e., $G(R/K)$. We claim that Φ is onto. Suppose $\lambda \in G(K/F)$, i.e., λ is an automorphism of K that fixes F. By Theorem 6.5, R is a root field of F, and so, by Lemma 6.4, λ can be extended to an automorphism λ^* of R. Therefore, $\lambda^* \in G(R/F)$ and

$$\Phi(\lambda^*) = \lambda^*|K = \lambda.$$

The first isomorphism theorem (Theorem 2.12) completes the proof. ∎

From this point, F is not only assumed to be a subfield of C, but is also assumed to contain all roots of unity.

Exercises   **6.11**   Let $R = F(\alpha)$, where α is a root of $x^k - a$, $a \in F$. Prove that there exist intermediate fields

$$F = K_0 \subset K_1 \subset \cdots \subset K_t = R,$$

where $K_{i+1} = K_i(\alpha_i)$, α_i is a root of $x^{n(i)} - a_i$, $a_i \in K_i$, and $n(i)$ is prime.

    6.12   If p is a prime and $a \in F$, then $x^p - a$ either has a root in F or is irreducible over F.

    [*Note:* If $f(x)$ has a root $a \in F$, then $f(x)$ is not irreducible, for it is divisible by $x - a$. The converse is false: If $f(x)$ factors, it need not have a root in F. For example, if F is the reals, then $f(x) = (x^2 + 1)(x^2 + 1)$ factors, but it has no real roots.]

    6.13   Let α be a root of $x^p - a$, $a \in F$, and p be a prime. Prove that $G(F(\alpha)/F)$ is a cyclic group of order p.

We summarize this investigation in the next theorem.

THEOREM 6.7   Let R be the root field of $f(x)$ over F. If $f(x)$ is solvable by radicals, then there exist subgroups G_i of $G = G(R/F)$ such that:

   (i) $G = G_0 \supset G_1 \supset \cdots \supset G_n = \{1\}$.

   (ii) $G_{i+1} \triangleleft G_i$, for all i.

   (iii) G_i/G_{i+1} is cyclic of prime order.

Proof   Define $G_i = G(R/K_i)$. We only remind the reader of previous work; (i) follows immediately from the definition of Galois group; (ii) follows from Lemma 6.6; (iii) follows from Exercises 6.11 and 6.13 and Lemma 6.6. ∎

The converse of this theorem is also true, but we shall not prove it here.

We have been led to the following concept.

Definition   A **subnormal**[2] **series** of G is a chain of subgroups

(*) $G = G_0 \supset G_1 \supset \cdots \supset G_n$

in which $G_{i+1} \lhd G_i$ for all i. The **factor groups** of the series (*) are the groups G_i/G_{i+1}; the **length** of the series (*) is the number of strict inclusions.

Alternatively, the length of the series is the number of factor groups with more than one element. Note that the factor groups are the only quotient groups we can always form, for we have seen (Exercise 3.32) that normality need not be transitive.

Definition   A finite group G is **solvable** in case it has a subnormal series with $G_n = \{1\}$ whose factor groups are cyclic of prime order.

In this terminology, Theorem 6.7 and its converse say that a polynomial $f(x)$ is solvable by radicals if and only if its Galois group $G(R/F)$ is a solvable group. Now Abel proved that there exists a polynomial $f(x)$ of degree 5 whose Galois group[3] is S_5. Since S_5 is not a solvable group (as we shall soon see), this polynomial is not solvable by radicals. Thus, the classical problem of the determination of the roots of a polynomial led inevitably to groups and to subnormal series, and there its solution (or nonsolution) lies. (We refer the interested reader to E. Artin's monograph, *Galois Theory*, and

---

[2] This terminology is not standard; most authors call this a normal series. We reserve the term *normal series* for those series in which each term is normal in the big group G.

[3] Galois outlined Galois theory in 1832 (six years after Abel proved the unsolvability of the quintic) when he was only 19; he was killed in a duel two years later.

B. L. van der Waerden's *Modern Algebra*, Vol. I (see Bibliography), for a more thorough discussion.)

The work of Abel and Galois has not only enriched the study of polynomials and fields, it has also contributed a new point of view to the study of groups. Let us give a brief review of what we have learned so far. Our first results arose from examining properties of a single subgroup via Lagrange's theorem. The second, deeper set of results arose from examining properties of a family of subgroups via the Sylow theorems (Theorems 5.9 and 5.10); this family of subgroups consists of the conjugates of a single subgroup, and so each member has the same order. Subnormal series will give results by allowing us to examine a family of subgroups of distinct orders, thus providing an opening wedge for an inductive proof.

The Jordan-Hölder Theorem

Our study of subnormal series begins with a theorem whose mysterious origin will appear as soon as it is applied.

THEOREM 6.8 (*Zassenhaus Lemma*)   Let $A^*, A, B^*,$ and B be four subgroups of a group G such that $A^* \lhd A$ and $B^* \lhd B$.

Then

$$A^*(A \cap B^*) \lhd A^*(A \cap B),$$

$$B^*(A^* \cap B) \lhd B^*(A \cap B),$$

and there is an isomorphism

$$\frac{A^*(A \cap B)}{A^*(A \cap B^*)} \approx \frac{B^*(A \cap B)}{B^*(A^* \cap B)}.$$

Proof   Let D be the subset $(A \cap B^*)(A^* \cap B)$. Now $B^* \lhd B$,

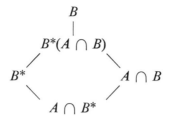

so that B^* is normal in the smaller group $B^*(A \cap B)$. By the second isomorphism theorem (Theorem 2.15), $A \cap B^* \lhd A \cap B$. In a similar manner, one sees that $A^* \cap B \lhd A \cap B$. It follows from Exercise 2.40 that the subset D is a normal subgroup of $A \cap B$. We shall prove that each of the quotient groups in the theorem is isomorphic to $(A \cap B)/D$.

Let $f: A^*(A \cap B) \to (A \cap B)/D$ be given as follows: If $x \in A^*(A \cap B)$, then $x = a^*c$, where $a^* \in A^*$ and $c \in A \cap B$; set $f(x) = Dc$. It is straightforward to check that f is a well defined homomorphism of $A^*(A \cap B)$ onto $(A \cap B)/D$ whose kernel is $A^*(A \cap B^*)$. By the first isomorphism theorem, $A^*(A \cap B^*) \lhd A^*(A \cap B)$ and

$$\frac{A^*(A \cap B)}{A^*(A \cap B^*)} \approx \frac{A \cap B}{D}.$$

If we interchange the letters A and B, the symmetry of the hypothesis shows that a similar homomorphism exists; hence, $B^*(A^* \cap B) \lhd B^*(A \cap B)$, and the other quotient group is also isomorphic to $A \cap B/D$; therefore, the two quotient groups of the theorem are isomorphic. ∎

We remark that the Zassenhaus lemma generalizes the second isomorphism theorem: Set $A^* = T$, $A = G$, $B^* = S \cap T$, and $B = S$, where S and T are subgroups of G with $T \lhd G$.

Definition   Let

(*) $G = G_0 \supset G_1 \supset \cdots \supset G_n$

and

(**) $G = H_0 \supset H_1 \supset \cdots \supset H_m$

be subnormal series of G; (**) is a **refinement** of (*) in case (**) = (*) or (**) is obtained from (*) by the insertion of subgroups.

The length of a refinement is thus at least as great as the length of the original series.

Definition   A subnormal series

$$G = G_0 \supset G_1 \supset \cdots \supset G_n = \{1\}$$

is a **composition series** in case each G_{i+1} is a maximal normal subgroup of G_i.

Exercises   6.14   A subnormal series with $G_n = \{1\}$ is a composition series if and only if each of its nontrivial factor groups is simple.
6.15   A composition series is a subnormal series of maximal length.
6.16   Every finite group has a composition series.
6.17   An abelian group has a composition series if and only if it is finite.
*6.18   A subgroup H is **subnormal** in G in case there is a subnormal series from G to H. Prove that a group G has a composition series if and only if G has both chain conditions on subnormal subgroups.

Consider the group $G = \sigma(30)$ with generator x; we write two composition series for G (normality is automatic, since G is abelian):

(*) $G \supset [x^5] \supset [x^{10}] \supset \{1\}$;

(**) $G \supset [x^2] \supset [x^6] \supset \{1\}$.

The factor groups of (*) are $G/[x^5]$, $[x^5]/[x^{10}]$, and $[x^{10}]$, i.e., $\sigma(5)$, $\sigma(2)$, and $\sigma(3)$. The factor groups of (**) are $G/[x^2]$, $[x^2]/[x^6]$, and $[x^6]$, i.e., $\sigma(2)$, $\sigma(3)$, $\sigma(5)$. In this case, these two composition series of G have the same length, and the factor groups can be "paired isomorphically" after rearranging them. We give a name to this phenomenon.

Definition   Two subnormal series (*) and (**) of G are **equivalent** if there is a one-to-one correspondence between the factor groups of (*) and (**) such that corresponding factor groups are isomorphic.

Observe that equivalent subnormal series have the same length. The two composition series for $\sigma(30)$ exhibited above are equivalent; the amazing fact is that this is true for every group G (possibly infinite) that has a composition series! Rather than prove this theorem directly, we prove an even stronger result.

THEOREM 6.9 (*Schreier*)   Any two subnormal series of an arbitrary group G have refinements that are equivalent.

Proof   Let

(*) $G = G_0 \supset G_1 \supset \cdots \supset G_n$

and

(**) $G = H_0 \supset H_1 \supset \cdots \supset H_m$

be subnormal series. In the first series, between each G_i and G_{i+1}, insert the groups $G_{i+1}(G_i \cap H_j)$, where $0 \leq j \leq m$. (These are the "numerators" of the groups in the Zassenhaus lemma.) The normality assertions of that lemma say that this refinement of (*) is a subnormal series with mn (not necessarily strict) inclusions. In the second series, between each H_j and H_{j+1}, insert the groups $H_{j+1}(H_j \cap G_i)$, where $0 \leq i \leq n$. This refinement also has mn inclusions. The first refinement looks like

$$\cdots \supset G_{i+1}(G_i \cap H_j) \supset G_{i+1}(G_i \cap H_{j+1}) \supset \cdots;$$

the second refinement looks like

$$\cdots \supset H_{j+1}(H_j \cap G_i) \supset H_{j+1}(H_j \cap G_{i+1}) \supset \cdots.$$

In essence, we have squeezed either subnormal series between each consecutive pair of groups in the other series. The isomorphism of Theorem 6.8 with the four subgroups G_{i+1}, G_i, H_{j+1}, and H_j is precisely what is needed to complete the proof. ∎

THEOREM 6.10 (*Jordan-Hölder*)[4]   Any two composition series of a group G are equivalent. Therefore, every group having a composition series determines a set of simple groups.

---

[4] Jordan proved that the orders of the factor groups of a composition series of G depend only on G; Hölder proved that the factor groups depend only on G.

Proof   Since composition series are subnormal series, any two composition series of G have equivalent refinements. That a composition series is a subnormal series of maximal length implies that it is equivalent to every refinement of itself; the theorem now follows. ∎

If one applies the Jordan-Hölder theorem to $G = \sigma(n)$, he may prove again the fundamental theorem of arithmetic, for the only abelian simple groups have prime order.

Solvable Groups

Solvable groups have been defined in connection with Galois theory. Since these groups form a large class of groups of purely group-theoretical interest as well, we give another definition of solvability which is more convenient to work with, and which is equivalent to our earlier definition when G is finite.

Definition   A group G is **solvable** if it has a subnormal series with last term $\{1\}$ and which has abelian factor groups. Such a subnormal series is called a **solvable series** of G.

Exercises   6.19   Any refinement of a solvable series is a solvable series.

6.20   A finite group is solvable (definition given above) if and only if it has a composition series with cyclic factor groups of prime order (earlier definition, page 107).

6.21   A solvable group with a composition series is finite.

6.22   Let $H \lhd G$, where G has a composition series. Prove that G has a composition series, one of whose terms is H.

Let us see how to manufacture solvable groups.

THEOREM 6.11   Any subgroup H of a solvable group G is solvable.

Proof   Let $G = G_0 \supset G_1 \supset \cdots \supset G_n = \{1\}$ be a solvable series for G; we claim that

$$H = H_0 \supset (H \cap G_1) \supset \cdots \supset (H \cap G_n) = \{1\}$$

is a solvable series for H. By the second isomorphism theorem,

$$H \cap G_{i+1} = (H \cap G_i) \cap G_{i+1} \lhd H \cap G_i,$$

so that we do have a subnormal series. Moreover, we have the diagram

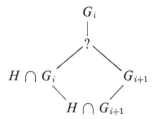

where $? = G_{i+1}(H \cap G_i)$. Therefore,

$$\frac{H \cap G_i}{H \cap G_{i+1}} \approx \frac{?}{G_{i+1}} \subset \frac{G_i}{G_{i+1}}.$$

Since G_i/G_{i+1} is abelian, so is its subgroup $?/G_{i+1}$, as desired. ∎

THEOREM 6.12 If G is solvable and $H \lhd G$, then G/H is solvable.

Proof Let $G = G_0 \supset G_1 \supset \cdots \supset G_n = \{1\}$ be a solvable series. Now $G \supset H \supset \{1\}$ is a subnormal series, so that, by Theorem 6.9, these two series have equivalent refinements. Therefore (Exercise 6.19), there is a solvable series

$$G = K_0 \supset K_1 \supset \cdots \supset H \supset \cdots \supset \{1\}.$$

Consider the series

$$G/H \supset K_1/H \supset K_2/H \supset \cdots \supset H/H = \{1\}.$$

By the third isomorphism theorem (Theorem 2.16), this is a subnormal series and $(K_i/H)/(K_{i+1}/H) \approx K_i/K_{i+1}$, which is abelian. Hence, G/H is solvable. ∎

(Another proof of this theorem, given shortly, does not use Theorem 6.9.)

THEOREM 6.13 Let $H \lhd G$. If both H and G/H are solvable, then G is solvable.

Proof   Let

$$G/H \supset K_1^* \supset K_2^* \supset \cdots \supset \{1\}$$

be a solvable series. By the correspondence theorem, we can construct the beginning of a solvable series from G to H, i.e., there are subgroups K_i with $K_{i+1} \lhd K_i$, K_i/K_{i+1} abelian, and

$$G = G_0 \supset K_1 \supset K_2 \supset \cdots \supset H.$$

Since H is solvable, it has a solvable series. If we hook these two series together at H, we obtain a solvable series for G. ∎

COROLLARY 6.14   If H and K are solvable, then $H \times K$ is solvable.

Proof   If $G = H \times K$, then $H \lhd G$ and $G/H \approx K$, so that G is solvable, by Theorem 6.13. ∎

COROLLARY 6.15   Every finite p-group G is solvable.

Proof   We perform an induction on $|G|$. By Theorem 5.4, $|Z(G)| \neq 1$. Therefore, $G/Z(G)$ is a p-group of order $< |G|$, and so is solvable, by induction. $Z(G)$ is solvable, for every abelian group is solvable. By Theorem 6.13, G is solvable. ∎

THEOREM 6.16   If $n \geq 5$, S_n is not solvable.

Proof   Since A_n is simple for $n \geq 5$, one composition series for S_n is

$$S_n \supset A_n \supset \{1\};$$

the factor groups are $\sigma(2)$ and A_n. By the Jordan-Hölder theorem, S_n is not solvable. ∎

Exercises   6.23   If S and T are solvable subgroups of G with $S \lhd G$, then ST is a solvable subgroup of G.

6.24   If $n \leq 4$, then S_n is solvable.

6.25   Any group of order p^2q is solvable, where p and q are primes. (Burnside has proved, using representation theory, i.e., the study of the homomorphisms of groups into groups of matrices, that any group of order $p^m q^n$ is solvable, where p and q are primes.)

*6.26 Any group of square-free order is solvable. (*Hint:* Use Exercise 5.32.)

6.27 The dihedral groups D_n are solvable.

6.28 The following two statements are equivalent: (1) Every group of odd order is solvable; (2) every finite nonabelian simple group has even order. (In a deep paper in 1963, W. Feit and J. Thompson proved the truth of these statements.)

Another approach to solvable groups is with commutator subgroups. The fact that we are dealing with abelian quotient groups suggests this approach at once.

Definition We define the **"higher"** commutator subgroups of G inductively:

$$G^{(0)} = G; \quad G^{(i+1)} = G^{(i)\prime},$$

i.e., $G^{(i+1)}$ is the commutator subgroup of $G^{(i)}$. The series of higher commutator subgroups is called the **derived series** of G.

We also want the following terminology.

Definition A subgroup H of G is **characteristic** in G in case $f(H) \subset H$ for every isomorphism $f: G \to G$; H is **fully invariant in** G in case $f(H) \subset H$ for every homomorphism $f: G \to G$.

Every fully invariant subgroup is characteristic, and every characteristic subgroup is normal.

Exercises 6.29 Let $G \neq \{1\}$ be a finite group. If G is solvable, then G contains a normal abelian subgroup $H \neq \{1\}$; if G is not solvable, then G contains a normal subgroup $H \neq \{1\}$ such that $H = H'$.

6.30 If $H \subset N \triangleleft G$ and H is characteristic in N, then $H \triangleleft G$. (Compare Exercise 5.31.)

6.31 For any group G, $Z(G)$ is characteristic (it need not be a fully invariant subgroup).

6.32 If G is an abelian p-group, then $G[p]$, the set of all elements in G of order $\leq p$, is fully invariant in G.

6.33   Every normal p-sylow subgroup of a finite group G is fully invariant in G.

6.34   Every $G^{(i)}$ is a fully invariant subgroup of G.

LEMMA 6.17   If $G = G_0 \supset G_1 \supset \cdots \supset G_n = \{1\}$ is a solvable series, then $G_i \supset G^{(i)}$ for all i.

Proof   We prove the lemma by induction on i. If $i = 0$, $G_i = G^{(i)} = G$. Suppose now that $G_i \supset G^{(i)}$; then $G_i' \supset G^{(i)\prime} = G^{(i+1)}$. Since G_i/G_{i+1} is abelian, $G_{i+1} \supset G_i'$, by Exercise 2.47. Therefore, $G_{i+1} \supset G^{(i+1)}$, as desired. ∎

THEOREM 6.18   A group G is solvable if and only if $G^{(n)} = \{1\}$ for some integer n.

Proof   Let $G = G_0 \supset G_1 \supset \cdots \supset G_n = \{1\}$ be a solvable series. By the lemma, $G_n \supset G^{(n)}$ and so $G^{(n)} = \{1\}$.

If $G^{(n)} = \{1\}$ for some n, then the series

$$G = G^{(0)} \supset G' \supset \cdots \supset G^{(n)} = \{1\}$$

is a solvable series for G. ∎

Definition   A **normal series** of G is a subnormal series of G in which each term is a normal subgroup of the big group G.

Observe that the derived series of a group G is a normal series. The reader should supply alternative proofs of Theorems 6.11 and 6.12 using this new characterization of solvability.

A Theorem of P. Hall

The main result of this section is a generalization of the Sylow theorems (Theorems 5.9 and 5.10) that holds in (and, in fact, characterizes) finite solvable groups.

Definition   A **minimal normal subgroup** N of G is a normal subgroup $\neq \{1\}$ that contains no proper subgroup that is normal in G.

LEMMA 6.19 Every minimal normal subgroup N of a finite solvable group G is an elementary abelian group.

Proof N' is a fully invariant subgroup of N so that $N' \lhd G$, by Exercise 6.30. Since N is a minimal normal subgroup of G, either $N' = N$ or $N' = \{1\}$. Since N is a subgroup of a solvable group, N is itself solvable. Therefore, $N \neq N'$ and $N' = \{1\}$, i.e., N is abelian. Because N is finite, it is the direct product of its sylow subgroups. By Exercises 6.33 and 6.30, N is a p-group. Finally, Exercises 6.32 and 6.30 imply that N is elementary. ∎

THEOREM 6.20 (*P. Hall*) Let G be a solvable group of order ab, where $(a,b) = 1$. Then G contains at least one subgroup of order a, and any two such are conjugate.

Proof The proof proceeds by induction on $|G|$.

  Case (i) G contains a normal subgroup H of order $a_1 b_1$, where a_1 divides a, b_1 divides b, and $b_1 < b$.

G/H is a solvable group of order $(a/a_1) \cdot (b/b_1)$ and so contains a subgroup $\hat{A}/H$ of order a/a_1. The subgroup $\hat{A}$ of G has order $ab_1 < ab$. Since $\hat{A}$ is also solvable, it contains a subgroup of order a, as desired.

Suppose A and A_1 are subgroups of G of order a. If $k = |AH|$, then k divides ab and k divides $aa_1 b_1$ (by the second isomorphism theorem). Since the a and b are relatively prime, we may conclude that k divides ab_1. On the other hand, Lagrange's theorem implies that $k = |AH|$ is divisible by a and by $a_1 b_1$; therefore, $|AH| = ab_1$. A similar argument shows that $|A_1 H| = ab_1$. Thus, AH/H and $A_1 H/H$ are subgroups of G/H of order a/a_1; by induction, these subgroups are conjugate (say, by $\bar{x} \in G/H$). If $x \in G$ goes into $\bar{x}$ under the natural map, it is quickly checked that $xAHx^{-1} = A_1 H$. Therefore, xAx^{-1} and A_1 are subgroups of $A_1 H$ of order a and so are conjugate, by induction. This completes case (i).

If there is some proper normal subgroup of G whose order is not divisible by b, the theorem is proved. We may therefore assume that b divides $|H|$ for every proper normal subgroup H. If H is a minimal normal subgroup, however, $|H| = p^m$ for some prime p, by Lemma 6.19. We conclude that $b = p^m$. Thus, H is a p-sylow subgroup of G; that H is normal implies (by Exercise 5.9) that H is the unique such subgroup. Our problem has now been reduced to the following case.

Case (ii) G has a unique minimal normal subgroup H (H must have order p^m).

Observe that since G is finite, every normal subgroup of G contains a minimal normal subgroup of G; in our present case, every proper normal subgroup of G must contain H.

Let K/H be a minimal normal subgroup of G/H. By Lemma 6.19 $|K/H| = q^n$, so that $|K| = p^m q^n$. Let S be a q-sylow subgroup of K and let N^* be the normalizer of S in G. We shall show that $|N^*| = a$.

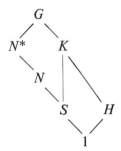

Observe that $HS \subset K$, and since $H \cap S = \{1\}$, $|HS| = |K|$; therefore, $K = HS$.

Since $K \lhd G$, every conjugate of S in G lies in K, so that all these subgroups are already conjugate in K. Thus, if N is the normalizer of S in K and c is the number of conjugates of S in G, we have

$$c = [G:N^*] = [K:N] = [HN:N] = [H:H \cap N],$$

the middle equality holding because $S \subset N$. If we can show that $H \cap N = \{1\}$, then $c = |H| = p^m$, and so $|N^*| = a$. We do this in two stages: (1) $H \cap N \subset Z(K)$; (2) $Z(K) = \{1\}$.

Let $x \in H \cap N$. If $k \in K$, then $k = hs$, where $h \in H$ and $s \in S$. Since $x \in H$, x commutes with h, for H is abelian. Hence, we need show only that x commutes with s. Now $(x^{-1}s^{-1}x)s \in S$, since $x \in N$; $x^{-1}(s^{-1}xs) \in H$, since H is normal. Therefore, $x^{-1}s^{-1}xs \in S \cap H = \{1\}$, and x commutes with s, as desired.

Finally, $Z(K)$ is a characteristic subgroup of K, and $K \lhd G$, so that $Z(K) \lhd G$. If $Z(K) \neq \{1\}$, then $Z(K)$ contains a minimal normal subgroup of G; thus $H \subset Z(K)$. This, together with $K = HS$, tells us that $S \lhd K$. By Exercise 6.33, $S \lhd G$ and so S, too, contains H, a contradiction.

Suppose A_1 is another subgroup of G of order a. Since $|A_1 K|$ is divisible by a and by $|K| = p^m q^n$, $|A_1 K| = |G| = ab$ so that $A_1 K = G$.

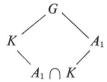

Therefore,

$$G/K = A_1 K/K \approx A_1/A_1 \cap K$$

implies $|A_1 \cap K| = q^n$. By the Sylow theorem, $A_1 \cap K$ is conjugate to S. Furthermore, $A_1 \cap K \lhd A_1$. Since conjugate subgroups have conjugate normalizers, A_1 must be the normalizer of $A_1 \cap K$ in G; (the normalizer of S in G is N^*, as we saw in the existence part of the proof; the fact that $|A_1| = |N^*|$ tells us, therefore, that A_1 is the largest subgroup of G containing $A_1 \cap K$ as a normal subgroup). Hence, A_1 and N^* are conjugate. ▌

Let us compare Hall's theorem to the Sylow theorems. Suppose $|G| = p^m a$, where $(p^m, a) = 1$. The Sylow theorems say that G has at least one subgroup of order p^m, and any two such are conjugate; Hall's theorem says that if G is solvable, G contains at least one subgroup of order a, and any two such are conjugate.

Definition   Let G be a group of order $p^m a$, where $(p^m, a) = 1$. A subgroup of G of order a is a **p-complement** of G.

Hall's theorem tells us that every finite solvable group has a p-complement, for every p. The converse of this statement is also true: If G is a finite group containing a p-complement for every p, then G is solvable. Notice that this converse gives an immediate proof of Burnside's theorem: If $|G| = p^m q^n$, then G is solvable. In this case, the p- and q-complements are just q- and p-sylow subgroups. Unfortunately, the proof of the converse (also due to P. Hall) makes use of Burnside's theorem, which we cannot prove here.

Central Series and Nilpotent Groups

Normal series other than the derived series can be associated with a group G; two important ones are the descending and ascending central series.

Notation   If H and K are subgroups of G, then
$$(H,K) = [h^{-1}k^{-1}hk : h \in H, k \in K].$$

Exercises   6.35   For any two subgroups H and K of G, $(H,K) = (K,H)$.

6.36 $G' = (G,G)$, and for all i, $G^{(i+1)} = (G^{(i)}, G^{(i)})$.

6.37   A subgroup H of G is normal if and only if $(H,G) \subset H$. (One often says that G **normalizes** H in this case.)

6.38 $(H,K) = \{1\}$ if and only if every element in H commutes with every element of K. (One often says that K **centralizes** H in this case.)

6.39   Let K be a normal subgroup of G with $K \subset H$. Prove that $H/K \subset Z(G/K)$ if and only if $(H,G) \subset K$.

6.40   Let $f: G \to L$ be a homomorphism onto. If $A \subset Z(G)$, then $f(A) \subset Z(L)$.

Definition   We define a chain of subgroups $\gamma_i(G)$ inductively: $\gamma_1(G) = G$; $\gamma_{i+1}(G) = (\gamma_i(G), G)$.

It is easy to see that $\gamma_{i+1}(G) \subset \gamma_i(G)$. Since $(\gamma_i(G), G) = \gamma_{i+1}(G)$, Exercise 6.37 says that $\gamma_{i+1}(G)$ is a normal subgroup of G, for all i.

Definition   The **descending central series** of G is the normal series
$$G = \gamma_1(G) \supset \gamma_2(G) \supset \cdots$$

Definition   We define a chain of subgroups inductively: $Z^0(G) = \{1\}$; $Z^{i+1}(G)$ is the subgroup of G corresponding to the center of $G/Z^i(G)$:
$$G \to G/Z^i(G)$$
$$Z^{i+1}(G) \to \text{center} = Z^{i+1}/Z^i$$
$$Z^i(G) \to \{1\}$$

$Z^i(G)$ is the ith **higher center** of G.

By the correspondence theorem, each $Z^i(G) \subset Z^{i+1}(G)$, and $Z^i(G)$ is a normal subgroup of G.

Definition   The **ascending central series** of G is
$$\{1\} = Z^0(G) \subset Z^1(G) \subset \cdots .$$

When no confusion can occur, we shall abbreviate $Z^i(G)$ by Z^i and $\gamma_i(G)$ by γ_i.

THEOREM 6.21 For any group G, $Z^m(G) = G$ if and only if $\gamma_{m+1}(G) = \{1\}$. Moreover,

$$\gamma_{i+1}(G) \subset Z^{m-i}(G) \qquad \text{for all } i.$$

Proof Assuming $Z^m = G$, we shall prove the inclusion holds by an induction on i. Both terms equal G when $i = 0$, so the induction begins. If $\gamma_{i+1} \subset Z^{m-i}$, then

$$\gamma_{i+2} = (\gamma_{i+1}, G) \subset (Z^{m-i}, G) \subset Z^{m-i-1},$$

the last inclusion following from Exercise 6.39. Since the inclusion holds for all i, it holds for $i = m$. Therefore,

$$\gamma_{m+1} \subset Z^0 = \{1\}.$$

Assuming that $\gamma_{m+1} = \{1\}$, we shall prove by induction on j that $\gamma_{m+1-j} \subset Z^j$ (this is the same inclusion as in the statement of the theorem, for the sum of the indices is $m + 1$). Both terms equal $\{1\}$ when $j = 0$, so the induction begins. If $\gamma_{m+1-j} \subset Z^j$, then there is a homomorphism

$$G/\gamma_{m+1-j} \to G/Z^j$$

which is onto. Now $\gamma_{m-j}/\gamma_{m+1-j} \subset Z(G/\gamma_{m+1-j})$, since $(\gamma_{m-j}, G) \subset \gamma_{m+1-j}$ and Exercise 6.39 holds. By Exercise 6.40,

$$\gamma_{m-j}Z^j/Z^j \subset Z(G/Z^j) = Z^{j+1}/Z^j.$$

Therefore, $Z^{j+1} \supset \gamma_{m-j}Z^j \supset \gamma_{m-j}$, as desired. Since the inclusion holds for all j, it holds for $j = m$. Therefore,

$$G = \gamma_1 \subset Z^m. \quad \blacksquare$$

Definition A group G is **nilpotent** if there is some integer m such that $\gamma_m(G) = \{1\}$.

A group G is nilpotent if the descending central series reaches $\{1\}$ or, equivalently, if the ascending central series reaches G. The nilpotent groups form a class of groups lying strictly between the abelian groups and the solvable groups. If G is abelian, then $\gamma_2(G) = \{1\}$, and so G is nilpotent. We shall soon see that every finite p-group is nilpotent, so that there do exist nilpotent groups that are not abelian.

It is easy to prove by induction that $G^{(i)} \subset \gamma_i(G)$ for all i; it follows that if $\gamma_m(G) = \{1\}$ for some m, then $G^{(m)} = \{1\}$, i.e., if G is nilpotent, then G is solvable. The group S_3 is a solvable group; we claim that it is not nilpotent. Every nilpotent group G has a nontrivial center: if m is the first integer for which $\gamma_{m+1}(G) = \{1\}$, then $\{1\} \neq \gamma_m(G) \subset Z^1(G) = Z(G)$. Therefore, S_3 is not nilpotent, for it is centerless.

THEOREM 6.22   Every subgroup of a nilpotent group G is nilpotent.

Proof   It is easily proved by induction that if $H \subset G$, then $\gamma_i(H) \subset \gamma_i(G)$ for all i. Therefore, $\gamma_m(G) = \{1\}$ implies $\gamma_m(H) = \{1\}$. ∎

THEOREM 6.23   If G is nilpotent and $H \triangleleft G$, then G/H is nilpotent.

Proof   If $f: G \rightarrow L$ is a homomorphism onto, then it is easily proved by induction that $\gamma_i(L) \subset f(\gamma_i(G))$ for all i. The theorem follows if we take f to be the natural map of G onto G/H. ∎

We have just proved the analogs for nilpotent groups of Theorems 6.11 and 6.12. Is the analog of Theorem 6.13 true? If $H \triangleleft G$ and both H and G/H are nilpotent, is G nilpotent? Again, S_3 is a counterexample; both A_3 and S_3/A_3 are abelian and hence nilpotent, but we have already seen that S_3 is not nilpotent. The analog of Corollary 6.14, however, is true.

Exercises   6.41 G is nilpotent if and only if there is a normal series

$$G = G_0 \supset G_1 \supset \cdots \supset G_n = \{1\}$$

such that $G_i/G_{i+1} \subset Z(G/G_{i+1})$ for all i.

6.42   If $H \subset Z(G)$ and G/H is nilpotent, then G is nilpotent.

6.43   The normalizer of H in G is the largest subgroup N such that $(H,N) \subset H$.

THEOREM 6.24 A direct product G of a finite number of nilpotent groups is nilpotent.

Proof An induction on the number of direct factors allows us to assume that $G = H \times K$. Another induction proves that

$$\gamma_i(H \times K) \subset \gamma_i(H) \times \gamma_i(K) \qquad \text{for all } i.$$

Let $M = \max \{m,n\}$, where $\gamma_m(H) = \{1\} = \gamma_n(K)$. Then $\gamma_M(H \times K) = \{1\}$, so that $H \times K$ is nilpotent. ∎

LEMMA 6.25 Every finite p-group G is nilpotent.

Proof We know, by Theorem 5.4, that G and all its nontrivial quotients have nontrivial centers. Therefore, if $Z^i \neq G$ for some i, then $Z^i \underset{\neq}{\subset} Z^{i+1}$. Since G is finite, we cannot have this inequality for all i. It follows that $Z^i = G$ for some i, i.e., G is nilpotent. ∎

This lemma is false without the finiteness assumption, for there exist infinite p-groups that are centerless.

The following theorem is a very satisfying characterization of finite nilpotent groups.

THEOREM 6.26 A finite group G is nilpotent if and only if G is the direct product of its sylow subgroups.

Proof If G is the direct product of its sylow subgroups, then G is nilpotent, by Theorem 6.24 and Lemma 6.25.

Let G be nilpotent and let H be a proper subgroup. We claim that if N is the normalizer of H in G, then $N \neq H$. There exists an i such that $H \supset \gamma_{i+1}(G)$, but $H \not\supset \gamma_i(G)$. Now

$$(\gamma_i, H) \subset (\gamma_i, G) \subset \gamma_{i+1} \subset H,$$

so that $\gamma_i \subset N$, by Exercise 6.43. Therefore, $N \neq H$.

Let P be a sylow subgroup of G, and let $N = N_G(P)$. We have seen in Exercise 5.11 that N is its own normalizer. It follows that N cannot be a proper subgroup of G; thus, $N = G$ and $P \lhd G$. Since P is an arbitrary sylow subgroup of G, G is the direct product of its sylow subgroups, by Exercise 5.12. ∎

Exercises   6.44   The dihedral group D_n is nilpotent if and only if n is a power of 2. (*Hint:* Use Exercise 5.15.)
*6.45 (*Wielandt*)   A finite group G is nilpotent if and only if every maximal subgroup of G is normal. (*Hint:* Use Exercise 5.11.) Conclude that the index of each maximal subgroup of G is prime.

Definition   If G is a group, we define its **Frattini subgroup** $\Phi(G)$ as the intersection of all the maximal subgroups of G.[5]

Definition   An element $y \in G$ is a **nongenerator** of G if whenever $G = [X,y]$, where X is a subset of G, then $G = [X]$.

Exercises (contd.)   6.46 $\Phi(G)$ is the set of nongenerators of G.
6.47 $\Phi(G)$ is a characteristic subgroup of G.
*6.48   If G is finite, $\Phi(G)$ is nilpotent. (*Hint:* Prove that every sylow subgroup of $\Phi(G)$ is normal in $\Phi(G)$.)
*6.49 (*Wielandt*)   If G is finite, then G is nilpotent if and only if $G' \subset \Phi(G)$.

Definition   A subset X of G is a **minimal set of generators** of G in case $G = [X]$, but no proper subset of X generates G.

Exercises (contd.)   *6.50   If G is a finite p-group, $G/\Phi(G)$ is a vector space over Z_p.
*6.51 (*Burnside Basis Theorem*)   If G is a finite p-group, any two minimal generating sets of G have the same number of elements. Moreover, if $x \notin \Phi(G)$, then $\{x\}$ can be extended to a minimal set of generators of G.
   The hypothesis that G is a p-group is necessary. If $G = [x] \approx \sigma(6)$, then two minimal generating sets of G are $\{x\}$ and $\{x^2,x^3\}$.
   The reader familiar with ring theory will note the analogy of the Frattini subgroup with the Jacobson radical. He will also note the

---

[5] Every finite group G contains maximal subgroups, so that the meaning of $\Phi(G)$ is clear in this case. There do exist infinite groups G that have no maximal subgroups; for such a group, $\Phi(G) = G$. This follows from the set-theoretical convention that the intersection of no subsets of G is all of G. This convention is more palatable when one realizes that the union of no subsets is empty and that the de Morgan laws should hold.

similarity of the Burnside basis theorem with the notion of the rank of a noetherian local ring.

For further results on solvable and nilpotent groups, we refer the reader to the books of Burnside, Hall, Kurosh, and Zassenhaus (see Bibliography). The forthcoming book of B. Huppert, *Endliche Gruppen*, is highly recommended.

Chapter 7

Extensions

The Extension Problem

If G is a group having a normal subgroup K, then we can "factor" G into the two groups K and G/K. The study of extensions involves the inverse question: Given K and G/K, to what extent may one recapture G?

Definition   If K and Q are groups, an **extension of K by Q** is a group G such that:
(i) G contains K as a normal subgroup.
(ii) $G/K \approx Q$.
(As a mnemonic, K denotes kernel and Q denotes quotient.)

In a heuristic sense, an extension G is a "product" of K and Q.

Examples   1   Both $\sigma(6)$ and S_3 are extensions of $\sigma(3)$ by $\sigma(2)$.
2   For any two groups K and Q, $K \times Q$ is an extension of K by Q (and also of Q by K).
3   Every extension of a solvable group by a solvable group is itself solvable; an extension of a nilpotent group by a nilpotent group need not be nilpotent (but see Exercise 6.42).

The extension problem formulated by Hölder is, given K and Q, to determine all extensions of K by Q. We can better understand the Jordan-Hölder theorem (discussed in Chapter 6) in the light of this problem. Let G be a group with the composition series

$$G = K_0 \supset K_1 \supset \cdots \supset K_{n-2} \supset K_{n-1} \supset K_n = \{1\}$$

127

and the corresponding factor groups

$$K_0/K_1 = Q_1, \cdots, K_{n-1}/K_n = Q_n.$$

Now $K_{n-1} = Q_n$, since $K_n = \{1\}$, but something more interesting happens at the next stage: $K_{n-2}/K_{n-1} = Q_{n-1}$, so that K_{n-2} is an extension of K_{n-1} by Q_{n-1}. If we could solve the extension problem, we could recapture K_{n-2} from K_{n-1} and Q_{n-1}, i.e., from Q_n and Q_{n-1}. Once we have K_{n-2}, we can attack K_{n-3} in a similar manner, for $K_{n-3}/K_{n-2} = Q_{n-2}$. Thus, a solution of the extension problem allows us to recapture K_{n-3} from Q_n, Q_{n-1}, and Q_{n-2}. We continue climbing up the composition series until we reach $K_0 = G$; to do this, we need extensions and the factor groups $Q_1, \cdots, Q_n$. The group G is thus a "product" of the Q, and the Jordan-Hölder theorem says that the simple groups occurring as factors in this "factorization" of G are uniquely determined by G. We could thus survey all finite groups if we knew all finite simple groups and if we could solve the extension problem. In particular, we could survey all finite solvable groups if we could solve the extension problem.

A solution of the extension problem consists of determining all groups G with $G/K \approx Q$. But what does "determining" a group G mean? We gave two answers to this question in Chapter 1 when we considered "knowing" a group G. One answer is that a multiplication table for G can be constructed; a second answer is that the isomorphism class of G can be characterized. Schreier solved the extension problem in the first sense; given K and Q, all multiplication tables of extensions G of K by Q can be constructed. On the other hand, no solution is known in the second sense. For example, given K and Q, Schreier's solution does not allow us to calculate the number of nonisomorphic extensions of K by Q.

We shall see that, in essence, the extensions of K by Q themselves form an abelian group! The computation of one of these groups is the Schur-Zassenhaus lemma (Theorem 7.15). More general techniques for computing groups of extensions will be considered in Chapter 10 when we discuss homological algebra.

Exercises   7.1   Any two extensions of K by Q have the same number of elements, namely, $|K| \, |Q|$.

7.2   There are exactly two nonisomorphic extensions of $\sigma(3)$ by

$\sigma(2)$; there is exactly one extension (up to isomorphism) of $\sigma(2)$ by $\sigma(3)$.

7.3   Every nonabelian group of order p^3, p prime, is an extension of $\sigma(p)$ by $\sigma(p) \times \sigma(p)$.

7.4   If G is an extension of K by Q, must G contain a subgroup isomorphic to Q?

7.5   If $(a,b) = 1$, and if K and Q are abelian groups of orders a and b, respectively, prove that there is only one abelian extension of K by Q.

Automorphism Groups

The coming construction is essential for a discussion of extensions; it is also of great intrinsic interest.

Definition   The **automorphism group** of a group G, denoted Aut(G), is the set of all automorphisms of G under the binary operation of composition.

It is easy to check that Aut(G) is a group; indeed, Aut(G) is a subgroup of S_G.

Definition   An automorphism α of G is **inner** if it is conjugation by an element of G, i.e., $\alpha(x) = axa^{-1}$ for some $a \in G$; otherwise, α is **outer**.

THEOREM 7.1   The set of all inner automorphisms of G, denoted $I(G)$, is a normal subgroup of Aut(G); furthermore,

$$I(G) \approx G/Z(G).$$

Proof   If $a \in G$, let f_a denote conjugation by a. The function $a \to f_a$ is easily seen to be a homomorphism of G into Aut(G). The image of this map is clearly $I(G)$, so that $I(G)$ is a subgroup of Aut(G). The kernel of this map is $Z(G)$, for the following statements are equivalent: a is in the kernel; f_a is the identity function on G; $axa^{-1} = x$ for all $x \in G$; $a \in Z(G)$. It follows from the first isomorphism theorem that $G/Z(G) \approx I(G)$.

In order to prove that $I(G) \lhd \mathrm{Aut}(G)$, we must show that if $\alpha \in \mathrm{Aut}(G)$, then $\alpha f_a \alpha^{-1}$ is an inner automorphism. In fact, $\alpha f_a \alpha^{-1} = f_{\alpha(a)}$, as the reader should check. ∎

Exercises   7.6   Prove that Aut $(S_3) \approx S_3$.

7.7   Prove that Aut$(V) \approx S_3$, where V is the 4-group. Conclude that nonisomorphic groups can have isomorphic automorphism groups.

7.8   Let G be an elementary abelian group of order p^n, where p is prime. Prove that Aut$(G) \approx GL(n,p)$, where $GL(n,p)$ is the multiplicative group of all $n \times n$ nonsingular matrices with entries in Z_p.

7.9   Let H and K be finite groups whose orders are relatively prime. Prove that Aut$(H \times K) \approx$ Aut$(H) \times$ Aut(K).

7.10   Let G be a finite group with Aut$(G) = \{1\}$. Prove that G has at most two elements. (The finiteness condition is unnecessary, but the reader may not possess the tools for dealing with the general case until Chapter 9.)

7.11   If p is a prime, then Aut$(\sigma(p)) \approx \sigma(p - 1)$.

Definition   A **unit** in a commutative ring with identity R is an element having a multiplicative inverse in R. The **group of units of** R, denoted $U(R)$, is the multiplicative group of all units in R.

Exercises (contd.)   7.12   Prove that Aut$(\sigma(n)) \approx U(Z_n)$ and hence has order $\varphi(n)$. (*Hint:* An integer k represents a unit in Z_n if and only if $(n,k) = 1$.)

*7.13   Prove that Aut $(\sigma(p^n))$ is cyclic if p is an odd prime. Prove that Aut$(\sigma(4))$ is cyclic, but that Aut$(\sigma(2^n)) \approx \sigma(2) \oplus \sigma(2^{n-2})$ for $n \geqq 3$.

*7.14   Give a complete set of invariants describing $U(Z_n)$.

7.15   Let X be the set of all conjugacy classes of a group G. Every automorphism α of G induces a permutation of X. Conclude that Aut(G) is a permutation group on X as well as a permutation group on G. This remark is the origin of the notion of **primitive** permutation groups (see **Burnside's** book, listed in the Bibliography, for further discussion of this topic).

7.16   Let G be a finite group, and let C be a conjugacy class of G consisting of h elements of order t. If no other conjugacy class of G

comprised of elements of order t has exactly h elements, then $\alpha(C) = C$ for every $\alpha \in \text{Aut}(G)$.

Theorem 7.1 suggests the following class of groups.

Definition   A group G is **complete** in case $Z(G) = \{1\}$ and every automorphism of G is inner.

If G is a complete group, then $\text{Aut}(G) \approx G$. An interesting fact that generalizes Exercise 7.6 is that almost all the symmetric groups are complete.

LEMMA 7.2   If $\alpha: S_n \to S_n$ is an automorphism that preserves transpositions, i.e., α sends any transposition into a transposition, then α is inner.

Proof   Recall that two elements of S_n are conjugate if and only if they have the same cycle structure, so that every conjugation of S_n preserves transpositions.

If $\pi \in S_n$ and $\gamma: S_n \to S_n$, we shall denote $\gamma(\pi)$ by π^γ.[1]

We shall prove by induction on t that there exist conjugations $\beta_2, \cdots, \beta_t$ such that $\beta_t^{-1} \cdots \beta_2^{-1}\alpha$ fixes $(12), \cdots, (1t)$. Now $(12)^\alpha = (ij)$; define β_2 to be conjugation by $(1i)(2j)$ (where our notation sets, e.g., $(1\,i) = $ identity if $1 = i$). Our quick way of computing conjugations (Lemma 3.9) shows that $(1\,2)^\alpha = (1\,2)^{\beta_2}$, and so $\beta_2^{-1}\alpha$ fixes $(1\,2)$.

Let $\gamma = \beta_t^{-1} \cdots \beta_2^{-1}\alpha$ be given by the inductive hypothesis. Now γ preserves transpositions, so that $(1\,t+1)^\gamma = (l\,k)$. Moreover $\{1,2\} \cap \{l,k\} \neq \phi$, otherwise $((1\,2)(1\,t+1))^\gamma = (1\,2)(l\,k)$ has order 2 while $(1\,2)(1\,t+1)$ has order 3, contradicting the fact that automorphisms preserve orders. For notational convenience, assume $(1\,t+1)^\gamma = (1\,k)$. We must have $k > t$ lest $(1\,k)^\gamma = (1\,t+1)^\gamma$, contradicting the fact that γ is one-to-one. Define $\beta_{t+1}: S_n \to S_n$ to be conjugation by $(k\,t+1)$. Now β_{t+1} fixes $(1\,2), \cdots, (1\,t)$ and $(1\,t+1)^{\beta_{t+1}} = (1\,t+1)^\gamma$, so that $\beta_{t+1}^{-1}\gamma = \beta_{t+1}^{-1}\beta_t^{-1} \cdots \beta_2^{-1}\alpha$ fixes $(1\,2), \cdots, (1\,t+1)$.

[1] It is a common practice to denote $\alpha(x)$ by x^α when $\alpha: G \to H$ is a homomorphism. In particular, if $\alpha: G \to G$ is conjugation by a, one even writes $\alpha(x) = x^\alpha = x^a = axa^{-1}$.

It follows that $\beta_n^{-1} \cdots \beta_2^{-1}\alpha$ fixes (1 2), $\cdots$, (1 n). Since these $n - 1$ transpositions generate S_n, by Exercise 3.20, $\beta_n^{-1} \cdots \beta_2^{-1}\alpha$ is the identity, and $\alpha = \beta_2 \cdots \beta_n \in I(S_n)$. ∎

THEOREM 7.3 S_n is complete if $n \neq 2$ and $n \neq 6$.

Proof   We remark that $S_2 \approx \sigma(2)$ is not complete because it has a center. If $n \geq 3$, we have seen in Exercise 3.33 that S_n is centerless.

Let C_1 be the conjugacy class of S_n consisting of all transpositions; every element in C_1 has order 2. Since every permutation is a product of disjoint cycles, the only elements in S_n of order 2 are products of disjoint transpositions; let C_k be the conjugacy class consisting of all products of k disjoint transpositions. We shall show that if $n \neq 6$, the size of each C_k ($k \neq 1$) is distinct from the size of C_1. Exercise 7.16 will then give $\alpha(C_1) = C_1$ for every $\alpha \in \text{Aut}(S_n)$, i.e., every $\alpha \in \text{Aut}(S_n)$ preserves transpositions. An application of Lemma 7.2 will then complete the proof.

There are $n(n - 1)/2$ transpositions in S_n. How many *sets* of k disjoint transpositions are there? Answer:

$$\frac{n(n - 1)}{2} \cdot \frac{(n - 2)(n - 3)}{2} \cdots \frac{(n - 2k + 2)(n - 2k + 1)}{2}.$$

How many *products* of k disjoint transpositions are there? If $\tau_1, \tau_2, \cdots, \tau_k$ are disjoint transpositions, they commute, and so the order in which they are written is irrelevant. There being $k!$ different orderings, the size of C_k is

$$\frac{1}{k!} \frac{1}{2^k} \, n(n - 1)(n - 2) \cdots (n - 2k + 1).$$

The problem is now reduced to the question: Can the size of C_k equal $n(n - 1)/2$; equivalently, does the following equation hold for $k > 1$?

(*) $(n - 2)(n - 3) \cdots (n - 2k + 1) = k!2^{k-1}.$

Since the left side is positive, we must have $n \geq 2k$. Therefore, for fixed n,

left side $\geq (2k - 2)(2k - 3) \cdots (2k - 2k + 1) = (2k - 2)!.$

An easy induction shows that if $k \geq 4$, then

$$(2k - 2)! > k!2^{k-1},$$

so that (*) can hold only if $k < 4$, regardless of the value of n. We may now assume that $k = 2$ or $k = 3$. It is easy to see that (*) never holds if $k = 2$, so that only the case $k = 3$ remains. Now, since $n \geq 2k$, we must have $n \geq 6$. If $n > 6$, the left side of (*) $> 5 \cdot 4 \cdot 3 \cdot 2 = 120$, while the right side of (*) $= 3!2^2 = 24$. (If $n = 6$ and $k = 3$, then (*) does hold.) We have shown that if $n \neq 6$, then there is no $k > 1$ for which (*) holds. Hence, if $n \neq 6$, the size of each C_k ($k \neq 1$) is distinct from the size of C_1. ∎

It is known that $\text{Aut}(S_6)/I(S_6) \approx \sigma(2)$, so that there is essentially only one outer automorphism of S_6. An explicit construction of an outer automorphism can be found in D. W. Miller, "On a theorem of Hölder," *Amer. Math. Monthly*, 65 (1958), pp. 252–254.

THEOREM 7.4 Let $H \lhd G$, where H is a complete group. Then H is a direct factor of G, i.e., there exists a normal subgroup K of G with $G = H \times K$.

Proof If $g \in G$, then $g^{-1}hg \in H$ for all $h \in H$, since $H \lhd G$. The function $h \to g^{-1}hg$ is thus an automorphism of H. Since every automorphism of H is inner, there exists an element $\eta \in H$ with $\eta^{-1}h\eta = g^{-1}hg$ for all $h \in H$. Let K be the **centralizer** of H:

$$K = \{x \in G : xh = hx \text{ for all } h \in H\}.$$

It is easy to check that K is a subgroup of G containing each $g\eta^{-1}$. We claim that $G = H \times K$. First of all, $HK = G$, for if $g \in G$, then $g = (g\eta^{-1})\eta$. Second, if $x \in H \cap K$, then $x \in Z(H) = \{1\}$, since H is centerless. Now $g^{-1}Kg = \eta^{-1}(\eta g^{-1})K(g\eta^{-1})\eta \subset \eta^{-1}K\eta$, since $g\eta^{-1} \in K$; furthermore, $\eta^{-1}K\eta \subset K$, by the definition of K. It follows that $K \lhd G$, and hence $G = H \times K$. ∎

Exercise *7.17 If G is simple of composite order, then $\text{Aut}(G)$ is complete.

Semidirect Products

A group G is the direct product of two normal subgroups K and Q in case $K \cap Q = \{1\}$ and $KQ = G$. A natural generalization of direct products is the situation in which only one of the subgroups is required to be normal.

Definition A group G is a **semidirect product of K by Q** in case G contains subgroups K and Q such that:
  (i) $K \triangleleft G$.
  (ii) $KQ = G$.
  (iii) $K \cap Q = \{1\}$.
It follows from the second isomorphism theorem that a semidirect product of K by Q is an extension of K by Q; a semidirect product is often called a **split extension.**

Exercises 7.18 S_n is a semidirect product of A_n by $\sigma(2)$.
  7.19 Let G be a finite solvable group of order ab, where $(a,b) = 1$. If G contains a normal subgroup K of order a, then G is a semidirect product of K by some group Q of order b. (*Hint:* Use P. Hall's theorem, Theorem 6.20.)
  7.20 If p is a prime, then $\sigma(p^n)$ is not a semidirect product (in which K and Q are proper subgroups).
  7.21 Both S_3 and $\sigma(6)$ are semidirect products of $\sigma(3)$ by $\sigma(2)$.

Exercise 7.21 is a bit jarring at first, for it says that in contrast to direct products, a semidirect product of K by Q is not determined up to isomorphism by the two subgroups. When we reflect on this, however, we see that a semidirect product should depend on how K is normal in G. We shall return to this point as soon as we establish a notational convention.

In discussing extensions G of K by Q, it is convenient to use the multiplicative notation for Q and the additive notation for G and its subgroup K (this is one of the few instances in which one uses the additive notation for a nonabelian group). Thus, if $k \in K$ and $g \in G$, the conjugate of k by g is written $g + k - g$.

Definition If $\pi\colon G \to Q$ is onto and $x \in Q$, then a **lifting** of x is an element $g \in G$ with $\pi(g) = x$.

The following rather technical lemma will enable us to translate the normality of K in G into a statement that involves K and Q but not G; it also describes the various ways that K can be normal in G.

The first form of the lemma is rather complicated, but it is the simpler, second version that is most interesting for us.

LEMMA 7.5 Let G be an extension of K by Q. There is a homomorphism $\theta \colon Q \to \operatorname{Aut}(K)/I(K)$ and there is an α_x in the coset $\theta(x)$ [i.e., $\theta(x) = I(K)\alpha_x$] such that

$$\alpha_x(k) = l(x) + k - l(x)$$

for every $k \in K$ and some lifting $l(x)$ of x.

Proof If $g \in G$, let $f_g \colon G \to G$ denote conjugation by g. Since $K \lhd G$, $f_g|K$ is an automorphism of K, and the function $\mu \colon G \to \operatorname{Aut}(K)$ defined by $\mu(g) = f_g|K$ is easily seen to be a homomorphism. If $g \in K$, then $\mu(g) \in I(K)$. As we saw in Exercise 2.43, since $I(K) \lhd \operatorname{Aut}(K)$, there is a homomorphism $\mu_\# \colon G/K \to \operatorname{Aut}(K)/I(K)$ defined by $\mu_\#(Kg) = I(K)\mu(g)$.

Now the first isomorphism theorem not only says that Q and G/K are isomorphic; it also says that $\lambda \colon Q \to G/K$ defined by $\lambda(x) = Kl(x)$ is an isomorphism, where $l(x)$ is any lifting of x. The composite $\theta = \mu_\#\lambda$ is a homomorphism from Q to $\operatorname{Aut}(K)/I(K)$. If $x \in Q$, $\theta(x) = \mu_\#\lambda(x) = \mu_\#(Kl(x)) = I(K)\mu(l(x))$. If we recall that $\mu(g)$ is just the restriction to K of conjugation by g, then setting $\alpha_x = \mu(l(x))$ means $\alpha_x(k) = l(x) + k - l(x)$.

This lemma is greatly simplified if we assume that K is abelian.

LEMMA 7.6 Let G be an extension of K by Q, where K is abelian. There is a homomorphism $\theta \colon Q \to \operatorname{Aut}(K)$ such that

$$\theta(x)(k) = l(x) + k - l(x)$$

for every $k \in K$ and every lifting $l(x)$ of x.

Proof Since K is abelian, $I(K) = \{1\}$. If $l'(x)$ is another lifting of x, then $l(x) = l'(x) + k_0$, and $l(x) + k - l(x) = l'(x) + k_0 + k - k_0 - l'(x) = l'(x) + k - l'(x)$. ∎

From now until we discuss the Schur-Zassenhaus lemma, we shall assume that K is abelian. Once a homomorphism $\theta \colon Q \to \operatorname{Aut}(K)$ is given, we shall usually abbreviate the expression $\theta(x)(k)$ by xk. The following formulas are valid for all $x, y \in Q$ and $k, k' \in K$:

$$x(k + k') = xk + xk';$$
$$(xy)k = x(yk);$$
$$1k = k.$$

(These formulas should remind the reader of the definition of a module. Indeed, a (possibly noncommutative) ring ZQ can be constructed, the *integral group ring of* Q, and the abelian group K is a left module admitting operators from this ring. This remark is the basis of further examinations of group extensions; for more details, we refer the reader to the book of S. MacLane, *Homology*, chap. IV.)

The object of our study is to recapture G from K and Q, and so we make the following definition.

Definition   Let K and Q be groups, K abelian, and $\theta: Q \to$ Aut(K) a homomorphism. An extension G of K by Q **realizes** θ in case

$$xk = l(x) + k - l(x)$$

for every $k \in K$ and every lifting $l(x)$ of x.

In this language, Lemma 7.6 says that every extension G of an abelian K by Q determines a θ that G realizes. The intuitive meaning of θ is that it describes how K is normal in G.

The extension problem is now posed as follows: Given an abelian K, a group Q, and a homomorphism $\theta: Q \to$ Aut(K), determine all extensions G of K by Q that realize θ (if there are any). (If one does not assume that K is abelian, he returns to the more complicated situation of Lemma 7.5; the reader is referred to the book of MacLane for a discussion of this case.)

Definition   Let K and Q be groups, K abelian, and $\theta: Q \to$ Aut(K). $K \times_\theta Q$ is the set of all ordered pairs $(k,x) \in K \times Q$ under the binary operation (written additively)

$$(k,x) + (k',y) = (k + xk', xy).$$

We note that θ is necessary so that xk' makes sense.

THEOREM 7.7   Let K and Q be groups, K abelian, and $\theta: Q \to$ Aut(K). Then $G = K \times_\theta Q$ is an extension of K by Q that realizes θ.

Proof   Let us first prove that $K \times_\theta Q$ is a group. Addition is associative:

$$[(k,x) + (k',y)] + (k'',z) \qquad (k,x) + [(k',y) + (k'',z)]$$
$$= (k + xk',xy) + (k'',z) \qquad = (k,x) + (k' + yk'',yz)$$
$$= (k + xk' + (xy)k'',xyz) \qquad = (k + x(k' + yk''),xyz).$$

Since $x(k' + yk'') = xk' + x(yk'')$ and $x(yk'') = (xy)k''$, the binary operation is associative.

The identity element is $(0,1)$, for

$$(0,1) + (k,x) = (0 + 1 \cdot k, 1 \cdot x) = (k,x).$$

The inverse of (k,x) is $(-x^{-1}k, x^{-1})$, for

$$(k,x) + (-x^{-1}k, x^{-1}) = (k + x(-x^{-1}k), xx^{-1}) = (0,1).$$

Let us identify K with the subgroup of G consisting of all pairs of the form $(k,1)$. Since the only "twist" occurs in the first coordinate, the map $\pi: G \to Q$ defined by $\pi(k,x) = x$ is a homomorphism. It is quickly checked that π is onto and that its kernel is K; hence, G is an extension of K by Q.

Does G realize θ? We must show that if $x \in Q$ and $k \in K$, then $xk = l(x) + k - l(x)$, where $l(x)$ is any lifting of x. Now $k \in K$, so that (by our identification) $xk = (xk,1)$; also, the definition of π yields $l(x) = (k',x)$ for some $k' \in K$. We compute:

$$(k',x) + (k,1) - (k',x) = (k' + xk,x) + (-x^{-1}k',x^{-1})$$
$$= (k' + xk + x(-x^{-1}k'),1)$$
$$= (xk,1),$$

for K is abelian. Therefore, G does realize θ. ∎

COROLLARY 7.8   If K is abelian, $K \times_\theta Q$ is a semidirect product of K by Q. Conversely, if G is a semidirect product of K by Q, where K is abelian, then there is a homomorphism $\theta: Q \to \text{Aut}(K)$ with $G \approx K \times_\theta Q$.

Proof   As in the preceding proof, we identify K with the set of all pairs $(k,1)$, and we note that $K \lhd G = K \times_\theta Q$, by Theorem 7.7. Let $Q_0 = \{(0,x): x \in Q\}$; Q_0 is a subgroup of G that is isomorphic to Q, $KQ_0 = G$ and $K \cap Q_0 = \{(0,1)\}$.

Conversely, let G be a semidirect product of K by Q written additively. Define $\theta: Q \to \text{Aut}(K)$ by $\theta(x)(k) = x + k - x$, and define $\alpha: K \times_\theta Q \to G$ by $\alpha(k,x) = k + x$; α is a homomorphism, since G realizes θ. We let the reader prove that α is a one-to-one correspondence. ∎

With these results, we have constructed all possible semidirect products of K by Q in the special case when K is abelian. As an illustration of the last theorem, we construct the group T of order 12 whose generators and relations were given in Exercise 5.28.

Example 4 The group T is a semidirect product of $\sigma(3)$ by $\sigma(4)$.
Let $\sigma(3) = [k]$ and let $\sigma(4) = [x]$. Now $\text{Aut}(\sigma(3)) \approx \sigma(2)$; define $\theta: \sigma(4) \to \text{Aut}(\sigma(3))$ by sending x into the generator. In detail, $\theta(x)$ is the automorphism

$$xk = 2k \quad \text{and} \quad x(2k) = k,$$

while x^2 acts on $[k]$ as the identity automorphism.
The group $\sigma(3) \times_\theta \sigma(4)$ has order $3 \times 4 = 12$. Let $a = (2k,x^2)$ and $b = (0,x)$. The reader may verify that

$$6a = (0,1) \quad \text{and} \quad 2b = 3a = 2(a + b),$$

which are the relations of T in additive notation.

Exercises 7.22 If p and q are distinct primes, construct all semidirect products of $\sigma(p)$ by $\sigma(q)$ by the methods of this section. Compare your results with Theorem 5.13.

7.23 Let $G = K \times_\theta Q$, where K is abelian. Show that $(k,x) \in Z(G)$ if and only if $x \in Z(Q)$, $yk = k$ for all $y \in Q$, and $xk' = k'$ for all $k' \in K$.

7.24 An extension G of K by Q is a **central extension** if $K \subset Z(G)$. Prove that G is a central extension of K by Q if and only if θ is trivial, and then $K \times_\theta Q$ is the direct product $K \times Q$.

Definition The **holomorph** of an abelian group K is $K \times_\theta \text{Aut}(K)$, where $\theta: \text{Aut}(K) \to \text{Aut}(K)$ is the identity function.

Exercises (contd.) 7.25 Let K be abelian and let G be its holomorph. Prove that every automorphism of K is the restriction of an inner automorphism of G.

We now generalize the construction of a holomorph to the general case when K is not necessarily abelian.

Exercises (contd.)   *7.26   For any group K, a **holomorphism** is a one-to-one correspondence $h: K \to K$ such that

$$h(xy^{-1}z) = h(x)h(y)^{-1}h(z)$$

for every $x,y,z \in K$. (Every automorphism of K is a holomorphism, as in every left or right translation.) Prove that the set of all holomorphisms, $\mathrm{Hol}(K)$, is a group under composition, and that $\mathrm{Hol}(K)$ is an extension of K by $\mathrm{Aut}(K)$. Moreover, every automorphism of K is the restriction of an inner automorphism of $\mathrm{Hol}(K)$.

*7.27   If K is abelian, prove that the two holomorphs of K given in the two preceding exercises are isomorphic.

7.28   Let G be an extension of K by Q, and let $\pi: G \to Q$ be a map of G onto Q having kernel K. Prove that G is a semidirect product of K by Q if and only if there is a homomorphism $l: Q \to G$ with $\pi \circ l = $ identity on Q.

Factor Sets

Since there are nonsimple groups that are not semidirect products (see, e.g., Exercise 7.20), our survey of extensions is still incomplete. Notice the sort of survey we already have; if we know K, Q, and θ, then we know $K \times_\theta Q$ in the sense that we can write a multiplication table for it.

We now examine arbitrary extensions given the data: K (which is abelian), Q, and $\theta: Q \to \mathrm{Aut}(K)$. This study is called the **cohomology of groups** because of the analogy with methods of cohomology theory in algebraic topology.

Suppose K is abelian, and G is an extension of K by Q realizing θ. We identify Q with G/K, and for each $x \in Q$, we choose a lifting $l(x) \in G$; for computational ease, choose $l(1) = 0$. Once these choices have been made, every element $g \in G$ has a unique expression of the form

$$g = k + l(x) \qquad x \in Q, k \in K;$$

(after all, $l(x)$ is a representative of a coset of K in G, and G is the disjoint union of these cosets). We have the following formulas:

(i) $l(x) + k = xk + l(x)$ for every $x \in Q$ and $k \in K$;
(this is the statement that G realizes θ).

(ii) $l(x) + l(y) = f(x,y) + l(xy)$ for some $f(x,y) \in K$;
($l(x) + l(y)$ and $l(xy)$ are representatives of the same coset of K).

Definition The function $f: Q \times Q \to K$ defined by formula (ii) is called a **factor set**[2] of G.

Notice that a factor set depends on the choice of liftings. If G is a semidirect product, Corollary 7.8 shows that there is a choice of liftings such that $f(x,y) = 0$ for every x and y in Q. In fact, it follows from property (ii) that $l: Q \to G$ is a homomorphism if and only if the corresponding factor set is identically zero. Thus, a factor set may fruitfully be thought of as a "measure" of G's deviation from being a semidirect product, for it tells how the backwards function l fails to be a homomorphism.

THEOREM 7.9 Let K be abelian and let $\theta: Q \to \text{Aut}(K)$. A function $f: Q \times Q \to K$ is a factor set if and only if it satisfies the formulas:

(i) $f(1,y) = 0 = f(x,1)$ for every $x,y \in Q$.
(ii) $xf(y,z) - f(xy,z) + f(x,yz) - f(x,y) = 0$
for every $x,y,z \in Q$.

Proof Suppose f is a factor set. This means that there is an extension G of K by Q realizing θ, a choice of liftings $l(x)$ has been made, and f satisfies

$$l(x) + l(y) = f(x,y) + l(xy).$$

Since we have assumed that $l(1) = 0$, $0 + l(y) = f(1,y) + l(1y)$, so that $f(1,y) = 0$; a similar calculation shows that $f(x,1) = 0$, so that (i) is established.

Formula (ii) arises from associativity; one need only calculate the consequences of $[l(x) + l(y)] + l(z) = l(x) + [l(y) + l(z)]$.

Suppose, conversely, that we have a function $f: Q \times Q \to K$

---

[2] The term *factor set* is a misnomer; *factor function* would be more suggestive. However, we conform to standard usage. Factor sets are often called **cocycles** to stress the analogy with cohomology theory.

which satisfies (i) and (ii). We shall construct an extension G of K by Q realizing θ and we shall choose liftings $l(x)$ such that f is the factor set determined by this data.

Let G be the set of all pairs $(k,x) \in K \times Q$ with the binary operation

$$(k,x) + (k',y) = (k + xk' + f(x,y), xy).$$

(Note the similarity to the construction of $K \times_\theta Q$.)

The proof that G is a group is quite similar to the proof of Theorem 7.7; formula (ii) is needed to prove associativity; the identity is $(0,1)$; the inverse of (k,x) is $(-x^{-1}k - x^{-1}f(x,x^{-1}), x^{-1})$.

That G is an extension of K by Q is also easy; identify K with all pairs of the form $(k,1)$ and define $\pi: G \to Q$ by $\pi(k,x) = x$. As in the proof of Theorem 7.7, one shows that G does realize θ.

Finally, make the choice of liftings $l(x) = (0,x)$. A straightforward computation shows that $l(x) + l(y) - l(xy) = (f(x,y),1)$, as desired. ∎

Definition $Z^2_\theta(Q,K)$ is the set of all factor sets $f: Q \times Q \to K$.

Exercise   7.29   Prove that $Z^2_\theta(Q,K)$ is an abelian group under the operation

$$(f + f')(x,y) = f(x,y) + f'(x,y).$$

We are near a solution of the extension problem. Given abelian K, Q, and θ, we can write down a multiplication table for an extension G of K by Q realizing θ once we are given a factor set. Moreover, factor sets are concrete objects that are succinctly characterized by Theorem 7.9.

It is quite possible that two factor sets f and f' give rise to the same extension. Indeed, let us again assume that we have an extension G, and recall that a factor set f is defined by

$$l(x) + l(y) = f(x,y) + l(xy).$$

The factor set f thus depends on the choice of liftings $l(x)$. If we choose a different set of liftings $l'(x)$, we get a second factor set f', defined by

$$l'(x) + l'(y) = f'(x,y) + l'(xy),$$

but, quite clearly, f' still gives the group G.

LEMMA 7.10   Let G be an extension of K by Q realizing θ; let $\{l(x)\}$ and $\{l'(x)\}$ be two choices of liftings that give rise to factor sets f and f'. There exists a function $\alpha: Q \to K$ with $\alpha(1) = 0$ and

$$f'(x,y) - f(x,y) = x\alpha(y) - \alpha(xy) + \alpha(x)$$

for every $x,y \in Q$.

Proof   For each $x \in Q$, $l(x)$ and $l'(x)$ are just different representatives of the same coset of K in G. There is thus an element $\alpha(x) \in K$ with

$$l'(x) = \alpha(x) + l(x).$$

Since we are consistently lifting 1 to 0, $l'(1) = l(1) = 0$, so that $\alpha(1) = 0$. We derive the main formula as follows:

$$\begin{aligned}
l'(x) + l'(y) &= \alpha(x) + l(x) + \alpha(y) + l(y) \\
&= \alpha(x) + x\alpha(y) + l(x) + l(y) \\
&\quad \text{(since } G \text{ realizes } \theta) \\
&= \alpha(x) + x\alpha(y) + f(x,y) + l(xy) \\
&= \alpha(x) + x\alpha(y) + f(x,y) - \alpha(xy) + l'(xy).
\end{aligned}$$

It follows that $f'(x,y) = \alpha(x) + x\alpha(y) + f(x,y) - \alpha(xy)$. We obtain the desired formula, since each term lies in the abelian group K. $\blacksquare$

Definition   A **coboundary** is a function $g: Q \times Q \to K$ such that

$$g(x,y) = x\alpha(y) - \alpha(xy) + \alpha(x)$$

for some $\alpha: Q \to K$ with $\alpha(1) = 0$. $B_\theta^2(Q,K)$ is the set of all coboundaries.

Exercise   7.30 $B_\theta^2(Q,K)$ is a subgroup of $Z_\theta^2(Q,K)$.

Now Lemma 7.10 says that factor sets arising from distinct choices of liftings lie in the same coset of B^2 in Z^2. We have been led to the following quotient group and equivalence relation.

Definition $H_\theta^2(Q,K)$ is defined to be $Z_\theta^2(Q,K)/B_\theta^2(Q,K)$ and is called the **second cohomology group.**

Definition   Two extensions G and G' of K by Q realizing θ are **equivalent** if there are factor sets f of G and f' of G' with $f' - f \in B_\theta^2(Q,K)$.

Observe that we have defined a relation on groups, not merely on factor sets: If one chooses other factor sets f_0 of G and f_0' of G', then $f_0' - f_0 = (f_0' - f') - (f_0 - f) + (f' - f) \in B_\theta^2(Q,K)$, since $f_0' - f'$ and $f_0 - f$ are in $B_\theta^2(Q,K)$, by Lemma 7.10.

Exercise   7.31 Let G and G' be extensions of K by Q realizing θ, where K is abelian. We have the diagram

where $\pi: G \to Q$ and $\pi': G' \to Q$ are onto. Prove that G is equivalent to G' if and only if there is an isomorphism $\gamma: G \to G'$ such that $\gamma(k) = k$ for all $k \in K$ and $\pi' \circ \gamma = \pi$. (*Hint:* Use multiplication tables for G and G' to define γ.)

It follows that equivalent extensions are isomorphic. Unfortunately, the converse is false, as we shall see in Chapter 10.

Exercise (contd.)   7.32 Let K be abelian and let $\theta: Q \to \text{Aut}(K)$. Prove that any two semidirect products of K by Q realizing θ are equivalent.

We summarize the results of this section in the following theorem.

THEOREM 7.11   Let K be abelian and let $\theta: Q \to \text{Aut}(K)$. The set E of all equivalence classes of extensions of K by Q realizing θ form an abelian group isomorphic to $H_\theta^2(Q,K)$ whose identity element is the class of the semidirect product.

Proof   If G is an extension of K by Q realizing θ, let $[G]$ denote its equivalence class, so that E is the set of all $[G]$. We now define a one-to-one correspondence $\lambda: H_\theta^2(Q,K) \to E$ as follows: $\lambda(f + B^2) = [G_f]$, where G_f is the extension determined by f that we constructed in Theorem 7.9. First of all, λ is well defined, for if both f and f' lie in the same coset of B^2, the definition of equivalence says that G_f and $G_{f'}$ are equivalent. Conversely, λ is one-to-one, for if $\lambda(f + B^2) = \lambda(f' + B^2)$, then G_f and $G_{f'}$ are equivalent, and so $f' - f \in B^2$. Furthermore, λ is onto, for if G is an extension and f is a factor set of G, then $\lambda(f + B^2) = [G]$.

By Exercise 1.16, there is a unique addition defined on E making it a group and λ an isomorphism. The last part of the theorem follows from the fact that an extension is a semidirect product if and only if it has a factor set in B^2. ∎

In Chapter 10, we shall give an explicit construction of the sum of two classes in E.

COROLLARY 7.12   Let K be abelian and let $\theta \colon Q \to \mathrm{Aut}(K)$. Every extension of K by Q realizing θ is a semidirect product if and only if $H^2_\theta(Q,K) = \{0\}$.

The Schur-Zassenhaus Lemma

We now apply the results of the preceding section.

THEOREM 7.13   Let K be an abelian group of order m, and let Q be a group of order n. If $(m,n) = 1$, then every extension G of K by Q is a semidirect product.

Proof   By Corollary 7.12, it suffices to prove that every factor set f lies in $B^2_\theta(Q,K)$.
Define $\sigma \colon Q \to K$ by

$$\sigma(x) = \sum_{y \in Q} f(x,y);$$

σ is well defined, since Q is finite and K is abelian. Now, if we sum the formula

$$xf(y,z) - f(xy,z) + f(x,yz) = f(x,y)$$

over all $z \in Q$, we obtain

$$x\sigma(y) - \sigma(xy) + \sigma(x) = nf(x,y);$$

(as z ranges over all elements of Q, so does yz for fixed y). Since $(m,n) = 1$, there are integers a and b with $am + bn = 1$. If we define $\alpha: Q \to K$ by $\alpha(x) = b\sigma(x)$, then $\alpha(1) = 0$ and

$$x\alpha(y) - \alpha(xy) + \alpha(x) = f(x,y).$$

This formula says that $f \in B^2_\theta(Q,K)$, as desired. ∎

THEOREM 7.14 Let K be an abelian group of order m, Q a group of order n, $(m,n) = 1$, and G an extension of K by Q. Then any two subgroups of G of order n are conjugate.

Proof Let Q_1 be a subgroup of G of order n. Now $K \cap Q_1 = \{1\}$, for if $a \in K \cap Q_1$, its order must divide m and n, and $(m,n) = 1$. Moreover, $|KQ_1| = |KQ_1|\,|K \cap Q_1| = |K|\,|Q_1| = |G|$, so that $KQ_1 = G$. It follows that G is a semidirect product of K by Q_1. If Q_2 is a second subgroup of G of order n, then G is a semidirect product of K by Q_2 as well. By Exercise 7.28, Q_1 consists of liftings $l_1(x)$, and Q_2 consists of liftings $l_2(x)$, where l_1 and l_2 are homomorphisms; it follows that the factor sets f_1 and f_2 determined by the $l_1(x)$ and by the $l_2(x)$ are each zero. Now, if $l_1(x) = \alpha(x) + l_2(x)$, then

$$0 = f_1(x,y) - f_2(x,y) = x\alpha(y) - \alpha(xy) + \alpha(x).^3$$

Summing over all $y \in Q$ gives the equation:

$$0 = xk - k + n\alpha(x)$$

where

$$k = \sum_{y \in Q} \alpha(y).$$

This is an equation in K. If $am + bn = 1$, and $h = bk$,

$$-\alpha(x) = xh - h = -h + xh.$$

We claim that $-h + Q_1 + h = Q_2$, for $-h + l_1(x) + h = -h + xh + l_1(x) = -\alpha(x) + l_1(x) = l_2(x) - l_1(x) + l_1(x) = l_2(x)$. ∎

THEOREM 7.15 (*Schur-Zassenhaus Lemma*) If K and Q are finite groups of orders m and n, respectively, and if $(m,n) = 1$, then every extension G of K by Q is a semidirect product.

---

[3] A function $\alpha: Q \to K$ such that $\alpha(xy) = \alpha(x) + x\alpha(y)$ (as this one is) is called a **crossed homomorphism**.

Proof   As we saw at the beginning of the proof of Theorem 7.14, it suffices to prove that G contains a subgroup of order n.

We perform an induction on m, noting that if $m = 1$, the theorem is trivial. Suppose K contains a proper subgroup T that is also normal in G. Then $K/T \lhd G/T$ and $(G/T)/(K/T) \approx G/K \approx Q$. If $|K/T| = m'$, then $m' < m$ and $|G/T| = m'n$. By induction, G/T contains a subgroup N/T of order n. Now $|N| = n|T|$ and $(n, |T|) = 1$, for $|T|$ divides $|K| = m$. Since $T \lhd N$ and $|T| < m$, the inductive hypothesis gives a subgroup of N, and hence of G, of order n.

We may now assume that K is a minimal normal subgroup of G. If p is a prime dividing m, and P is a p-sylow subgroup of K, then a check of its order shows that P is also a p-sylow subgroup of G, since $(m, n) = 1$. Furthermore, since $K \lhd G$, P has the same number of conjugates in G as in K, so that $[G : N_G(P)] = [K : N_K(P)]$. By Lagrange's theorem,

$$[N_G(P) : N_K(P)] = [G : K] = n.$$

Since $N_K(P) = K \cap N_G(P)$, the second isomorphism theorem gives $[KN_G(P) : K] = [N_G(P) : N_K(P)] = n$, so that $|KN_G(P)| = n|K| = |G|$.

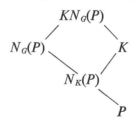

Since $KN_G(P)$ is a subgroup of G, it follows that $KN_G(P) = G$. Applying the second isomorphism theorem once more gives

$$N_K(P) = K \cap N_G(P) \lhd N_G(P)$$

and

$$N_G(P)/N_K(P) = N_G(P)/(K \cap N_G(P))$$
$$\approx KN_G(P)/K = G/K \approx Q.$$

If $N_G(P)$ is a proper subgroup of G, then $|N_K(P)| < m$, and so $N_G(P)$ contains a subgroup of order n, by induction. Therefore, we may assume that $N_G(P) = G$, i.e., that $P \lhd G$.

Since $K \supset P$ and K is a minimal normal subgroup of G, $K = P$. Now $Z(P)$ is a characteristic subgroup of P, so that $P \lhd G$ implies

$Z(P) \lhd G$. Again, minimality implies $Z(P) = P$, for a finite p-group has a nontrivial center. But now P is abelian, and the proof is completed by Theorem 7.13. ∎

The generalization of Theorem 7.14 is true: Under the hypotheses of the Schur-Zassenhaus lemma (Theorem 7.15), any two subgroups of order n are conjugate. One first proves this theorem by first assuming that either K or Q is solvable. Since $(m,n) = 1$, one of these groups must have odd order, and hence one of K or Q must be solvable, by the theorem of Feit and Thompson (see Exercise 6.28).

Exercises   7.33   Use the Schur-Zassenhaus lemma and Exercise 7.22 to reclassify all groups of order pq, where p and q are distinct primes.

7.34   Prove that every group of order p^2q, where $p > q$ are primes, has a normal p-sylow subgroup, and classify all such groups.

7.35   Using Corollary 5.17, reclassify all groups of order 12.

*7.36   Let $p_1 < p_2 < \cdots < p_t$ be primes such that $(p_i, p_j - 1) = 1$ for all $i < j$. Prove that every group G of order $n = p_1 p_2 \cdots p_t$ is cyclic. (*Hint:* Use Exercise 5.32, which states that G must contain a normal p_t-sylow subgroup.)

We sketch a proof that there exist sets of primes $\{p_1, p_2, \cdots, p_t\}$ for arbitrarily large t that satisfy the hypothesis of the exercise. Let $p_1 = 3$, and suppose that we have found $p_1 < p_2 < \cdots < p_t$ with $(p_i, p_j - 1) = 1$ for all $i < j$. We quote a theorem of Dirichlet: If $(a,b) = 1$, then the arithmetic progression $a, a + b$, $a + 2b, \cdots, a + mb, \cdots$ contains infinitely many primes. Since $(2, p_1 p_2 \cdots p_t) = 1$, there is a positive integer m such that $p_{t+1} = 2 + mp_1 p_2 \cdots p_t$ is prime; $\{p_1, p_2, \cdots, p_{t+1}\}$ satisfies the desired conditions.

The reader may test his group-theoretical muscles on the following problem: For which integers n is every group of order n abelian? The number $5929 = 7^2 11^2$ should be considered before any false conjectures are made.

7.37   Use extensions to construct all groups of order p^3, where p is prime.

Chapter 8

Some Simple Groups

Finite Fields

The Jordan-Hölder theorem (see Chapter 6) tells us that once we know extensions and simple groups, we know all groups that possess composition series. Several families of simple groups are known (in addition to the cyclic groups of prime order and the large alternating groups), and our main concern in this chapter is the exhibition of one of these families, the projective unimodular groups. These are essentially groups of matrices of determinant 1 whose entries are allowed to lie in (almost) any field. Since these groups are finite only when the underlying field is finite, we begin our discussion by examining the finite fields. We first recall several definitions from Chapter 4.

Definition   Let R be a commutative ring with 1. An **ideal** I in R is a nonempty subset of R such that:
   (i) $a - b \in I$ whenever $a, b \in I$;
   (ii) $ra \in I$ whenever $a \in I$ and $r \in R$.

Definition   An ideal I in R is **principal** in case there is an element $a \in I$ such that every $b \in I$ is a multiple of a; I is denoted (a) in this case.

Definition   A **principal ideal domain** is a domain in which every ideal is principal.

Two examples of principal ideal domains are Z and $F[x]$, where F is a field.

149

THEOREM 8.1 (*Construction of a Quotient Ring*)   Let R be a commutative ring with 1 and let I be an ideal in R. There exists a ring S and a ring homomorphism π of R onto S whose kernel is I.

Proof   Under addition, R is an abelian group and I is a subgroup. Therefore, R/I is an additive abelian group, and the natural map $\pi\colon R \to R/I$ is a group homomorphism of R onto R/I whose kernel is I.[1]

In order that $S = R/I$ be a ring, we define

$$(r + I)(r' + I) = rr' + I.$$

This is a well defined multiplication, for if $r + I = s + I$ and $r' + I = s' + I$, then $rr' - ss' = r(r' - s') + (r - s)s' \in I$; hence, $rr' + I = ss' + I$. The reader should verify that R/I is a ring under the given operations. Finally, since $\pi(r) = r + I$, π is a ring homomorphism. ∎

Definition   The ring just constructed is denoted R/I and is called the **quotient ring** of R modulo I.

Exercises   8.1   If $R = Z$ and $I = (m)$, then R/I is isomorphic to Z_m, the integers modulo m.

8.2   The first isomorphism theorem (Theorem 2.12) holds for commutative rings: If $f\colon R \to S$ in a ring homomorphism with kernel I, then I is an ideal and $R/I \approx$ image f.

8.3   The correspondence theorem (Theorem 2.17) holds for commutative rings, if one replaces "normal subgroup" by "ideal."

8.4   Let R be a commutative ring with 1. R is a field if and only if R contains no proper ideals.

Definition   An ideal I in R is **prime** in case $I \neq R$ and $rr' \in I$ implies either r or r' lies in I.

Exercises (*contd.*)   8.5   The prime ideals in Z are (0) and (p), where p is a prime.

---

[1] The zero element in R/I is thus $I = 0 + I$.

8.6   If F is a field, the prime ideals in $F[x]$ are (0) and $(\varphi(x))$, where $\varphi(x)$ is a polynomial irreducible in $F[x]$.

THEOREM 8.2   Let R be a commutative ring with 1. An ideal I in R is a prime ideal if and only if R/I is a domain.

Proof   If I is a prime ideal, we must show that R/I contains no zero-divisors. Suppose $(r + I)(r' + I) = 0$, i.e., $rr' + I = I$. Then $rr' \in I$; since I is a prime ideal, one of these factors, say, r, lies in I. Hence, $r + I = 0$.
    Suppose R/I is a domain. If $rr' \in I$, then $(r + I)(r' + I) = 0$ in R/I, so that one of the factors is 0, i.e., either r or r' lies in I. Thus I is a prime ideal. ∎

Definition   Let R be a commutative ring with 1. An ideal I in R is a **maximal ideal** in case $I \neq R$ and there is no larger proper ideal of R that contains I.

THEOREM 8.3   Let R be a commutative ring with 1. An ideal I in R is a maximal ideal if and only if R/I is a field.

Proof   If I is a maximal ideal, then the correspondence theorem for rings (Exercise 8.3) implies that R/I has no proper ideals. By Exercise 8.4, R/I is a field. To prove the converse, just reverse this argument. ∎

COROLLARY 8.4   Every maximal ideal in R is a prime ideal.

    In general, the converse of this corollary is false. For example, if $R = F[x,y]$, polynomials in two variables over a field F, one verifies that (x) is a prime ideal contained in the larger proper ideal (x,y). There is one important class of rings, however, for which the converse of the corollary is true.

THEOREM 8.5   If R is a principal ideal domain, every nonzero prime ideal I is a maximal ideal.

Proof   Let J be an ideal with $I \subsetneq J$. Since R is a principal ideal domain, there are elements a and b in R with $I = (a)$ and $J = (b)$. Now $a \in J = (b)$, so there is an $r \in R$ with $a = rb$. Since I is a prime ideal, either $r \in I$ or $b \in I$. Were b in I, then $J \subset I$, a contradiction. Therefore, $r \in I$, so that $r = sa$ for some $s \in R$. Hence, $a = rb = sab$, and $1 = sb$. The ideal (b) thus contains 1, and so $(b) = R$. We conclude that I is a maximal ideal. ∎

Definition   A **prime field** is a field having no proper subfields.

THEOREM 8.6   Every prime field K is isomorphic to either Z_p or the rationals.

Proof   If 1 is the unit element of K, let $R = \{n \cdot 1 : n \in Z\} \subset K$; it is easily checked that R is a domain. Further, the map $f: Z \to R$ defined by $f(n) = n \cdot 1$ is a ring homomorphism of Z onto R. By the first isomorphism theorem, $R \approx Z/I$, where I is the kernel of f. Since R is a domain, I is a prime ideal. If $I = (p)$, then $R \approx Z/(p) \approx Z_p$. In this case, R is a field, and so $R = K$. If $I = (0)$, then $R \approx Z$; it follows that K contains a subfield S isomorphic to the rationals, for K must contain the multiplicative inverse of each nonzero element in R. Since K is a prime field, $K = S$. ∎

THEOREM 8.7   Every field F contains a unique prime field K.

Proof   Let K be the intersection of all subfields of F; recall that every subfield of F contains 1, so that $K \neq \{0\}$. The reader may now prove that K is a prime field and that K is the only prime field contained in F. ∎

Definition   Let F be a field whose prime field is K. F has **characteristic** p if $K \approx Z_p$; otherwise, F has **characteristic** 0.

Observe that if F has characteristic p, then $pa = 0$ for every $a \in F$.

COROLLARY 8.8   If F is a finite field, then F has exactly p^n elements, where p is a prime.

Proof Since F is finite, it must have characteristic p, for some prime p. Moreover, F is a finite-dimensional vector space over Z_p. If F has dimension n, then one may choose a basis of F and count exactly p^n vectors $(k_1, k_2, \cdots, k_n)$, where $k_i \in Z_p$. $\blacksquare$

We remark that there do exist infinite fields of characteristic p, e.g., all rational functions over Z_p (a rational function is a quotient of two polynomials).

The next question is whether there are any finite fields aside from the Z_p. In order to exhibit them, we must generalize the method of adjoining a root of a polynomial to a field. In Chapter 6, this process was simple because we could work within the complex numbers. We must be wily here, however, for there is no such larger field available to us at the outset.

LEMMA 8.9 Let K be a field and let $\varphi(x)$ be irreducible in $K[x]$. There exists a field F containing a root of $\varphi(x)$ and a subfield isomorphic to K.

Proof Let $R = K[x]$ and let I be the ideal $(\varphi(x))$. Since $\varphi(x)$ is irreducible, I is a prime ideal (Exercise 8.6). Moreover, since R is a principal ideal domain, I is even a maximal ideal. By Theorem 8.3, R/I is a field.

We set $F = R/I$. If $\varphi(x) = \sum k_i x^i$, where $k_i \in K$, then

$$\varphi(x + I) = \sum k_i(x + I)^i = \sum k_i(x^i + I)$$
$$= \sum (k_i x^i + I) = (\sum k_i x^i) + I = \varphi(x) + I.$$

Since $\varphi(x) \in I$, $\varphi(x) + I = I$, the zero element of F. Therefore, the element $x + I$ in F is a root of $\varphi(x)$.

Finally, the reader may verify that $\{k + I: k \in K\}$ is a subfield of F that is isomorphic to K. $\blacksquare$

THEOREM 8.10 If K is a field and $f(x) \in K[x]$, there is a field F containing K over which $f(x)$ is a product of linear factors.

Proof We perform an induction on the degree d of $f(x)$. If $d = 1$, then K itself is the desired field. If $d > 1$, then $f(x) = \varphi(x)g(x)$, where $\varphi(x)$ is an irreducible polynomial. By Lemma 8.9, there is a field F_0 containing K and a root α of $\varphi(x)$. In $F_0[x]$, $\varphi(x) = (x - \alpha)\psi(x)$, and so $f(x) = (x - \alpha)\psi(x)g(x)$. Since $\psi(x)g(x)$ has degree less than d, the inductive hypothesis provides a field F containing F_0 (hence, K and α) in which $\psi(x)g(x)$ (hence, $f(x)$) is a product of linear factors. ∎

Exercises   8.7 If R is a commutative ring with 1, then the binomial theorem holds, i.e., if $a,b \in R$, then

$$(a + b)^n = a^n + \binom{n}{1}a^{n-1}b + \cdots + \binom{n}{n-1}ab^{n-1} + b^n.$$

8.8   If F is a field of characteristic $p > 0$, then for every $a,b \in G$,

$$(a + b)^{p^k} = a^{p^k} + b^{p^k}, \quad k > 0.$$

8.9   If F is a finite field with exactly q elements, then every element in F is a root of $x^q - x$. (*Hint:* Use Lagrange's theorem, Theorem 2.7, on the nonzero elements of F.)

Definition   Let F be a field, and let

$$f(x) = a_nx^n + a_{n-1}x^{n-1} + \cdots + a_0 \in F[x].$$

The **derivative** of $f(x)$, denoted $f'(x)$, is the polynomial

$$f'(x) = na_nx^{n-1} + (n - 1)a_{n-1}x^{n-2} + \cdots + a_1 \in F[x].$$

Exercises (contd.)   8.10   Prove the usual formulas of Calculus for the derivatives of sums and products of polynomials in $F[x]$.

8.11   Let $f(x) \in F[x]$. Then $f(x)$ and $f'(x)$ have a nonconstant common factor if and only if $f(x)$ has repeated roots.

THEOREM 8.11   Let p be a prime and n be a positive integer. There exists a field F with exactly p^n elements.

Proof   Let $q = p^n$, and consider the polynomial

$$f(x) = x^q - x \in Z_p[x].$$

By Theorem 8.10, there is a field F_0 containing Z_p in which $f(x)$ is a product of linear factors. Note that since F_0 contains Z_p, it has characteristic p.

Let F be the subset of F_0 consisting of all the roots of $f(x)$. Since

$f(x)$ has degree q, $|F| \leq q$. To prove that $|F| = q$, it suffices to prove that all the roots of $f(x)$ in F_0 are distinct, i.e., that $f(x)$ has no repeated roots. Now $f'(x) = qx^{q-1} - 1 = -1$, since F_0 has characteristic p. We now apply Exercise 8.11.

Let us now prove that F is a field. If a and b are roots of $f(x)$, then, using Exercise 8.8, $(a - b)^q = a^q - b^q = a - b$, i.e., $a - b$ is a root of $f(x)$. Hence, F is a group under addition. Further, $(ab)^q = a^q b^q = ab$, so that ab is also a root of $f(x)$; thus, F is a commutative ring. Finally, if $f(a) = 0$ and $a \neq 0$, then $a^{q-1} = 1$; the inverse of a is thus a^{q-2}. Therefore, F is a field having precisely $q = p^n$ elements. $\blacksquare$

THEOREM 8.12   Any two fields having exactly p^n elements are isomorphic.

Proof   If $|F| = p^n$, then by Exercise 8.9, every element in F is a root of $f(x) = x^{p^n} - x$. In the language of Chapter 6, F is a *root field* of $f(x)$. The reader may now adapt the proof of Lemma 6.4 to prove its analog: Any two root fields of $f(x)$ over Z_p are isomorphic. Our result now follows. $\blacksquare$

It was Galois who discovered these finite fields, and they are called **Galois fields** in his honor. The field with p^n elements is thus denoted $GF(p^n)$.

The General Linear Group

Groups of nonsingular matrices are as natural an object of study as groups of permutations. In investigating the structure of these groups, we shall discover a new family of simple groups.

Definition   Let K be a field. The **general linear group** $GL(m,K)$ is the multiplicative group of all nonsingular $m \times m$ matrices over K.

If $K = GF(q)$, one usually denotes this group $GL(m,q)$. A slight generalization of the result of Exercise 7.8 is that $GL(m,q) \approx \text{Aut}(W)$, where W is a direct sum of m copies of $\sigma(q)$.

THEOREM 8.13 $|GL(m,q)| = (q^m - 1)(q^m - q) \cdots (q^m - q^{m-1})$.

Proof Let V be an m-dimensional vector space over $GF(q)$, and let $\{\alpha_1, \alpha_2, \cdots, \alpha_m\}$ be an ordered basis. If we regard $GL(m,q)$ as linear transformations on V, then we can exhibit a one-to-one correspondence between $GL(m,q)$ and the family of all ordered bases of V. If $T \in GL(m,q)$, then $\{T\alpha_1, T\alpha_2, \cdots, T\alpha_m\}$ is an ordered basis of V (because T is nonsingular); if $\{\beta_1, \beta_2, \cdots, \beta_m\}$ is an ordered basis of V, there is a unique $T \in GL(m,q)$ with $T\alpha_i = \beta_i$ for all i.

An ordered basis of V consists of vectors $\{\beta_1, \beta_2, \cdots, \beta_m\}$. Since there are q^m vectors in V, there are $q^m - 1$ choices for β_1 (the zero vector is not a candidate). Having chosen β_1, the only restriction on β_2 is that it not lie in the subspace spanned by β_1; there are thus $q^m - q$ choices for β_2. More generally, having chosen an independent set $\{\beta_1, \beta_2, \cdots, \beta_i\}$, the only restriction on β_{i+1} is that it not lie in the subspace spanned by $\{\beta_1, \beta_2, \cdots, \beta_i\}$; there are thus $q^m - q^i$ choices for β_{i+1}. Therefore, there are exactly $(q^m - 1)(q^m - q) \cdots (q^m - q^{m-1})$ ordered bases of V. ∎

Notation If K is a field, then K^* is the multiplicative group of its nonzero elements.

Definition A **primitive element** of $GF(q)$ is a generator of $GF(q)^*$; (we saw in Exercise 4.17 that $GF(q)^*$ is a cyclic group).

Let ρ be a primitive element of $GF(q)$.

Definition If t is a nonnegative integer, then

$$M(t) = \{A \in GL(m,q): \det A = \text{power of } \rho^t\}.$$

LEMMA 8.14 Let t be a divisor of $q - 1$. If $\Omega = |GL(m,q)|$, then $M(t)$ is a normal subgroup of $GL(m,q)$ of order Ω/t.

Proof We use the correspondence theorem (Theorem 2.17) in the setting

$$\det: GL(m,q) \to GF(q)^*.$$

If t is a divisor of $q - 1 = |GF(q)^*|$, then the cyclic subgroup $[\rho^t]$ of $GF(q)^*$ has order $(q - 1)/t$, and hence index t. Furthermore, $[\rho^t] \lhd GF(q)^*$, for the latter group is abelian. Since $M(t)$ is the subgroup of $GL(m,q)$ that corresponds to $[\rho^t]$, $M(t) \lhd GL(m,q)$ and it has index t and hence order Ω/t. ∎

THEOREM 8.15   Let $q - 1 = p_1 p_2 \cdots p_k$, where the p are (not necessarily distinct) primes. The following normal series is the beginning of a composition series:

$$GL(m,q) = M(1) \supset M(p_1) \supset M(p_1 p_2) \supset \cdots \supset M(q - 1).$$

Proof   We have already seen above that each of the terms in this series is normal in $GL(m,q)$. Furthermore, if $\Omega = |GL(m,q)|$,

$$\left| \frac{M(p_1 p_2 \cdots p_i)}{M(p_1 p_2 \cdots p_{i+1})} \right| = \frac{\Omega/p_1 p_2 \cdots p_i}{\Omega/p_1 p_2 \cdots p_{i+1}} = p_{i+1}.$$

Since the factor groups have prime order, they are simple. ∎

The last subgroup in the above chain, $M(q - 1)$, is of special interest; it consists of all matrices of determinant $\rho^{q-1} = 1$.

Definition   A matrix is **unimodular** if it has determinant 1.

Definition   Let K be a field. The **special linear group** $SL(m,K)$ is the multiplicative group of all $m \times m$ unimodular matrices over K.

If $K = GF(q)$, one usually denotes this group $SL(m,q)$.
One would discover the subgroup SL without recalling determinants, for SL is the commutator subgroup of GL. It is clear that $(GL)' \subset SL$, since GL/SL is abelian; the reverse inclusion is not so obvious, and it will follow from the main results of this chapter.
We introduce the following elementary matrices in order to analyze the structure of the subgroup $SL(m,K)$.

Definition   Let λ be a nonzero element of K and $i \neq j$ integers between 1 and m. A **transvection** $B_{ij}(\lambda)$ is an $m \times m$ matrix differing from the identity matrix E in that it has λ as its ijth entry.

If E_{ij} is the $m \times m$ matrix with 1 in the ijth place and 0 elsewhere, then $B_{ij}(\lambda) = E + \lambda E_{ij}$.
We recall two elementary facts of matrix theory. First, every transvection is unimodular. Second, if A is an $m \times m$ matrix whose

kth row is a vector α_k (so that we may denote A by $(\alpha_1, \alpha_2, \cdots, \alpha_m)$), then $B_{ij}(\lambda)A$ is the matrix $(\alpha_1, \cdots, \alpha_i + \lambda\alpha_j, \cdots, \alpha_m)$.

LEMMA 8.16   If $A \in GL(m,K)$, then $A = UD(\mu)$, where U is a product of transvections (hence lies in $SL(m,K)$), and $D(\mu)$ is the diagonal matrix with diagonal entries $\{1, 1, \cdots, 1, \mu\}$.

Proof   Since we continue to assume that the reader is familiar with the elements of matrix theory, we present only a sketch of the proof.

We shall simplify A as much as possible by using only the elementary row operations corresponding to the matrices $B_{ij}(\lambda)$. Since A is nonsingular, not every entry a_{11} in the first column is 0. Adding some row to the second if necessary, we may assume $a_{21} \neq 0$. Now add $a_{21}^{-1}(1 - a_{11})$ times the second row to the first row to get 1 in the 11 position. We may now clean out the remainder of the first column so that all other entries in it are 0. Repeat this process on the second column, so that finally $a_{22} = 1$ and the other entries in column 2 are 0. Unfortunately, we may have dirtied the first column a bit, so return and clean it once more. There are now two tidy columns; go on to the third one. This process ends with a matrix $D(\mu)$.

In terms of matrix multiplication, we have shown that $WA = D(\mu)$, where W is a product of transvections. Since the inverse of $B_{ij}(\lambda)$ is $B_{ij}(-\lambda)$, which is again a transvection, $A = W^{-1}D(\mu)$ is the desired factorization. ∎

THEOREM 8.17 $GL(m,K)$ is a semidirect product of $SL(m,K)$ by K^*; $SL(m,K)$ is generated by transvections.

Proof   First of all, $SL(m,K) \lhd GL(m,K)$. If Δ is the set of all diagonal matrices $D(\mu)$ (notation as in the lemma), then Δ is a subgroup of $GL(m,K)$ isomorphic to K^*. Since $\det(D(\mu)) = \mu$, $\Delta \cap SL(m,K) = \{E\}$, so that GL is a semidirect product of SL by K^*.

If $A = UD(\mu)$ is a factorization of an element A of GL, as in the lemma, then $\det A = \mu$. It follows that if A is unimodular, $D(\mu) = D(1) = E$, and so $A = U$ is a product of transvections. ∎

THEOREM 8.18   The center of $SL(m,K)$, which we denote Z_0, consists of all scalar matrices kE with $k^m = 1$.

Proof   We shall prove that if $A \in Z_0$, then A must be a scalar matrix kE; the condition on k follows from unimodularity.

If A commutes with the transvection $E + E_{ij}$, then $AE_{ij} = E_{ij}A$. Now AE_{ij} has the first column of A as its jth column, with 0 elsewhere; $E_{ij}A$ has the jth row of A as its first row, with 0 elsewhere.

$$AE_{ij} = \begin{bmatrix} a_{11} \\ a_{21} \\ \vdots \end{bmatrix} \qquad E_{ij}A = \begin{bmatrix} a_{ji} & a_{j2} & \cdots \\ & 0 & \end{bmatrix}$$

Since these are equal, $a_{11} = a_{jj}$, while the other entries are 0. The same argument works if we replace 1 by i. Therefore A is scalar if it commutes with every transvection. ∎

THEOREM 8.19   If Z_0 is the center of $SL(m,q)$, then $|Z_0| = d$, where $d = (m, q - 1)$.

Proof   By Theorem 8.18, we must determine the number of elements $k \in GF(q)$ with $k^m = 1$. If ρ is a primitive element of $GF(q)$, then ρ has order $q - 1$. Define

$$\tau = \rho^{(q-1)/d}.$$

There are exactly d distinct powers of τ, and $(\tau^i)^m = 1$ for all i.

We shall now prove that if $(\rho^t)^m = 1$, then ρ^t is a power of τ. Since $\left(\dfrac{m}{d}, \dfrac{q-1}{d} \right) = 1$, there are integers a and b with $\dfrac{am}{d} + \dfrac{b(q-1)}{d} = 1$. It follows that $\rho^t = \tau^{bt}$, as desired. ∎

The following technical lemma will be needed often; it says that if $A \in H \lhd SL$, then anything similar to A is almost in H.

LEMMA 8.20   Let $H \lhd SL(m,K)$, and let $A \in H$. If A is similar to

$$C = \begin{bmatrix} & & & b_1 \\ & C' & & b_2 \\ & & & \vdots \\ & & & \\ a_1 & a_2 & \cdots & y \end{bmatrix},$$

where C' is an $(m - 1) \times (m - 1)$ matrix, then there is a nonzero $\mu \in K$ such that H contains

$$\begin{bmatrix} & & & \mu^{-1}b_1 \\ & C' & & \mu^{-1}b_2 \\ & & & \vdots \\ & & & \\ \mu a_1 & \mu a_2 & \cdots & y \end{bmatrix}.$$

Proof   There is a nonsingular P with $C = P^{-1}AP$. Now $P = UD(\mu)$, where U is unimodular. Therefore,

$$C = (UD(\mu))^{-1}AUD(\mu)$$
$$= D(\mu)^{-1}U^{-1}AUD(\mu)$$

so that

$$D(\mu)CD(\mu)^{-1} = U^{-1}AU \in H.$$

The reader may check that this last matrix is the desired one. ∎

Exercise   8.12   Let $H \lhd SL(m,K)$ and let H contain

$$\begin{bmatrix} A & 0 \\ 0 & B \end{bmatrix},$$

where B is a $k \times k$ matrix that is not scalar. Prove that H contains a matrix

$$\begin{bmatrix} E & 0 \\ 0 & D \end{bmatrix},$$

where E is an identity matrix and D is a $k \times k$ matrix that is not scalar. (*Hint:* Take an appropriate commutator.) Observe that analogous hypotheses on A instead of B guarantee a matrix of the form $\begin{bmatrix} C & 0 \\ 0 & E \end{bmatrix}$ in H.

PSL(2,K)

Our preceding discussion allows us to extend the normal series of Theorem 8.15 one step further:

$$GL(m,K) \supset \cdots \supset SL(m,K) \supset Z_0.$$

Moreover, Z_0 is an abelian group, so that its composition factors are no secret if it is finite. Let us investigate the last factor group of this series.

Definition   The **projective unimodular group** $PSL(m,K)$ is the group $SL(m,K)/Z_0$.

If $K = GF(q)$, one usually writes $PSL(m,q)$.

THEOREM 8.21   If $d = (m, q - 1)$, then
$$|PSL(m,q)| = \frac{(q^m - 1)(q^m - q) \cdots (q^m - q^{m-1})}{d(q - 1)}.$$

Proof   If $\Omega = |GL(m,q)|$, then $|SL(m,q)| = \Omega/q - 1$, by Lemma 8.14. Theorem 8.21 now follows from Theorems 8.13 and 8.19. ∎

We first show that $PSL(m,K)$ is of intrinsic interest.

Exercise   8.13   If K is a field, let $LF(K)$ denote the set of all unimodular linear fractional transformations

$$f(x) = \frac{ax + b}{cx + d},$$

where $a,b,c,d \in K$ and $ad - bc = 1$. Prove that $LF(K)$ is a group (the binary operation is composition of functions) isomorphic to $PSL(2,K)$. (This construction can be generalized to the general case $m > 2$.)

Definition   If $V_{n+1}(K)$ is an $(n + 1)$-dimensional vector space over a field K, define an equivalence relation on $V_{n+1}(K)$ by $\alpha \equiv \beta$ in case there is a nonzero $k \in K$ with $k\alpha = \beta$.

Define n-dimensional **projective space** $P_n(K)$ as the set of equivalence classes of vectors in $V_{n+1}(K)$. Now every nonsingular linear transformation $T: V_{n+1}(K) \rightarrow V_{n+1}(K)$ defines a map $T^*: P_n(K) \rightarrow P_n(K)$ by

$$T^*[\alpha] = [T\alpha];$$

T^* is called a **projective transformation**. If T is unimodular, then T^* is called a **projective unimodular transformation**.

Exercise   8.14   The set of all projective unimodular transformations of $P_n(K)$ forms a group isomorphic to $PSL(n + 1, K)$.

For the remainder of this section, we concentrate on the case $m = 2$ with the aim of proving that the groups $PSL(2, q)$ are simple when $q > 3$.

LEMMA 8.22   If a normal subgroup H of $SL(2, q)$ contains a transvection $B_{ij}(\mu)$, then $H = SL(2, q)$.

Proof   By Theorem 8.17, it suffices to prove that H contains every transvection.

If we conjugate $B_{12}(\mu)$ by a unimodular matrix, we have

$$\begin{bmatrix} a & b \\ c & d \end{bmatrix}\begin{bmatrix} 1 & \mu \\ 0 & 1 \end{bmatrix}\begin{bmatrix} d & -b \\ -c & a \end{bmatrix} = \begin{bmatrix} 1 - \mu ac & \mu a^2 \\ -\mu c^2 & 1 + \mu ac \end{bmatrix}.$$

In particular, this conjugate is $B_{12}(\mu a^2)$ if $c = 0$, and it is $B_{21}(-\mu c^2)$ if $a = 0$. Furthermore, these matrices lie in H, since H is normal.

The map $k \rightarrow k^2$ is an endomorphism of the abelian group K^* whose kernel consists of all k with $k^2 = 1$. Since K is a field, the polynomial $x^2 - 1$ has at most two roots, and so the kernel has order 1 or order 2 (it has order 1 if K has characteristic 2). It follows that at least half the elements of K^* are squares.

Let

$$\Gamma = \{\lambda \in K: B_{12}(\lambda) \in H\} \cup \{0\}.$$

It is easy to see that Γ is a subgroup of K (where we consider K only as an additive group). Moreover, we know that Γ contains 0 and all elements of the form μa^2. Therefore, Γ contains more than half the elements of K, and so $\Gamma = K$, by Lagrange's theorem. Hence, H contains all transvections of the form $B_{12}(\lambda)$, and a similar argument shows that H contains all transvections of the form $B_{21}(\lambda)$. $\blacksquare$

The transvections thus play the same role in the study of the special linear groups as the 3-cycles play in the study of the alternating groups. We now prove the main theorem of this section.

THEOREM 8.23   The groups $PSL(2,q)$ are simple if and only if $q > 3$.

Proof   First of all, Theorem 8.21 gives

$$|PSL(2,q)| = \begin{cases} (q + 1)(q^2 - q) & \text{if } q \text{ is even;} \\ \frac{1}{2}(q + 1)(q^2 - q) & \text{if } q \text{ is odd.} \end{cases}$$

Therefore, $|PSL(2,2)| = 6$ and $|PSL(2,3)| = 12$, so that these groups cannot be simple.

Let H be a normal subgroup of $SL(2,q)$ which contains a matrix not in Z_0. By the correspondence theorem, it suffices to prove that $H = SL(2,q)$.

Suppose H contains a matrix

$$A = \begin{bmatrix} r & 0 \\ s & t \end{bmatrix},$$

where $r \neq \pm 1$. If

$$S = \begin{bmatrix} 1 & 0 \\ 1 & 1 \end{bmatrix},$$

then H also contains

$$SAS^{-1}A^{-1} = \begin{bmatrix} 1 & 0 \\ 1 - t^2 & 1 \end{bmatrix}.$$

Since $\det A = 1 = rt$, $t \neq \pm 1$ and $1 - t^2 \neq 0$. This last matrix is thus a transvection, and so $H = SL(2,q)$, by Lemma 8.22.

To complete the proof, we have only to produce a matrix in H whose top row is $(r \quad 0)$ where $r \neq \pm 1$. Let M be a matrix in H that is not in Z_0. For later use, we remark that when the ground field has characteristic distinct from 2, we may assume that M has non-zero trace: If trace $M = 0$, then M^2 has trace $= -2 \neq 0$. Moreover, M is similar to either a diagonal matrix or a matrix

$$\begin{bmatrix} 0 & -1 \\ 1 & x \end{bmatrix},$$

for the only rational canonical forms for 2×2 matrices are: (i) a direct sum of two 1×1 companion matrices, i.e., a diagonal matrix; (ii) a 2×2 companion matrix (which has the above form because M is unimodular). In the first event, we have our desired matrix (since $M \notin Z_0$, and M is unimodular). In the second event, H contains, by Lemma 8.20, a matrix

$$C = \begin{bmatrix} 0 & -\mu^{-1} \\ \mu & x \end{bmatrix}.$$

If now

$$T = \begin{bmatrix} \alpha^{-1} & 0 \\ 0 & \alpha \end{bmatrix},$$

H contains the matrix

$$U = TCT^{-1}C^{-1} = \begin{bmatrix} \alpha^{-2} & 0 \\ \mu x(\alpha^2 - 1) & \alpha^2 \end{bmatrix}.$$

We are done if $\alpha^{-2} \neq \pm 1$, i.e., if $\alpha^4 \neq 1$. If $q > 5$, such a nonzero α does exist in $GF(q)$, for the polynomial $z^4 - 1$ has at most four roots in a field. If $q = 4$, then every $\alpha \in GF(4)$ satisfies the equation $\alpha^4 = \alpha$, so that if $\alpha \neq 1$, then $\alpha^4 \neq 1$. Therefore, only the case $q = 5$ remains.

In this last case, H still contains the matrices C and U. As we remarked earlier, we may assume that the original matrix M has nonzero trace, for the characteristic is now not 2. Since C is similar to M, both have the same trace, so that the entry x in C is nonzero. Choose $\alpha \in GF(5)$ ($\approx Z_5$) so that $1 - \alpha^2 \neq 0$; note that $\alpha^2 = -1$. The lower left corner of U, $\lambda = \mu x(\alpha^2 - 1)$, is nonzero, and so

$$U = \begin{bmatrix} -1 & 0 \\ \lambda & -1 \end{bmatrix}.$$

Hence, $U^2 = B_{21}(-2\lambda) \in H$, so that H contains a transvection. It follows from Lemma 8.22 that $H = SL(2,5)$. ∎

We have exhibited an infinite family of simple groups; are any of its members distinct from simple groups we already know? Using the formula of Theorem 8.21, we see that both $PSL(2,4)$ and $PSL(2,5)$ have order 60. By Exercise 5.34, any two simple groups of order 60 are isomorphic; therefore

$$PSL(2,4) \approx A_5 \approx PSL(2,5).$$

If $q = 7$, however, we do get a new simple group, for $|PSL(2,7)| = 168$, which is neither prime nor $\frac{1}{2}n!$. If we take $q = 8$, we see that there is a simple group of order 504.

Exercises   8.15   If K is a field of characteristic $\neq 2$, then

$$x = \left(\frac{x+1}{2}\right)^2 - \left(\frac{x-1}{2}\right)^2$$

for every $x \in K$. Use this remark to prove that $PSL(2,K)$ is simple for every, possibly infinite, field K of characteristic not 2. (*Hint:* The finiteness of K was used only in the consideration of the subgroup Γ in the proof of Lemma 8.22.)
(It is known that $PSL(2,K)$ is simple for every infinite field K.)
8.16   Prove that $PSL(2,2) \approx S_3$.
8.17   Is $SL(2,3) \approx S_4$? Prove that $PSL(2,3) \approx A_4$. (*Hint:* Prove that $PSL(2,3)$ contains no element of order 6.)
8.18   What is the 2-sylow subgroup of $SL(2,3)$?
8.19   What are the composition factors of $GL(2,7)$?
8.20   Prove that the commutator subgroup of $GL(2,q)$ is $SL(2,q)$ when $q > 3$. What are the commutator subgroups of $GL(2,3)$ and $GL(2,2)$?

PSL(m,K)

We shall prove in this section that $PSL(m,K)$ is simple for every field K and all $m \geq 3$. As a consequence of this, we shall be able to exhibit two nonisomorphic simple groups having the same finite order.
Let us generalize Lemma 8.22 for $m > 2$.

LEMMA 8.24   If a normal subgroup H of $SL(m,K)$ contains a transvection $B_{ij}(\mu)$, then $H = SL(m,K)$.

Proof   We have already proved the lemma for $m = 2$, so we may assume that $m > 2$. The following facts should be verified by the reader: for all indices k, l, s, t,
(i) $B_{kl}^{-1}(\lambda) = B_{kl}(-\lambda)$.
(ii) $B_{kl}(\lambda) = E + \lambda E_{kl}$.
(iii) $E_{kl}E_{st} = \delta_{ls}E_{kt}$,
where δ_{ls} is the Kronecker delta.[2]

[2] $\delta_{ls} = 0$ if $l \neq s$ and $\delta_{ls} = 1$ if $l = s$.

Since $m > 2$, there is an index k distinct from i and j. Since H is normal, the following commutator lies in H:

$$B_{ij}(\mu)B_{jk}(\lambda)B_{ij}(-\mu)B_{jk}(-\lambda).$$

Rules (ii) and (iii) may be used to show that this product is $B_{ik}(\lambda\mu)$. Since λ is an arbitrary nonzero element of K, so is $\lambda\mu$; hence, H contains every transvection with first index i and second index $k \neq j$. Moreover, the same formula gives every $B_{kj}(\lambda\mu) \in H$ (where we now take the commutator of B_{ki} and B_{ij}). Thus, H contains all transvections with second index j and any first index $k \neq i$. We have shown that if we begin with a transvection $B_{ij}(\mu)$, then H contains every transvection with the possible exceptions of $B_{ij}(\lambda)$, where $\lambda \neq \mu$. But these are also in H if we begin the process anew with $B_{ik}(\mu)$, which we now know is in H. ∎

Our proof of the simplicity of $PSL(m,K)$ is by induction on m, where $m \geq 3$. The following theorem is needed for the inductive step; it also provides some extra information about normal subgroups of $SL(m,K)$.

THEOREM 8.25 Suppose that $PSL(m,K)$ is simple, for some fixed $m \geq 3$. If a normal subgroup H of $SL(m,K)$ contains a non-scalar matrix, then $H = SL(m,K)$.

Remark The point of this theorem is that we are not assuming H contains the center Z_0.

Proof If $PSL(m,K)$ is simple, then Z_0 is a maximal normal subgroup of $SL(m,K)$; hence, $HZ_0 = SL(m,K)$. It follows that H contains A, a scalar multiple of a transvection:

$$A = \begin{bmatrix} \alpha & \mu & & & & \\ 0 & \alpha & & & & \\ & & \alpha & & & \\ & & & \cdot & & \\ & & & & \cdot & \\ & & & & & \cdot \\ & & & & & & \alpha \end{bmatrix},$$

and its inverse:

$$A^{-1} = \begin{bmatrix} \alpha^{-1} & -\mu\alpha^{-2} & & & & \\ 0 & \alpha^{-1} & & & & \\ & & \alpha^{-1} & & & \\ & & & \cdot & & \\ & & & & \cdot & \\ & & & & & \cdot \\ & & & & & & \alpha^{-1} \end{bmatrix}.$$

If $K = GF(2)$, then A is a transvection and we are done, by Lemma 8.24. If $K \neq GF(2)$, then there is a nonzero element $\beta \in K$ with $-\mu\alpha^{-2} + \beta \neq 0$. Recalling Exercise 4.36, A^{-1} is similar to B, where

$$B = \begin{bmatrix} \alpha^{-1} & -\mu\alpha^{-2} + \beta & & & & \\ 0 & \alpha^{-1} & & & & \\ & & \alpha^{-1} & & & \\ & & & \cdot & & \\ & & & & \cdot & \\ & & & & & \cdot \\ & & & & & & \alpha^{-1} \end{bmatrix},$$

and $B \in H$, by Lemma 8.20; (it is here that we use the hypothesis that $m \geq 3$). Since $AB = B_{12}(\alpha\beta)$, H contains a transvection, and so $H = SL(m,K)$. ∎

We now begin the induction.

THEOREM 8.26 $PSL(3,K)$ is simple for every field K.

Proof   Let H be a normal subgroup of $SL(3,K)$ which contains Z_0, and let $A \in H$ be a nonscalar matrix. There are only three possible canonical forms for A:
  (i)   a direct sum of three 1×1 companion matrices;
  (ii)   a direct sum of a 2×2 and a 1×1 companion matrix;
  (iii)   a 3×3 companion matrix.

  Case (i). A is similar to

$$D = \begin{bmatrix} a & 0 & 0 \\ 0 & b & 0 \\ 0 & 0 & c \end{bmatrix},$$

where D is not scalar. Therefore, we may assume that $a^{-1}c \neq 1$. By Lemma 8.20, $D \in H$. If

$$B = \begin{bmatrix} 1 & 0 & 0 \\ 0 & 1 & 0 \\ 1 & 0 & 1 \end{bmatrix},$$

then

$$BDB^{-1}D^{-1} = \begin{bmatrix} 1 & 0 & 0 \\ 0 & 1 & 0 \\ 1 - a^{-1}c & 0 & 1 \end{bmatrix} \in H,$$

and this is a transvection.

Case (ii). A is similar to

$$D = \begin{bmatrix} 0 & a & 0 \\ 1 & b & 0 \\ 0 & 0 & c \end{bmatrix}.$$

If $B = B_{32}(1)$, then

$$M = BDB^{-1}D^{-1} = \begin{bmatrix} 1 & 0 & 0 \\ 0 & 1 & 0 \\ -ca^{-1} & 1 & 1 \end{bmatrix} \in H.$$

Now the characteristic polynomial of M is $(x - 1)^3$. Since $M \neq E$ and M satisfies $(x - 1)^2$, the minimum polynomial of M is $(x - 1)^2$. Since the characteristic roots of M are all equal to 1, they lie in K, and so M is similar to its Jordan canonical form

$$J = \begin{bmatrix} 1 & 0 & 0 \\ 1 & 1 & 0 \\ 0 & 0 & 1 \end{bmatrix}.$$

By Lemma 8.20, the transvection J is in H.

Case (iii). A is similar to a 3×3 companion matrix, so that

$$C = \begin{bmatrix} 0 & 0 & a \\ 1 & 0 & b \\ 0 & \mu & c \end{bmatrix} \in H,$$

by Lemma 8.20. Therefore, H contains the commutator

$$D = C^{-1}B_{21}(-1)CB_{21}(1) = \begin{bmatrix} 1 & 0 & -a \\ 1 & 1 & 0 \\ 0 & 0 & 1 \end{bmatrix}$$

as well as

$$D^{-1} = \begin{bmatrix} 1 & 0 & a \\ -1 & 1 & -a \\ 0 & 0 & 1 \end{bmatrix}.$$

Notice that det $C = \mu a = 1$, so that $a \neq 0$. But H also contains the commutator

$$B_{21}(1)DB_{21}(-1)D^{-1} = \begin{bmatrix} 1 & 0 & 0 \\ 0 & 1 & -a \\ 0 & 0 & 1 \end{bmatrix},$$

and this is a transvection.[3] ∎

THEOREM 8.27 $PSL(m,K)$ is simple for every field K and all $m \geq 3$.

Proof   The theorem is proved by an induction on m, where $m \geq 3$. We have just completed the initial step $m = 3$.

Let $H \lhd SL(m,K)$, where $m > 3$ and H properly contains Z_0. Now H contains a nonscalar matrix A, and A is similar to a direct sum of companion matrices

$$\begin{bmatrix} C_1 & & & & \\ & C_2 & & & \\ & & \cdot & & \\ & & & \cdot & \\ & & & & \cdot \\ & & & & & C_t \end{bmatrix};$$

by Lemma 8.20, this matrix lies in H if we adjust the last row and column.

If $t > 1$, then Exercise 8.12 gives a matrix in H of the form

$$\begin{bmatrix} E & 0 \\ 0 & D \end{bmatrix},$$

where D is a $k \times k$ matrix that is not scalar. We may assume that $k \geq 3$: if, for example, $k = 2$, then let

$$D = \begin{bmatrix} 1 & 0 & 0 \\ 0 & a & b \\ 0 & c & d \end{bmatrix}.$$

---

[3] The reader may wonder why we did not use the fact that $PSL(2,K)$ is simple in the proof. The reason is that we would then have been forced to include special proofs for the exceptional cases $GF(2)$ and $GF(3)$.

Let S^* be the following isomorphic copy of $SL(k,K)$ inside of $SL(m,K)$:

$$S^* = \left\{ \begin{bmatrix} E & 0 \\ 0 & U \end{bmatrix} : U \in SL(k,K) \right\}.$$

Now $S^* \cap H \lhd S^*$ and $\begin{bmatrix} E & 0 \\ 0 & D \end{bmatrix}$ is a nonscalar matrix in this intersection. Since $PSL(k,K)$ is simple, by induction, Theorem 8.25 gives $S^* \cap H = S^*$, i.e., $S^* \subset H$. It follows that H contains a transvection.

The last case is when $t = 1$, i.e., the original matrix A is similar to a companion matrix. Thus, H contains an adjusted companion matrix

$$C = \begin{bmatrix} 0 & 0 & \cdots & 0 & a_1 \\ 1 & 0 & \cdots & 0 & a_2 \\ 0 & 1 & \cdots & 0 & a_3 \\ \cdot & \cdot & & \cdot & \cdot \\ \cdot & \cdot & & \cdot & \cdot \\ \cdot & \cdot & & \cdot & \cdot \\ 0 & 0 & \cdots & \mu & a_m \end{bmatrix},$$

where $\mu = a_1^{-1}$. Our multiplication is easier if we think of C as a linear transformation; there is a basis $\alpha_1, \alpha_2, \cdots, \alpha_m$ with

$$C\alpha_1 = \alpha_2,$$
$$\cdot$$
$$\cdot$$
$$\cdot$$
$$C\alpha_{m-1} = \mu\alpha_m,$$
$$C\alpha_m = \sum a_i\alpha_i.$$

The inverse of C also lies in H; its action is given by

$$C^{-1}\alpha_1 = -a_2\mu\alpha_1 - a_3\mu\alpha_2 - \cdots - a_{m-1}\mu\alpha_{m-2} - a_m\alpha_{m-1} + \mu\alpha_m,$$
$$C^{-1}\alpha_2 = \alpha_1,$$
$$\cdot$$
$$\cdot$$
$$\cdot$$
$$C^{-1}\alpha_{m-1} = \alpha_{m-2},$$
$$C^{-1}\alpha_m = \mu^{-1}\alpha_{m-1}.$$

If B is the transvection $B_{21}(1)$, then

$$B = \begin{bmatrix} 1 & 0 & 0 \\ 1 & 1 & 0 \\ 0 & 0 & E \end{bmatrix},$$

and

$$B\alpha_1 = \alpha_1 + \alpha_2 \quad \text{and} \quad B\alpha_i = \alpha_i \quad \text{for } i \geq 2.$$

The transformation $D = BCB^{-1}C^{-1}$ acts as follows:

$$D\alpha_1 = \alpha_1 + \alpha_2 + a_2\mu\alpha_3$$
$$D\alpha_2 = \alpha_2 - \alpha_3; \quad D\alpha_i = \alpha_i \quad \text{if } i \geq 3.$$

The matrix of D relative to the basis of α is in H, and

$$D = \begin{bmatrix} 1 & 0 & 0 & \\ 1 & 1 & 0 & \\ a_2\mu & -1 & 1 & \\ & & & E \end{bmatrix}.$$

If

$$S^* = \left\{ \begin{bmatrix} U & 0 \\ 0 & E \end{bmatrix} : U \in SL(3,K) \right\},$$

then $S^* \approx SL(3,K)$ and $H \cap S^* \lhd S^*$. Since $H \cap S^*$ contains D, a nonscalar matrix, $H \cap S^* = S^*$, by Theorem 8.25. Therefore, $S^* \subset H$ and H contain a transvection. This completes the proof of the theorem. ∎

Elegant geometric proofs of these theorems may be found in Artin's book, *Geometric Algebra*; the reader will also find simplicity proofs for other families of linear groups there. Another excellent reference is the book of Dieudonné, *Sur les groups classiques* (see Bibliography).

Exercises 8.21 Prove that the commutator subgroup of $GL(m,K)$ is $SL(m,K)$ for $m \geq 3$.

8.22 Let K be a subfield of F, and let A be a square matrix over K. If A is similar over F to a matrix B (whose entries may lie in F), then A^n is scalar if and only if B^n is scalar.

8.23 Let K be a subfield of F, where K is a finite field having q elements; let $m(x)$ be an irreducible polynomial in $K\lceil x \rceil$ of degree d. If α is a root of $m(x)$ in F, then

$$\alpha^{q^d} = \alpha$$

and the roots of $m(x)$ are

$$\alpha, \alpha^q, \alpha^{q^2}, \cdots, \alpha^{q^{d-1}}.$$

(*Hint:* Show that $(m(x))^q = m(x^q)$ by using Exercises 8.8 and 8.9.)
Observe that $|PSL(3,4)| = 20,160 = \frac{1}{2}\,8!$, so that $PSL(3,4)$ and A_8 have the same order.

THEOREM 8.28 $PSL(3,4)$ and A_8 are not isomorphic. Therefore, there are nonisomorphic finite simple groups having the same order.

Proof A_8 contains $(12345)(678)$, an element of order 15. We shall prove that $PSL(3,4)$ contains no element of order 15, and this will prove the theorem.

Let A be a 3×3 unimodular matrix over $GF(4)$, and let $c(x)$ be its characteristic polynomial. By Theorem 8.10, there is a field F containing $GF(4)$ in which $c(x)$ is a product of linear factors; thus, F contains all the characteristic roots of A.

Since a conjugate of an element in a group has the same order as the element, we need only examine the canonical form of A. Furthermore, the center of SL is the scalar matrices, so that Exercise 8.22 allows us to examine canonical forms over F instead of over $GF(4)$. This last remark allows us to assume that all characteristic roots of A are in F, so that we may use the Jordan canonical form of A.

There are only three possible Jordan canonical forms for a 3×3 matrix:

(i)   a 3×3 Jordan block:

$$B = \begin{bmatrix} a & 0 & 0 \\ 1 & a & 0 \\ 0 & 1 & a \end{bmatrix};$$

(ii)   a direct sum of a 1×1 and a 2×2 Jordan block:

$$B = \begin{bmatrix} a & 0 & 0 \\ 0 & b & 0 \\ 0 & 1 & b \end{bmatrix};$$

(iii)   a direct sum of three 1×1 Jordan blocks:

$$B = \begin{bmatrix} a & 0 & 0 \\ 0 & b & 0 \\ 0 & 0 & c \end{bmatrix}.$$

If $\mu \in GF(4)$ is nonzero, then $\mu^3 = 1$. Therefore, if A^{15} (hence B^{15}) is a scalar matrix, then $A^{45} = E$; hence, $B^{45} = E$. Since F has characteristic 2 and 45 is odd, Exercises 4.32 and 4.33 show that odd powers of the first two canonical forms for B cannot be scalar. Only the diagonal matrix (iii) remains.

Suppose the characteristic polynomial $c(x)$ of B is irreducible over $GF(4)$. By Exercise 8.23, the roots a, b, c of $c(x)$ are given by α, α^4, α^{16}, and $\alpha^{64} = \alpha$. Hence, $\alpha^{63} = 1$. Since $B^{45} = E$, $\alpha^{45} = 1$; therefore, $\alpha^9 = 1$, $B^9 = E$, and B does not represent an element of order 15 in PSL.

At the other end of the spectrum is the case in which all characteristic roots of B already lie in $GF(4)$. As we remarked above, this implies that $B^3 = E$, so there is no element of order 15 here.

The final case is $c(x) = (x - a)m(x)$, where $a \in GF(4)$ and $m(x)$ is an irreducible polynomial over $GF(4)$ of degree 2. Exercise 8.23 says that the roots of $m(x)$ are α and α^4; furthermore, it says that $\alpha^{16} = \alpha$, i.e., $\alpha^{15} = 1$; hence, α is a 15th root of unity. Since $GF(16)$ contains every 15th root of unity (i.e., every root of $x^{15} - 1$ over $GF(2)$), we may assume that $F = GF(16)$. Let ρ be a primitive 15th root of unity in F. There is an integer t such that $\alpha = \rho^t$ and $\alpha^4 = \rho^{4t}$. Note that the nonzero elements of $GF(4)$ are ρ^5, ρ^{10}, and $\rho^{15} = 1$. Hence,

$$B = \begin{bmatrix} a & 0 & 0 \\ 0 & \rho^t & 0 \\ 0 & 0 & \rho^{4t} \end{bmatrix},$$

where $a = \rho^5$, ρ^{10}, or ρ^{15}. We claim that for either of these choices of a, B^5 is a scalar matrix, and so cannot represent an element of order 15 in PSL. For example, suppose $a = \rho^5$. Since B is unimodular, $\rho^{5+5t} = 1$, i.e., $\rho^{5t} = \rho^{10}$. The diagonal entries of B^5 are ρ^{25}, $\rho^{5t} = \rho^{10}$, and $\rho^{20t} = \rho^{40}$, all of which equal ρ^{10}. This completes the proof of the theorem. ∎

Chapter 9

Infinite Abelian Groups

The First Reduction:
Torsion and Torsion-Free

A valuable viewpoint in studying an infinite abelian group G is to consider G as an extension of more manageable groups. Of course this reduces the study of G to the study of an extension problem and the study of the more manageable groups. In our first reduction, the more manageable groups are torsion and torsion-free.

Before we begin, it is convenient to agree upon notation and to make some quite formal definitions. First, all groups are abelian and are written additively; second, the trivial group having one element is denoted 0 (instead of $\{0\}$).

Definition   In the following diagram, capital letters denote groups and arrows denote homomorphisms.

$$\begin{array}{ccc} A & \xrightarrow{\alpha} & B \\ {\scriptstyle\beta'}\downarrow & {\scriptstyle\alpha'} & \downarrow{\scriptstyle\beta} \\ A' & \xrightarrow{\alpha'} & B' \end{array}$$

This diagram **commutes** in case $\beta\alpha = \alpha'\beta'$.

A special case of such a diagram is a triangular diagram, i.e., one of the homomorphisms is an identity. A common example is

$$\begin{array}{ccc} & B' & \\ {\scriptstyle f}\nearrow & & \uparrow{\scriptstyle g} \\ A & \xrightarrow{i} & B \end{array}$$

where A is a subgroup of B, and i is the inclusion. This diagram commutes if $gi = f$, i.e., $g|A = f$. Another way of saying this is that g **extends** f.

We say that a larger diagram composed of squares and triangles **commutes** if each component diagram commutes.

Here is a second formal definition.

Definition   Let

(*) $\cdots \rightarrow A_{k+2} \xrightarrow{f_{k+2}} A_{k+1} \xrightarrow{f_{k+1}} A_k \xrightarrow{f_k} A_{k-1} \rightarrow \cdots$

be a sequence of groups and homomorphisms; this sequence is **exact** in case the image of each map is equal to the kernel of the next map.

Exercises   9.1   If $0 \rightarrow A \xrightarrow{f} B$ is an exact sequence, then f is one-to-one.

9.2   If $B \xrightarrow{g} C \rightarrow 0$ is an exact sequence, then g is onto.

9.3   If $0 \rightarrow A \rightarrow B \rightarrow C \rightarrow 0$ is an exact sequence, then B is an extension of A by C.

9.4   In the exact sequence (*), f_{k+2} is onto if and only if f_k is one-to-one.

Definition   If G is abelian, the **torsion**[1] **subgroup** of G, denoted tG, is the set of all elements in G of finite order.

Since G is abelian, tG is a subgroup of G.

Definition   A group G is **torsion** in case $tG = G$; G is **torsion-free** in case $tG = 0$.

THEOREM 9.1   Every abelian group G is an extension of a torsion group by a torsion-free group.

Proof   It suffices to prove that G/tG is torsion-free. Suppose $n\bar{x} = 0$ for some $\bar{x} \in G/tG$ and some integer $n \neq 0$. If we lift $\bar{x}$ to $x \in G$, then $nx \in tG$; hence, there is an integer $m \neq 0$ with $mnx = 0$. Since $mn \neq 0$, $x \in tG$, and so $\bar{x} = 0$. ∎

[1] This terminology comes from algebraic topology, where a space is "twisted" if it has homology groups containing elements of finite order.

Theorem 9.1 reduces the study of arbitrary abelian groups to the study of torsion groups, torsion-free groups, and an extension problem. Our first question is to determine whether this particular extension problem is only virtual or if there is a group whose torsion subgroup is not a direct summand.[2] Let us first generalize one of our methods of manufacturing groups.

Let K be a nonempty set (possibly infinite), and for each $k \in K$, let there be given a group A_k.

Definition   The **direct product**[3] of the A_k, denoted $\prod\limits_{k \in K} A_k$ is the group consisting of all elements $\langle a_k \rangle$ in the cartesian product of the A_k under the binary operation:

$$\langle a_k \rangle + \langle a'_k \rangle = \langle a_k + a'_k \rangle.$$

Definition   The **direct sum** of the A_k, denoted $\sum\limits_{k \in K} A_k$, is the subgroup of $\prod\limits_{k \in K} A_k$ consisting of all elements $\langle a_k \rangle$ almost all of whose coordinates are 0, i.e., only finitely many a_k are nonzero.

If the index set K is finite, then

$$\prod_{k \in K} A_k = \sum_{k \in K} A_k;$$

if the index set K is infinite, the product and the sum are distinct (and are isomorphic only in rare cases).

Exercises   9.5   Let $\{A_k\}$ be a family of abelian groups. Prove that $t(\Pi A_k) \subset \Pi t A_k$ and $t(\sum A_k) = \sum t A_k$. Show that the first inclusion is proper for the special case when the index set K is the positive integers and $A_k = \sigma(p^k)$ for some prime p.

9.6   Define a function $p_i \colon \prod\limits_{k \in K} A_k \to A_i$ by $p_i(\langle a_k \rangle) = a_i$. Prove that each p_i is a homomorphism of $\prod\limits_{k \in K} A_k$ onto A_i. (p_i is called the ith **projection**.) The restriction of p_i (also called a projection) maps $\sum\limits_{k \in K} A_k$ onto A_i as well.

---

[2] If an abelian group is a semidirect product, then it is a direct product (or, in additive terminology, a direct sum).

[3] Also called the *strong direct sum*, or the *complete direct sum*.

9.7   Let $\{A_k\}$ be a family of subgroups of G. Prove that $G \approx \sum A_k$ if and only if every nonzero element $g \in G$ has a unique expression of the form $g = a_{k_1} + \cdots + a_{k_n}$, where $a_{k_i} \in A_{k_i}$, the k_i are distinct, and each $a_{k_i} \neq 0$.

9.8   Let $\{A_k\}$ be a family of subgroups of G. Prove that $G \approx \sum A_k$ if and only if $G = \left[\bigcup_k A_k\right]$, and for every i,

$$A_i \cap \left[\bigcup_{k \neq i} A_k\right] = 0.$$

9.9   Let $\{A_k\}$ be a family of subgroups of G. Prove that $G \approx \sum A_k$ if and only if, given any abelian group H and any set of homomorphisms $f_k \colon A_k \to H$, there exists a unique homomorphism $f \colon G \to H$ that extends each f_k, i.e., if $i_k \colon A_k \to G$ is the inclusion, there is a unique f such that all the following diagrams commute:

$$
\begin{array}{ccc}
 & G & \\
{\scriptstyle i_k}\nearrow & & \downarrow {\scriptstyle f} \\
A_k & \underset{f_k}{\longrightarrow} & H
\end{array}
$$

(*Hint:* First consider the case $H = \sum A_k$ in order to get maps $f \colon G \to \sum A_k$ and $g \colon \sum A_k \to G$. To show that f is an isomorphism, use the uniqueness hypothesis in a second diagram in which $H = G$.)

9.10   Let A be a subgroup of G. Prove that A is a direct summand of G if and only if there is a homomorphism $p \colon G \to A$ such that $p(a) = a$ for every $a \in A$.

9.11   Let $\{A_k\}$ be a family of subgroups of G. Prove that $G \approx \Pi A_k$ if and only if there exist homomorphisms $p_k \colon G \to A_k$ with $p_k|A_k =$ identity, and given any abelian group H and any set of homomorphisms $f_k \colon H \to A_k$, there is a unique homomorphism $f \colon H \to G$ such that $p_k f = f_k$, for all k, i.e., there is a unique f such that all the following diagrams commute:

$$
\begin{array}{ccc}
 & G & \\
{\scriptstyle p_k}\swarrow & & \uparrow {\scriptstyle f} \\
A_k & \underset{f_k}{\longleftarrow} & H
\end{array}
$$

Definition   Let $x \in G$ and let n be an integer; x is **divisible by n** in case there is an element $y \in G$ with $ny = x$.

Exercises (contd.)   9.12   Let $x \in G$ have order n; if $(m,n) = 1$, then x is divisible by m.

THEOREM 9.2   There exists an abelian group G whose torsion subgroup is not a direct summand.

Proof   Let P be the set of all primes, and let $G = \prod_{p \in P} \sigma(p)$.

We claim that there is no nonzero element x in G that is divisible by every prime p. If $qy = x$, then $\langle qy_p \rangle = \langle x_p \rangle$, i.e., $qy_p = x_p$ for every p. In particular, if $q = p$, then $x_p = 0$. Therefore, if x is divisible by every prime p, then each coordinate of x is 0, and so $x = 0$.

Our next assertion is that $tG = \sum \sigma(p)$ (compare with Exercise 9.5). Clearly, $\sum \sigma(p) \subset tG$. Suppose $x = \langle x_p \rangle \in G$ and $mx = 0$ for some $m \neq 0$; then $mx_p = 0$ for each p. Since $x_p \in \sigma(p)$, $m \equiv 0$ (mod p) for every p for which $x_p \neq 0$. There are thus only finitely many coordinates x_p different from 0, lest m be divisible by infinitely many different primes; hence, $tG \subset \sum \sigma(p)$.

We shall now show that G/tG contains a nonzero element that is divisible by every prime. Were tG a direct summand of G, then $G \approx tG \oplus (G/tG)$ would also contain such a nonzero element, contradicting the first part of our proof. Consider the element $\langle a_p \rangle + tG$ in G/tG, where a_p is a generator of $\sigma(p)$. If q is a prime, then, by Exercise 9.12, for each $p \neq q$, there is an element $x_p \in \sigma(p)$ with $qx_p = a_p$. Hence, if we define $x_q = 0$, then

$$q\langle x_p \rangle = \langle a_p \rangle - y$$

where y has 0 in each coordinate save the qth, where it has a_q. Therefore, $y \in tG$ and

$$q(\langle x_p \rangle + tG) = \langle a_p \rangle - y + tG = \langle a_p \rangle + tG.$$

We have shown that $\langle a_p \rangle + tG$ is divisible by every prime; since this element is nonzero, tG cannot be a direct summand of G. ∎

THEOREM 9.3   Every torsion group G is the direct sum of p-primary groups.

Proof   For any prime p, let

$$G_p = \{x \in G : x \text{ has order some power of } p\}.$$

(G_p is the p-**primary component** of G.) The reader may now prove that $G = \sum G_p$, using our proof of the primary decomposition theorem (Theorem 4.4) as his model. ∎

THEOREM 9.4   Let G and H be torsion; $G \approx H$ if and only if $G_p \approx H_p$ for all primes p.

Proof   Let $f: G \to H$ be an isomorphism, and let $g: H \to G$ be its inverse. One checks easily that $f(G_p) \subset H_p$, and by symmetry, that $g(H_p) \subset G_p$. Let $f_p = f|G_p$ and $g_p = g|H_p$. Both $f_p g_p$ and $g_p f_p$ are identities, so that $G_p \approx H_p$.

Conversely, if $f_p: G_p \to H_p$ are isomorphisms, then there is an isomorphism $f: G \to H$ defined by $\langle x_p \rangle \to \langle f_p(x_p) \rangle$. ∎

Because of these two theorems, the study of torsion groups is reduced to the study of p-primary groups.

The Second Reduction:
Divisible and Reduced

If we had asked the reader in Chapter 1 to give examples of infinite abelian groups, he probably would have responded with the integers, the rationals, and the reals. In this section, we study a common generalization of the latter two groups, the divisible groups. We shall see that every group is an extension of a divisible group by a group having no divisible subgroups.

Definition   A group G is **divisible** in case each $x \in G$ is divisible by every $n > 0$.

Exercises   9.13   We shall henceforth denote the additive group of rationals by Q. Prove that the following groups are divisible: Q; additive group of real numbers; additive group of complex numbers; multiplicative group of positive reals; multiplicative group of non-zero elements of an algebraically closed field.

9.14   The group G/tG constructed in Theorem 9.2 is divisible.

9.15   A quotient of a divisible group is divisible.

9.16   A direct sum (direct product) of groups is divisible if and only if each summand (factor) is divisible.

9.17   A torsion-free divisible group is a vector space over Q. (*Hint:* Verify the axioms.)

The reader knows that every finite dimensional vector space V over a field F has a basis and that any two bases of V have the same number of elements. We now prove the infinite analogs of these theorems; because this may be the reader's first contact with Zorn's lemma (see Appendix IV), we proceed leisurely.

Definition   Let V be a vector space over a field F. A subset X of V is **dependent** in case there exist a finite number of vectors $x_1, x_2, \cdots, x_n$ in X and nonzero scalars $a_1, a_2, \cdots, a_n \in F$ such that $\sum a_i x_i = 0$; otherwise, X is **independent**. A subset X **spans** V in case every vector in V is a finite linear combination of vectors in X. A **basis** of V is an independent subset that spans V.

Example   Let $V = Q[x]$, the vector space of all polynomials in x over Q. A basis of V is the set $\{1, x, x^2, \cdots, x^m, \cdots\}$.

THEOREM 9.5   If V is a vector space over a field F, then V has a basis. In fact, every independent subset I of V is contained in a basis.

Proof   Let $\mathcal{S}$ be the family of all independent subsets of V containing I; partially order $\mathcal{S}$ by ordinary inclusion. Let $\{X_\alpha\}$ be a simply ordered subset of $\mathcal{S}$, i.e., the X_α are independent subsets of V containing I, and given any two of them, one contains the other. From this it follows that, given any finite number of these X_α, one contains all the others. Now let X be the union of these X_α. It is trivial that X contains each X_α, but we must verify that $X \in \mathcal{S}$ in order that it be an upper bound. Suppose $x_1, x_2, \cdots, x_n \in X$ and $\sum a_i x_i = 0$. Now each x_i got into X by being in X_{α_i} for some α_i. There being only finitely many X_{α_i}, one contains all the others; hence, $x_1, x_2, \cdots, x_n$ all lie in this one X_α, which is, by hypothesis, independent. Therefore, each $a_i = 0$ and X is independent.

By Zorn's lemma, there is a maximal independent subset Y of V that contains I. We claim that Y is a basis of V, for which it now suffices to prove that Y spans V. Suppose $x \in V$ and x is not a linear combination of elements in Y. Consider the set $Y' = Y \cup \{x\}$. Y' is an independent set containing I, as the reader may easily check, and this contradicts the maximality of Y. ∎

COROLLARY 9.6   Let V be a vector space over F. Considering V as an abelian group, V is a direct sum of copies of F.

Proof   Let $B = \{x_k : k \in K\}$ be a basis of V, and let F_k denote the one-dimensional subspace generated by x_k. Clearly, each F_k is isomorphic, as a group, to the additive group F.

We claim that the additive group V is isomorphic to $\sum\limits_{k \in K} F_k$. Since B spans V, every nonzero vector $\alpha \in V$ has an expression $\alpha = \sum r_{k_i} x_{k_i}$, where the r are nonzero elements of F and all the x are distinct; furthermore, each $r_{k_i} x_{k_i} \in F_{k_i}$. Since B is independent, this is the only expression for α of this kind. By Exercise 9.7, $V \approx \sum F_k$. ∎

COROLLARY 9.7   (i)   Every torsion-free divisible group G is a direct sum of copies of Q;
(ii)   An abelian group G in which every nonzero element has prime order p is a direct sum of copies of $\sigma(p)$.

Proof   (i) By Exercise 9.17, G is a vector space over Q. (ii) In the proof of Lemma 4.5, it was verified that G admits a scalar multiplication by elements in Z_p, and the additive group Z_p is isomorphic to $\sigma(p)$. ∎

We see in particular that the additive group of real numbers is a vector space over Q. A basis of this vector space is usually called a **Hamel basis,** and it is useful for constructing certain analytical counterexamples. For example, a Hamel basis may be used to exhibit a discontinuous function f on the reals satisfying the functional equation

$$f(x + y) = f(x) + f(y)$$

for all real numbers x and y. (If c is the cardinal of the continuum, there are 2^c such functions f and only c continuous real-valued functions.)

Exercises   *9.18   Let G be an abelian group of bounded order, i.e., $nG = 0$ for some $n > 0$. Prove that G is a direct sum of cyclic groups. (*Hint:* Use Theorem 9.3 and our proof of the basis theorem, Theorem 4.6.)

*9.19 Let G be a (not necessarily abelian) group, and suppose $|\text{Aut } (G)| = 1$. Prove that G has at most two elements. (The reader now has the power to complete Exercise 7.10.)

9.20 Let V be a vector space over a field F. Prove that any two bases of V have the same number of elements.

Hints:

(i) The reader need only consider the case in which V is not finite-dimensional, for the other case is well known.

(ii) The following theorem of set theory may be used: Let X be an infinite set, and let S be the collection of all finite subsets of X; X and S have the same number of elements.

Definition   Let V_1 and V_2 be vector spaces over F. V_1 and V_2 **have the same dimension** if there are bases B_1 of V_1 and B_2 of V_2 that have the same number of elements.

Exercises (contd.)   9.21 Let V and W be vector spaces over F, where F is isomorphic to either Q or Z_p. Show that, as abelian groups, $V \approx W$ if and only if V and W have the same dimension.

The easiest example to exhibit of a torsion divisible group is Q/Z; in particular, its p-primary components are p-primary divisible groups.

Definition   If p is a prime, $\sigma(p^\infty)$ denotes the p-primary component of Q/Z.

Exercises   9.22 Let $A^{(p)}$ denote the set of all rationals between 0 and 1 of the form m/p^n, where $m,n \geq 0$, under the binary operation "addition modulo 1." For example, if $p = 2$, then $\frac{1}{2} + \frac{1}{2} = 0$, $\frac{1}{2} + \frac{3}{4} = \frac{1}{4}$, etc. Prove that $A^{(p)}$ is a p-primary group and that $Q/Z \approx \sum A^{(p)}$; conclude that $A^{(p)} \approx \sigma(p^\infty)$.

9.23 Show that $\sigma(p^\infty)$ is generated by elements $a_1, a_2, a_3 \cdots$, where $pa_1 = 0, pa_2 = a_1, \cdots, pa_{n+1} = a_n, \cdots$. If $[a_n]$ is the cyclic subgroup of $\sigma(p^\infty)$ generated by a_n, then $[a_n] \approx \sigma(p^n)$, $[a_n] \subset [a_{n+1}]$ for all n, and

$$\sigma(p^\infty) = \bigcup_{n=1}^{\infty} [a_n].$$

9.24   Every proper subgroup of $\sigma(p^\infty)$ is finite, and the set of subgroups is well ordered by inclusion. (It is an open question whether there exists an infinite nonabelian group all of whose proper subgroups are finite.)

9.25   Prove that $\sigma(p^\infty)$ has the DCC but not the ACC.

9.26   For a fixed prime p, let G be the set of all pth power roots of unity, i.e., all complex numbers of the form $\exp(2\pi ik/p^n)$, where $k \in Z$ and $n \geq 0$. Prove that G is a multiplicative group isomorphic to $\sigma(p^\infty)$.

Our immediate goal is the classification of divisible groups.

THEOREM 9.8 (*The Injective Property*)   Let A be a subgroup of B, and let $f\colon A \to D$ be a homomorphism, where D is divisible. Then f can be extended to a homomorphism $F\colon B \to D$, i.e., an F exists making the adjoined diagram commute.

$$D$$
$$f \nearrow \quad \uparrow$$
$$0 \to A \to B$$

Proof   We use Zorn's lemma. Consider the set $\mathcal{S}$ of all pairs (S,h) where S is a subgroup of B containing A and $h\colon S \to D$ extends f; $\mathcal{S}$ is nonempty, for $(A,f) \in \mathcal{S}$. We partially order $\mathcal{S}$ by decreeing $(S_1,h_1) \leq (S_2,h_2)$ in case $S_1 \subset S_2$ and h_2 extends h_1. If $\{(S_\alpha,h_\alpha)\}$ is a simply ordered subset of $\mathcal{S}$, define (S_0,h_0) as follows: $S_0 = \bigcup_\alpha S_\alpha$; if $s \in S_0$, then $s \in S_\alpha$ for some α; define $h_0(s) = h_\alpha(s)$. We leave to the reader the proof that $(S_0,h_0) \in \mathcal{S}$ and that it is an upper bound of $\{(S_\alpha,h_\alpha)\}$. By Zorn's lemma, there exists a maximal pair, (M,h). We shall show that $M = B$, which will complete the proof.

Suppose there is an element $b \in B$ that is not in M. Define $M_1 = M + [b]$; clearly, $M \underset{\neq}{\subset} M_1$, so that it suffices to extend h to M_1 to reach a contradiction.

Case (i) $M \cap [b] = 0$. Then $M_1 = M \oplus [b]$. Define $g\colon [b] \to D$ to be the zero map. By Exercise 9.9, there is a map $F\colon M_1 \to D$ extending h (and g).

Case (ii) $M \cap [b] \neq 0$. Let k be the smallest positive integer for which $kb \in M$; then every element y in M_1 has the unique expression $y = m + tb$, where $0 \leq t < k$. Let $c = kb$; since $c \in M$, $h(c)$ is defined. Since D is divisible, there is an element $x \in D$ with $kx = h(c)$.

Define $F: M_1 \to D$ by $F(m + tb) = h(m) + tx$. We leave to the reader the straightforward computation that F is a homomorphism extending h. ∎

COROLLARY 9.9   Let D be a subgroup of G, where D is divisible. Then D is a direct summand of G.

Proof   Consider the diagram

$$
\begin{array}{c}
D \\
{}^{I}\nearrow \ \uparrow \\
0 \to D \to G
\end{array}
$$

where I is the identity map. By Theorem 9.8, there is a homomorphism $p: G \to D$ such that $p(d) = d$ for every $d \in D$. By Exercise 9.10, D is a direct summand of G. ∎

Exercises   9.27   An abelian group G is divisible if and only if it has the injective property. (*Hint:* Extend homomorphisms from nZ into G to homomorphisms from Z into G.)
9.28 G is divisible if and only if $pG = G$ for every prime p; if G is p-primary, G is divisible if and only if $G = pG$.
9.29   Let G be a nonzero group. Prove that there exists a non-trivial homomorphism $f: G \to Q/Z$.

Definition   If G is an abelian group, dG is the subgroup of G generated by all the divisible subgroups of G.

LEMMA 9.10 dG is a divisible subgroup of G (which contains every divisible subgroup of G).

Proof   Since the parenthetical remark follows immediately from the definition of dG, we need prove only that dG is divisible. Let $n > 0$ and let $x \in dG$; then $x = x_1 + \cdots + x_k$, where each x_i is in a divisible subgroup D_i of G. Since D_i is divisible, there is an element $y_i \in D_i$ with $ny_i = x_i$. Hence, $y_1 + \cdots + y_k \in dG$ and $n(y_1 + \cdots + y_k) = x$. ∎

Definition   An abelian group G is **reduced** if $dG = 0$.

THEOREM 9.11   Every abelian group $G = dG \oplus R$, where R is reduced.

Proof   Since dG is divisible, $G = dG \oplus R$ for some subgroup R (by Corollary 9.9). If R contains a divisible group D, then $dG \oplus D$ is a divisible subgroup of G. But dG contains every divisible subgroup of G, so that $D = 0$ and R is reduced. ∎

Exercise   9.30   Let G and H be abelian groups. $G \approx H$ if and only if $dG \approx dH$ and $G/dG \approx H/dH$.

The reader should note the similarity of the roles of the subgroups tG and dG. We have seen that every abelian group is an extension (not necessarily split) of a torsion group by a torsion-free group. Now we see that every abelian group is also an extension (always split) of a divisible group by a reduced group.

LEMMA 9.12   Let G and H be divisible p-primary groups. Then $G \approx H$ if and only if $G[p] \approx H[p]$.[4]

Proof   Necessity is simple, so that we prove only sufficiency. Let $f: G[p] \to H[p]$ be an isomorphism. We may consider f as mapping $G[p] \to H$, so that the injective property implies the existence of a map $F: G \to H$ extending f; we claim that F is an isomorphism.

(i) F is one-to-one. Let x be a nonzero element of G of order p^n; we show by induction on n that if $F(x) = 0$, then $x = 0$. If $n = 1$, then $x \in G[p]$ and $F(x) = f(x)$; since f is an isomorphism, $x = 0$. Suppose now that x has order p^{n+1} and $F(x) = 0$. If we set $y = px$, then y has order p^n and $F(y) = 0$. By induction, $y = 0$, which contradicts the fact that x has order p^{n+1}.

(ii) F is onto. Let y be a nonzero element of H of order p^n; we show by induction on n that y is in the image of F. If $n = 1$, then $y \in H[p]$ so that $y \in \text{image } f \subset \text{image } F$. Suppose $p^{n+1}y = 0$ and $p^n y \neq 0$. By induction, there is an $x \in G$ with $F(x) = p^n y$. Since G is divisible, there is a $z \in G$ with $p^n z = x$. Thus, $p^n(y - F(z)) = 0$. Using induction again, there is an element $z' \in G$ with $F(z') = y - F(z)$, and so $F(z' + z) = y$. ∎

---

[4] Recall that $G[p] = \{x \in G: px = 0\}$.

THEOREM 9.13 Every divisible group D is the direct sum of copies of Q and of copies of $\sigma(p^\infty)$ (for various primes p).

Proof It is easy to check that tD is divisible, so that $D \approx tD \oplus (D/tD)$. Since D/tD is a torsion-free divisible group, it is a direct sum of copies of Q, by Corollary 9.7. Let G be the p-primary component of tD; G is divisible. If dimension $G[p]$ (as a vector space over the integers modulo p) is r, let H be the direct sum of r copies of $\sigma(p^\infty)$. Now H is a p-primary divisible group with $H[p] \approx G[p]$. By Lemma 9.12, $G \approx H$. ∎

The structure of divisible groups is not very complicated. One question yet remains: When are two divisible groups isomorphic? If D is a divisible group, let $D_\infty = D/tD$ and $D_p = (tD)[p]$; observe that D_∞ is a vector space over Q and D_p is a vector space over Z_p.

THEOREM 9.14 If D and D' are divisible groups, then $D \approx D'$ if and only if (i) D_∞ and D'_∞ have the same dimension; (ii) for each p, D_p and D'_p have the same dimension.

Proof Left to the reader. ∎

Exercises 9.31 Let G and H be divisible groups, each of which is isomorphic to a subgroup of the other. Prove that $G \approx H$. Is this true if we drop the adjective "divisible"?
9.32 If G and H are divisible and $G \oplus G \approx H \oplus H$, prove that $G \approx H$.
9.33 If T is the circle group, i.e., the reals modulo the integers, then $T \approx \coprod_p \sigma(p^\infty)$.

Free Abelian Groups

We now consider an important class of groups that is, in a certain sense, dual to the divisible groups. The reader will see properties of these groups that will remind him of several of the theorems we have just proved.

Definition F is a **free abelian group on** $\{x_k\}$ in case F is a direct sum of infinite cyclic groups Z_k, where $Z_k = [x_k]$.

THEOREM 9.15   If F is free on $\{x_k\}$, every nonzero element $x \in F$ has the unique expression

$$x = m_{k_1}x_{k_1} + \cdots + m_{k_n}x_{k_n},$$

where the m are nonzero integers and the k_i are distinct.

Proof   Exercise 9.7. ∎

THEOREM 9.16   Let

$$F = \sum_{i \in I} Z_i \quad \text{and} \quad G = \sum_{j \in J} Z_j$$

be free abelian groups. Then $F \approx G$ if and only if I and J have the same number of elements.

Proof   Imbed each Z_i in a copy of the rationals, Q_i. Thus, $F = \sum Z_i \subset \sum Q_i = V$; similarly, $G = \sum Z_j \subset \sum Q_j = W$. Now V and W are both vector spaces over Q. If $f: F \to G$ is an isomorphism, define $f^*: V \to W$ by

$$f^*(\sum q_i x_i) = \sum q_i f(x_i),$$

where $q_i \in Q$ and $[x_i] = Z_i$. It is easy to check that f^* is a (well defined) isomorphism between V and W *qua* abelian groups. By Exercise 9.21, V and W have the same dimension (as vector spaces). Since the set $\{x_i\}$ is a basis of V, I and J have the same number of elements.

Sufficiency is easy and is left to the reader. ∎

We sketch an alternative proof of Theorem 9.16. Suppose F is free on $\{x_i\}$ and p is a prime. Then F/pF is a vector space over Z_p, and $\{x_i + pF\}$ is a basis. Hence, a free set of generators of F has the same number of elements as a basis of F/pF. The proof is now completed by appealing to Exercise 9.20.

Definition   Let F be free on $\{x_i : i \in I\}$ and let G be free on $\{y_j : j \in J\}$; F and G **have the same rank** if I and J have the same number of elements. If I is finite and has n elements, we say that F has rank n.

Theorem 9.16 says that two free abelian groups F and G are isomorphic if and only if they have the same rank. In particular, if $F = G$, any two free sets of generators of F have the same number of elements. The reader will not be misled by the analogy: vector space-free abelian group; basis-free set of generators; dimension-rank. In order to stress this analogy, we make the following definition.

Definition   A **basis** of a free abelian group F is a free set of generators of F.

THEOREM 9.17   Let F be free with basis $\{x_k\}$, G an arbitrary abelian group, and $f: \{x_k\} \to G$ any function. There is a unique homomorphism $g: F \to G$ such that

$$g(x_k) = f(x_k) \qquad \text{for all } k.$$

Proof   If $Z_k = [x_k]$, we define $f_k: Z_k \to G$ by $f_k(mx_k) = mf(x_k)$. It is clear that each f_k is a homomorphism, so that the hypotheses of Exercise 9.9 are satisfied. ∎

COROLLARY 9.18   Every abelian group G is a quotient of a free abelian group.

Proof   We first show that if X is any set, there exists a free abelian group F having X as a basis. If X consists of one element x, an infinite cyclic group Zx can be constructed that has x as a generator. For the general case, set $F = \sum_{x \in X} Zx$.

To prove the corollary, let F be the free abelian group with basis G. By Theorem 9.17, the identity function on G extends to a homomorphism $g: F \to G$, and g is clearly onto. Therefore G is a quotient of F. ∎

The construction of a free abelian group on an arbitrary set X is quite convenient. For example, in one version of the Cauchy integral theorem, one wishes to integrate a holomorphic function over a finite number of curves, and these curves must be added and subtracted.

In this case, one forms the free abelian group on X, where X is the set of curves, so that addition and subtraction make sense.

THEOREM 9.19 (*The Projective Property*)   Let $\beta: B \to C$ be a homomorphism of B onto C. If F is free and $\alpha: F \to C$ is a homomorphism, then there is a homomorphism $\gamma: F \to B$ with $\beta\gamma = \alpha$, i.e., there is a γ making the adjoined diagram commute.

$$
\begin{array}{ccc}
 & F & \\
\gamma \swarrow & & \downarrow \alpha \\
B \underset{\beta}{\to} & C & \to 0
\end{array}
$$

Proof   Let $\{x_k\}$ be a basis of F. For each k, there is an element $b_k \in B$ with $\beta(b_k) = \alpha(x_k)$; this follows from the fact that β is onto. Define a function $f: \{x_k\} \to B$ by $f(x_k) = b_k$. By Theorem 9.17, there is a homomorphism $\gamma: F \to B$ such that $\gamma(x_k) = b_k$. In order to check that $\beta\gamma = \alpha$, it suffices to evaluate each on a set of generators of F, e.g., on $\{x_k\}$. But $\beta\gamma(x_k) = \beta(b_k) = \alpha(x_k)$, as desired.   ∎

COROLLARY 9.20   Let G be an abelian group and let $\beta: G \to F$ be onto, where F is free. Then

$$G = \text{kernel } \beta \oplus S,$$

where $S \approx F$.

Proof   Consider the diagram

$$
\begin{array}{ccc}
 & F & \\
 & \downarrow I & \\
G \overset{\beta}{\to} & F & \to 0,
\end{array}
$$

where I is the identity map. Since F has the projective property, there is a homomorphism $\gamma: F \to G$ with $\beta\gamma = I$. By set theory, γ is one-to-one, so that $S = \text{image } \gamma \approx F$. We let the reader prove, using Theorem 4.1, that $G = \text{kernel } \beta \oplus S$.   ∎

THEOREM 9.21   Every subgroup H of a free abelian group F is free; moreover, rank $H \leq$ rank F.

Proof   Let $\{x_k: k \in K\}$ be a basis of F. If I is a subset of the index set K, define

$$F(I) = \sum_{k \in I} [x_k].$$

Let $\mathcal{S}$ be the set of all pairs (B,I), where $I \subset K$ and $H \cap F(I)$ is free with a basis B such that $|B| \leq |I|$. Such pairs do exist: e.g., (ϕ,ϕ). Partially order $\mathcal{S}$ by defining

$$(B,I) \leq (B',I')$$

to mean $B \subset B'$ and $I \subset I'$. Since an ascending union of independent sets B is also independent, the reader may verify that the hypotheses of Zorn's lemma are satisfied. Therefore, there exists a maximal pair (B_0,I_0). We claim that $I_0 = K$, which will complete the proof (since $F(K) = F$). Suppose $I_0 \neq K$, i.e., there is an index $k \notin I_0$; let $I_0^* = \{I_0,k\}$. Then $F(I_0) \subset F(I_0^*)$ and

$$\frac{F(I_0^*) \cap H}{F(I_0) \cap H} = \frac{F(I_0^*) \cap H}{F(I_0^*) \cap H \cap F(I_0)}$$

$$\approx \frac{(F(I_0^*) \cap H) + F(I_0)}{F(I_0)} \subset \frac{F(I_0^*)}{F(I_0)}.$$

Now $F(I_0^*)/F(I_0) \approx Z$, so that the original quotient is 0 or Z (for every subgroup of Z is cyclic). If the quotient is 0, then $F(I_0^*) \cap H = F(I_0) \cap H$; therefore $(B_0,I_0^*) \in \mathcal{S}$ and is larger than the maximal pair (B_0,I_0), a contradiction. If the quotient is isomorphic to Z, then $F(I_0) \cap H$ is a direct summand of $F(I_0^*) \cap H$ and the complementary summand $L \approx Z$ (Corollary 9.20). Let $L = [b]$ and let $B_0^* = \{B_0,b\}$. The pair $(B_0^*,I_0^*) \in \mathcal{S}$ and is larger than (B_0,I_0), a contradiction. Therefore $I_0 = K$ and the theorem is proved. ∎

Exercises **9.34** An abelian group is finitely generated if and only if it is a quotient of a free abelian group of finite rank. Conclude that a direct summand of a finitely generated abelian group is also finitely generated.

9.35 Every subgroup H of a finitely generated abelian group G is itself finitely generated; if G can be generated by r elements, so can H. (We shall show later that both statements are false if we delete the adjective "abelian.")

9.36 The multiplicative group of positive rationals is a free abelian group of (countably) infinite rank. (See Exercise 1.22.)

*9.37** If F is a free abelian group of finite rank n, then $\mathrm{Aut}(F)$ is isomorphic to the multiplicative group of all $n \times n$ matrices of determinant ± 1 that have entries in Z.

*9.38   Let F be a free abelian group of rank n, and let H be a subgroup of rank $k < n$. Prove that F/H contains an element of infinite order.

9.39   An abelian group is free if and only if it has the projective property.

THEOREM 9.22   Every abelian group G can be imbedded in a divisible group.

Proof   By Corollary 9.18, there is a free abelian group F with $G \approx F/R$, for some subgroup R of F. Now $F = \sum Z$, so that $F \subset \sum Q$ (just imbed each Z in a copy of the rationals, Q). Therefore,

$$G \approx F/R \subset (\sum Q)/R,$$

and this last group is divisible, being a quotient of a divisible group. ∎

COROLLARY 9.23   An abelian group G is divisible if and only if it is a direct summand of every group containing it.

Proof   Necessity is Corollary 9.9. In order to prove sufficiency, first imbed G in a divisible group D, and then recall that every direct summand of a divisible group is divisible. ∎

There is an analogy between theorems about free abelian groups and divisible groups, which may be formalized as follows: Given a commutative diagram containing exact sequences, its *dual* is the commutative diagram containing exact sequences obtained by reversing the direction of all arrows. For example, the dual of "$0 \to A \to B$" is "$B \to A \to 0$," i.e., subgroup and quotient group are dual. We let the reader prove that "direct summand" is its own dual, sum and product are dual (see Exercises 9.9 and 9.11), and projective and injective are dual.

Finitely Generated Abelian Groups

In this section we apply our techniques to classify an important class of abelian groups. We first present some preparatory exercises.

Exercises 9.40 Every finitely generated subgroup A of Q is cyclic. (*Hint:* If A has generators $a_1/b_1, \cdots, a_n/b_n$, set $b = \Pi\, b_i$, and consider the map $f: A \to Z$ defined by $f(x) = bx$.)
9.41 If G is torsion-free and $x \in G$, define

$$\langle x \rangle = \{y \in G: my \in [x] \text{ for some } m \in Z, m \neq 0\}.$$

Prove that $\langle x \rangle$ is isomorphic to a subgroup of Q. (*Hint:* If $y \in \langle x \rangle$, then $my = nx$, where m and n are integers and $m \neq 0$.)
9.42 If G is torsion-free and $x \in G$, then $G/\langle x \rangle$ is also torsion-free.

THEOREM 9.24 (*Basis Theorem*) Every finitely generated abelian group G is a direct sum of cyclic groups.

Proof Let $G = [x_1, x_2, \cdots, x_n]$; we prove the theorem by induction on n. If $n = 1$, then G is cyclic, and we are done. Suppose $n > 1$.
Case (i) G is torsion-free. $G/\langle x_n \rangle$ is generated by $n - 1$ elements, and by Exercise 9.42, it is torsion-free. By induction, $G/\langle x_n \rangle$ is free abelian, and so, by Corollary 9.20, $G = \langle x_n \rangle \oplus$ (free abelian). Now $\langle x_n \rangle$ is finitely generated (Exercise 9.34) and a subgroup of Q (Exercise 9.41), and hence is cyclic (Exercise 9.40). Therefore, G is free abelian.
Case (ii) General case. G/tG is a finitely generated torsion-free group, so that it is free abelian, by case (i). By Corollary 9.20, $G = tG \oplus$ (free abelian). By Exercise 9.34, tG is finitely generated and torsion, so that it is finite (Exercise 4.28). By the basis theorem for finite groups, tG is a direct sum of cyclic groups. ∎

THEOREM 9.25 (*Fundamental Theorem of Finitely Generated Abelian Groups*) Every finitely generated abelian group G is the direct sum of primary and infinite cyclic groups, and the number of summands of each kind depends only on G.

Proof We know that $G \approx tG \oplus (G/tG)$. The uniqueness for tG is precisely the fundamental theorem of finite abelian groups; the uniqueness of the number of infinite cyclic summands is Theorem 9.16. ∎

We must confess that there is a proof of Theorem 9.24 which is one paragraph long (See Fuchs, *Abelian Groups*, p. 40). We have excluded that proof because it is not clear what "makes it tick," whereas our proof follows naturally from other interesting theorems we wished to present.

Torsion Groups

Torsion groups can be quite complicated, but there are two special classes of torsion groups that are quite manageable: divisible torsion groups and direct sums of cyclic groups. We shall prove that every torsion group is an extension of a direct sum of cyclics by a divisible, but our proof requires an investigation of a distinguished kind of subgroup whose definition generalizes that of direct summand. The definition is technical, so that it shall be followed by many exercises that will familiarize the reader with the concept.

Definition   A subgroup S of G is **pure in** G in case

$$nG \cap S = nS$$

for every integer n.

It is always true that $nG \cap S \supset nS$, so that it is only the reverse inclusion that is significant. Therefore, purity says that whenever $s = ng$ (where $s \in S$ and $g \in G$), there is an element $s' \in S$ with $s = ns'$. In other words, if an element of S is divisible by n in the big group, it is also divisible by n in the subgroup S.

If $G = [x]$ is infinite cyclic and if $S = [2x]$, then S is not pure, for $s = 2x$ is divisible by 2 in G, but there is no element y *in* S with $2y = 2x$.

Exercises   9.43   Any direct summand of G is pure in G.

9.44   If G/S is torsion-free, then S is pure; conclude that tG is a pure subgroup of G. Conclude further that a pure subgroup need not be a direct summand.

9.45   If G is torsion-free, a subgroup S of G is pure if and only if G/S is torsion-free.

9.46   Purity is transitive, i.e., if K is pure in H and H is pure in G, then K is pure in G.

9.47   If G is torsion-free, any intersection of pure subgroups is pure. Conclude that if X is a subset of G (where G is torsion-free), then there is a smallest pure subgroup of G containing X; we denote this subgroup $\langle X \rangle$ and call it the **pure subgroup of** G **generated by** X.

9.48 Let $x \in G$, where G is torsion-free. Show that the pure subgroup generated by x is

$$\{y \in G \colon my \in [x] \text{ for some } m \neq 0\} ;$$

(compare Exercise 9.41).

9.49 A pure subgroup of a divisible group is divisible.

9.50 Give examples of a group in which the intersection of two pure subgroups is not pure; in which the subgroup generated by two pure subgroups is not pure.

9.51 The ascending union of pure subgroups is pure, i.e., if $S_1 \subset S_2 \subset \cdots$ are pure subgroups of G, so is $\bigcup S_n$.

9.52 Show that the ascending union of direct summands need not be a direct summand. (*Hint:* Consider the group $G = \Pi \, \sigma(p)$, and let $S_n = \sigma(p_1) \oplus \cdots \oplus \sigma(p_n)$.)

9.53 Let S be pure in G, and let $y \in G/S$. Show that y can be lifted to $x \in G$, where x and y have the same order.

LEMMA 9.26 Let T be pure in G. If $T \subset S \subset G$ and S/T is pure in G/T, then S is pure in G.

Proof If $x \in G$, we shall denote its coset in G/T by $\bar{x}$. Suppose that $ng = s$, where $s \in S$. Then $n\bar{g} = \bar{s}$, so that the purity of S/T guarantees an element $\bar{s}' \in S/T$ with $n\bar{s}' = \bar{s}$. Lifting this equation to G gives

$$ns' - s = t,$$

for some $t \in T$. Hence $ns' - ng = t$, so that the purity of T yields $t' \in T$ with $ns' - ng = nt'$. Juggling, we obtain $s = n(s' - t')$; since $T \subset S$, $s' - t' \in S$, and so S is pure in G. ∎

LEMMA 9.27 A p-primary group G which is not divisible contains a pure cyclic subgroup.

Proof Suppose there is an $x \in G[p]$ which is divisible by p^k but not by p^{k+1}; let $p^k y = x$. We let the reader prove that $[y]$ is pure in G; (Exercise 9.12 says that one need only check powers of p).

We may, therefore, assume that each $x \in G[p]$ is divisible by every power of p. We shall prove, by induction on k, that if $p^k x = 0$, then x is divisible by p. If $k = 1$, $x \in G[p]$, and our claim is certainly true. Suppose $p^{k+1}x = 0$. If $y = p^k x$, then $y \in G[p]$; hence, there is an element $z \in G$ with

$$p^{k+1}z = y = p^k x.$$

Thus $p^k(pz - x) = 0$ so that, by induction, there is a $w \in G$ with $pw = pz - x$. Therefore

$$x = p(z - w),$$

as desired. We have shown that $G = pG$, so that G is divisible, by Exercise 9.28. This contradiction completes the proof. ∎

Definition   A subset X of nonzero elements of a group G is **independent** in case $\sum m_\alpha x_\alpha = 0$ implies each $m_\alpha x_\alpha = 0$, where $x_\alpha \in X$ and $m_\alpha \in Z$.

Our earlier definition of independence (in a vector space) had the m_α scalars in a field, but more important, the conclusion there was that each $m_\alpha = 0$; here we pay our respects to the elements of finite order and conclude only that each $m_\alpha x_\alpha = 0$.

LEMMA 9.28   A set X of nonzero elements of G is independent if and only if

$$[X] = \sum_{x \in X} [x].$$

Proof   Let $x_0 \in X$, and let $y \in [x_0] \cap [X - \{x_0\}]$. Then $y = mx_0$ and $y = \sum m_\alpha x_\alpha$, where each $x_\alpha \neq x_0$. Therefore,

$$-mx_0 + \sum m_\alpha x_\alpha = 0,$$

so that each term is 0, by independence. Hence, $0 = mx_0 = y$.
The proof of the converse is left to the reader. ∎

Definition   A subset X of G is **pure-independent** if X is independent and $[X]$ is a pure subgroup of G.

LEMMA 9.29   Let G be a p-primary group. If X is a maximal pure-independent subset of G (i.e., X is contained in no larger such), then $G/[X]$ is divisible.

Proof   By Lemma 9.27, if $G/[X]$ is not divisible, it contains a pure cyclic subgroup $[\bar{y}]$. Since $[X]$ is pure in G, $\bar{y}$ may be lifted to an element $y \in G$, where y and $\bar{y}$ have the same order (Exercise 9.53). We claim that $X^* = \{X, y\}$ is pure-independent, which will contradict the maximality of X. First of all,

$$[X] \subset [X^*] \subset G$$

and $[X^*]/[X] = [\bar{y}]$, which is pure in $G/[X]$. By Lemma 9.26, $[X^*]$ is pure in G. Secondly, suppose

$$my + \sum m_\alpha x_\alpha = 0, \quad x_\alpha \in X, \quad m_\alpha, m \in Z.$$

In $G/[X]$, this equation becomes $m\bar{y} = 0$. Since y and $\bar{y}$ have the same order, $my = 0$; since X is independent, each $m_\alpha x_\alpha = 0$. Hence, X^* is independent, and so it is pure-independent. ∎

Definition   Let G be a torsion group. A subgroup B of G is a **basic subgroup** of G in case:
   (i) B is a direct sum of cyclic groups.
   (ii) B is pure in G.
   (iii) G/B is divisible.

THEOREM 9.30 (*Kulikov*)   Every torsion group G contains a basic subgroup.

Proof   If we show that every p-primary group has a basic subgroup, then it follows from the primary decomposition that every torsion group has a basic subgroup. Assume, therefore, that G is p-primary.
   If G is divisible, then $B = 0$ is a basic subgroup. If G is not divisible, then G does contain pure-independent subsets (Lemma 9.27). Since both purity and independence are preserved by ascending unions, so is pure-independence. Therefore, Zorn's lemma may be applied to provide a maximal pure-independent subset X of G. The previous two lemmas show that $B = [X]$ is a basic subgroup. ∎

   It is known that a torsion group G may possess many basic subgroups, but any two of them are isomorphic.

COROLLARY 9.31   Every torsion group is an extension of a direct sum of cyclic groups by a divisible group.

COROLLARY 9.32 (*Prüfer*)   Let G be a group of bounded order, i.e., $nG = 0$ for some integer $n > 0$. Then G is a direct sum of cyclic groups.

Proof[5]   Let B be a basic subgroup of G. Then G/B is divisible, and $n(G/B) = 0$. It follows that $G/B = 0$, i.e., $B = G$. ∎

Exercise   9.54   Exhibit an extension of a direct sum of cyclic groups by a divisible group that does not split.

We have already classified divisible groups. If we can classify direct sums of cyclic groups, then we have classified all torsion groups modulo the extension problem. The question we ask is: If G and H are each direct sums of cyclic groups, when is $G \approx H$? The answer is essentially the same as that for finite groups given in Chapter 4.

Definition   If G is p-primary, consider the vector spaces over Z_p:

$$G\{n\} = \frac{p^n G \cap G[p]}{p^{n+1} G \cap G[p]}.$$

If G and H are p-primary groups, G and H **have the same Ulm invariants** if, for each $n \geq 0$, $G\{n\}$ and $H\{n\}$ have the same dimension.

THEOREM 9.33   Let G be a p-primary group that is a direct sum of cyclic groups. The number of summands of G isomorphic to $\sigma(p^{n+1})$ is the dimension of $G\{n\}$.[6] Moreover, if G and H are each p-primary and direct sums of cyclic groups, then $G \approx H$ if and only if G and H have the same Ulm invariants.

Proof   The direct translations of the proofs of Theorems 4.7 and 4.8 are left to the reader. ∎

Exercise   9.55   Prove that $t\left(\prod\limits_{n=1}^{\infty} \sigma(p^n)\right)$ is not a direct sum of cyclic groups.

---

[5] An alternative proof is outlined in Exercise 9.18.

[6] The reader should be able to phrase this sentence so that it says that two sets have the same number of elements.

There is one instance when one can guarantee that a pure subgroup is a direct summand.

THEOREM 9.34 Let S be a pure subgroup of G with $nS = 0$ for some $n > 0$; then S is a direct summand of G.

Proof Let $\pi: G \rightarrow G/(S + nG)$ be the natural map. Clearly, this quotient is of bounded order (n times it is 0), so that it is a direct sum of cyclic groups, by Prüfer's theorem (Corollary 9.32). Let $G/(S + nG) = \sum \sigma(r_\alpha)$, where $\bar{x}_\alpha$ is a generator of $\sigma(r_\alpha)$. For each α, lift $\bar{x}_\alpha$ to $x_\alpha \in G$. Then $r_\alpha x_\alpha \in S + nG$, and so

$$r_\alpha x_\alpha = s_\alpha + nh_\alpha,$$

where $s_\alpha \in S$ and $h_\alpha \in G$. Now r_α divides n, so that

$$s_\alpha = r_\alpha \left(\frac{n}{r_\alpha} h_\alpha - x_\alpha \right).$$

Since S is pure, there is an element $s'_\alpha \in S$ with $s_\alpha = r_\alpha s'_\alpha$. Set

$$y_\alpha = x_\alpha - s'_\alpha.$$

We have lifted and adjusted so that $r_\alpha y_\alpha = nh_\alpha$ and $\pi(y_\alpha) = \bar{x}_\alpha$. Let $K = [nG$, the $y_\alpha]$; we claim that $G = S \oplus K$.

(i) $S \cap K = \{0\}$. Let $x \in S \cap K$. Since $x \in K$, $x = \sum m_\alpha y_\alpha + nh$; since $x \in S$, $\pi(x) = 0$. Hence, $0 = \sum m_\alpha \bar{x}_\alpha$, so that r_α divides m_α for each α. But we know that $r_\alpha y_\alpha \in nG$, so that surely $m_\alpha y_\alpha \in nG$. Therefore, $x = \sum m_\alpha y_\alpha + nh \in nG$; since S is pure, there is an element $s' \in S$ with $x = ns'$. But $nS = 0$, so that $0 = ns' = x$.

(ii) $S + K = G$. If $g \in G$, then $\pi(g) = \sum m_\alpha \bar{x}_\alpha$. Since $\pi(\sum m_\alpha y_\alpha) = \sum m_\alpha \bar{x}_\alpha$, $g - \sum m_\alpha y_\alpha = s + nh \in S + nG$. Therefore, $g = s + (nh + \sum m_\alpha y_\alpha) \in S + K$. $\blacksquare$

COROLLARY 9.35 If tG is of bounded order, then tG is a direct summand of G. In particular, tG is a direct summand if it is finite.

COROLLARY 9.36 An indecomposable abelian group G is either torsion or torsion-free.

Proof   Let us suppose that G is an indecomposable group that is neither torsion nor torsion-free, i.e., tG is a proper subgroup of G. Now tG is not divisible, lest it be a summand, and so tG contains a pure cyclic subgroup σ, by Lemma 9.27. It follows from Theorem 9.34 that σ is a summand of G, a contradiction. $\blacksquare$

Exercises   9.56   Exhibit a group G that is not a direct sum of (possibly infinitely many) indecomposable groups.

     9.57   A torsion group G is indecomposable if and only if G is primary and cyclic or $G \approx \sigma(p^\infty)$ for some prime p.

     9.58 (*Kaplansky*)   In the following, G is an infinite abelian group.
  (a) If every proper subgroup of G is finite, then $G \approx \sigma(p^\infty)$ for some p;
  (b) If G is isomorphic to every proper subgroup, then $G \approx Z$;
  (c) If G is isomorphic to every proper quotient, then $G \approx \sigma(p^\infty)$ for some p;
  (d) If every proper quotient of G is finite, then $G \approx Z$.

A complete classification of all *countable* torsion groups exists; it is due to Ulm and Zippin. The proof presupposes a knowledge of ordinal and cardinal numbers, so that we refer the interested reader to Kaplansky's monograph, *Infinite Abelian Groups* (see Bibliography), for details. The reader will also find there a necessary and sufficient condition (due to Kulikov) that a torsion group be a direct sum of cyclic groups.

Torsion-Free Groups

We close this chapter with the classification of a restricted class of torsion-free groups: those of rank 1. At present, there is not even an adequate classification of the groups of finite rank, although it is known that counterexamples to almost every conjecture about direct sums can be found among these groups. We refer the reader to the book of Fuchs, *Abelian Groups* (see Bibliography), for further information.

When we restrict our attention to torsion-free groups, our two previous definitions of independence are equivalent, for $mx = 0$ if and only if $m = 0$ or $x = 0$.

Definition   The **rank** of a torsion-free group G is the number of elements in a maximal independent subset of G.

Observe that a free abelian group is torsion-free, and our two notions of rank coincide for these groups.

Exercises   9.59   Every torsion-free group G can be imbedded in a vector space V over Q. (*Hint:* First imbed G in a divisible group D and then consider the natural map $D \to D/tD$.)

9.60   A torsion-free group G has rank at most r if and only if G can be imbedded in an r-dimensional vector space over Q. Conclude that rank is well defined in the sense that any two maximal independent subsets of G have the same number of elements.

9.61   Let

$$0 \to A \to B \to C \to 0$$

be an exact sequence of torsion-free groups. Then

$$\text{rank } A + \text{rank } C = \text{rank } B.$$

Conclude that any torsion-free group of rank 1 is indecomposable.

Our starting point in examining the groups of rank 1 is that each of them is isomorphic to a subgroup of Q (Exercise 9.60). Let us first present three nonisomorphic subgroups of Q.

G_1:   All rationals whose denominator is square-free.
G_2:   All **dyadic rationals,** i.e., all rationals of the form $m/2^k$.
G_3:   All rationals whose decimal expansion is finite.

It is instructive to prove that no two of the groups G_1, G_2, G_3, Z, Q are isomorphic.

A perceptive observation is that each of these groups can be described by the numbers that are allowed to be denominators. (G_3 may be alternatively described as those rationals whose denominators are restricted to be powers of 10.)

Let $p_1, p_2, \cdots, p_n, \cdots$ be the sequence of primes.

Definition   A **characteristic** is a sequence

$$(k_1, k_2, \cdots, k_n, \cdots)$$

where each k_n is a nonnegative integer or the symbol ∞.

If G is a subgroup of Q, and if $x \in G$ is nonzero, then x determines a characteristic in the following way: What is the highest power of p_n that divides x in G? That is, for which nonnegative integers k is there an element $y \in G$ satisfying

$$p_n^k y = x?$$

If there is a largest such exponent k, we call it k_n; if there is no largest such exponent, we set $k_n = \infty$.[7]

It is convenient to write each nonzero integer as a formal infinite product $\Pi p_i^{\alpha_i}$, where the p_i range over all the primes and $\alpha_i \geq 0$; (of course almost all the $\alpha_i = 0$). Let $m = \Pi p_i^{\alpha_i}$ and $n = \Pi p_i^{\beta_i}$ be given integers. If $a \in G$ has characteristic $(k_1, k_2, \cdots)$, then the definition of characteristic says that there is an $x \in G$ satisfying $mx = na$ if and only if $\alpha_i \leq k_i + \beta_i$ for all i (by convention, $\infty + \beta_i = \infty$).

Each of the five groups of rank 1 exhibited above contains $x = 1$. Its characteristic in each group is

Z: $(0, 0, 0, \cdots)$;
Q: $(\infty, \infty, \infty, \cdots)$;
G_1: $(1, 1, 1, \cdots)$;
G_2: $(\infty, 0, 0, \cdots)$;
G_3: $(\infty, 0, \infty, 0, 0, 0, \cdots)$.

Unfortunately, distinct nonzero elements of the same group G may give rise to distinct characteristics. For example, if $G = G_2 = $ dyadic rationals, the characteristic of 1 is

$$(\infty, 0, 0, \cdots)$$

while the characteristic of $126 = 2 \cdot 3^2 \cdot 7$ is

$$(\infty, 2, 0, 1, 0, 0, \cdots).$$

We are led to the following definition.

Definition   Two characteristics are **equivalent** if
   (i)   they have ∞ in the same coordinates;
   (ii)   they differ in at most a finite number of coordinates.

[7] k_n is called the p_n-**height** of x.

It is easy to check that this is an equivalence relation; an equivalence class of characteristics is called a **type.**

LEMMA 9.37   Let G be a subgroup of Q, and let x and x' be nonzero elements of G. Then the characteristics of x and of x' are equivalent.

Proof   First of all, if $x' = mx$ for some integer m, then the characteristics of x and of x' are equivalent: x' is divisible by any power of p_i that divides x (plus only a few more); x' is divisible by every power of p_i if and only if x is.

Let us now pass to the general case. Since G is a subgroup of Q, there are integers m and n such that

$$mx = nx'.$$

The characteristic of x is equivalent to that of $mx = nx'$, which is equivalent to that of x'. $\blacksquare$

As a result of this lemma, if G is a group of rank 1 (i.e., a subgroup of Q), we may define the **type** of G, $\tau(G)$, as the type of a nonzero element of G.

THEOREM 9.38   Let G and G' be torsion-free groups of rank 1. Then $G \approx G'$ if and only if $\tau(G) = \tau(G')$.

Proof   Suppose $f \colon G \to G'$ is an isomorphism. If $x \in G$ is nonzero, then one verifies easily that x and $f(x)$ have the same characteristic. Therefore, $\tau(G) = \tau(G')$.

Assume that $\tau(G) = \tau(G')$ and (without loss of generality) that G and G' are subgroups of Q. If a and a' are nonzero elements of G and G', respectively, then their characteristics $(k_1, k_2, \cdots)$ and $(k_1', k_2', \cdots)$ differ in only a finite number of places. If we agree that the notation $\infty - \infty$ means 0, then we may define a rational number λ by

$$\lambda = \Pi\, p_i^{k_i - k_i'}$$

It follows from the definition of equivalence and our convention concerning ∞ that almost all the $k_i - k_i' = 0$.

Define $f \colon G \to Q$ by $f(x) = \mu x$, where $\mu = \lambda a'/a$. Note that distributivity implies that f is a homomorphism. Now a rational x is in G if and only if there are integers $m = \Pi p_i^{\alpha_i}$ and $n = \Pi p_i^{\beta_i}$ with $mx = na$ and $\alpha_i \le \beta_i + k_i$ for all i; a rational y is in G' if and only if there are integers m and n with $my = na'$ and $\alpha_i \le \beta_i + k'_i$, for all i. We claim that image $f \subset G'$. If $x \in G$, then $mx = na$ and $\alpha_i \le \beta_i + k_i$; hence, $m(\mu x) = n\mu a = (n\lambda)a'$. Since $\alpha_i \le (\beta_i + k_i - k'_i) + k'_i$, it follows that $\mu x = f(x) \in G'$. In a similar manner, the reader may see that if $g: G' \to Q$ is defined by $g(x') = \mu^{-1} x'$, then image $g \subset G$. Therefore, f and g are inverse, and $G \approx G'$. ∎

THEOREM 9.39   If τ is a type, then there exists a group G of rank 1 with $\tau(G) = \tau$.

Proof   Let $(k_1, k_2, \cdots, k_n, \cdots)$ be a characteristic in τ. We define a group G as the subgroup of Q generated by all rationals of the form $1/m$, where, for all n, p_n^t divides m if and only if $t \le k_n$. It is easy to check that G is a group of rank 1 and that the element 1 in G has the given characteristic. ∎

Exercises   9.62   If G is a subring of Q, then G is also a torsion-free additive group of rank 1. Prove that the characteristic of 1 in G has only 0 and ∞ as entries.

9.63   Prove that two distinct subrings of Q are not isomorphic as additive groups.

*9.64   There are uncountably many nonisomorphic subgroups of Q.

*9.65   If G is any abelian group, the set of all endomorphisms of G is a ring if we define multiplication as composition and addition by $(f + g)(x) = f(x) + g(x)$.

If G is torsion-free of rank 1, prove that the endomorphism ring of G is isomorphic to a subring of Q. (*Hint:* Use the injective property of Q.)

*9.66   Give an example of two nonisomorphic groups having isomorphic endomorphism rings.

9.67   Let G and H be torsion-free of rank 1. If there are nonzero elements $x \in G$ and $y \in H$ with $G/[x] \approx H/[y]$, prove that $G \approx H$. What is the relation between $G/[x]$ and the characteristic of x?

Every theorem in this chapter may be generalized for modules over principal ideal domains; they may be then interpreted as an analysis of linear transformations operating on infinite-dimensional spaces.

Chapter 10

Homological Algebra

The Hom Functors

In Chapter 1 we raised the twin questions of describing groups and describing homomorphisms, but our emphasis to this point has been upon groups. In this chapter we focus upon homomorphisms with the ultimate goal of computing some groups of extensions. We restrict ourselves here to abelian groups, but the reader should regard this study as an introduction to the more general theory that includes $H^2_\theta(Q,K)$ and the Schur-Zassenhaus lemma (Theorem 7.15).

For the remainder of this chapter, *group* means abelian group.

The fundamental abstraction we need is that of a functor, which we define at once. Let α be the class of all abelian groups; if $A \in \alpha$, we write $1:A$ for the identity map on A.

Definition   A function $T: \alpha \to \alpha$ is a **covariant** (additive) **functor** if, whenever $\alpha: A \to B$ is a homomorphism, there is a homomorphism $T(\alpha): T(A) \to T(B)$ such that:

(a) $T(1:A) = 1:T(A)$.
(b) $T(\beta\alpha) = T(\beta)T(\alpha)$ (where $\beta: B \to C$).
(c) $T(\alpha + \gamma) = T(\alpha) + T(\gamma)$ (where $\gamma: A \to B$).

The following construction gives an important example of a covariant functor.

Definition   Let G be a fixed group. Define a function $T: \alpha \to \alpha$ by $T(A) = \mathrm{Hom}(G,A)$, the group of all homomorphisms of G into A under the binary operation

$$(f + g)(x) = f(x) + g(x).$$

If $\alpha: A \to B$, we define $T(\alpha): T(A) \to T(B)$ as follows: If $f \in T(A) =$ Hom(G,A), then $f: G \to A$; define $T(\alpha)(f) = \alpha f: G \to B$.

THEOREM 10.1 If G is a group, then $T =$ Hom$(G, \ )$ is a covariant functor.

Proof The verifications of the axioms are automatic. ▮

Definition A function $T: \mathcal{Q} \to \mathcal{Q}$ is a **contravariant** (additive) **functor** if, whenever $\alpha: A \to B$ is a homomorphism, there is a homomorphism $T(\alpha): T(B) \to T(A)$ such that:

(a) $T(1:A) = 1: T(A)$.
(b) $T(\beta\alpha) = T(\alpha)T(\beta)$ (where $\beta: B \to C$).
(c) $T(\alpha + \gamma) = T(\alpha) + T(\gamma)$ (where $\gamma: A \to B$).

Observe that the main difference between covariant and contravariant functors is that the latter changes the direction of arrows.

THEOREM 10.2 If K is a group, then $S =$ Hom$(\ ,K)$ is a contravariant functor.

Proof If $A \in \mathcal{Q}$, define $S(A) =$ Hom(A,K). If $\alpha: A \to B$, define $S(\alpha):$ Hom$(B,K) \to$ Hom(A,K) by $S(\alpha)(g) = g\alpha$, where $g: B \to K$. The remaining details are left to the reader. ▮

We now have examples of functors of either variance; if we use the term *functor* without a modifier, then what we say is to be true for every functor, contra or co.

Exercises 10.1 The identity functor $J: \mathcal{Q} \to \mathcal{Q}$, defined by $J(A) = A$ and $J(\alpha) = \alpha$, is a covariant functor.
  10.2 The **zero map** $\alpha: A \to B$ is the homomorphism defined by $\alpha(x) = 0$ for all $x \in A$. If T is a functor, then $T(\alpha) = 0$ for every zero map α, and $T(0) = 0$, where 0 is the zero group. (*Hint:* Use additivity.)

10.3 If $\alpha: A \to B$ is an isomorphism and T is a functor, then $T(\alpha)$ is an isomorphism.

10.4 Which of the following are functors?

(a) $T(G) = tG$ and $T(f) = f|tG$.

(b) $T(G) = dG$ and $T(f) = f|dG$.

(c) $T(G) = G \oplus A$ (where A is fixed) and $T(f) = f \oplus 1:A$.

(d) $T(G) = G \oplus G$ and $T(f) = f \oplus f$.

10.5 Let $A_1, A_2, \cdots, A_n$ be a finite set of groups, and let T be a functor; prove that $T(\sum A_k) \approx \sum T(A_k)$. (*Hint:* Use Exercise 4.9.) (We shall soon see that this is false if we delete the adjective "finite.")

Definition A **short exact sequence** is an exact sequence of the form:

(*) $$0 \to A \xrightarrow{\alpha} B \xrightarrow{\beta} C \to 0;$$

(*) is **split** in case there is a map $\gamma: B \to A$ with $\gamma\alpha = 1:A$.

Exercises (contd.) 10.6 The short exact sequence (*) is split if and only if there is a map $\delta: C \to B$ with $\beta\delta = 1:C$.

10.7 If the short exact sequence (*) is split, then $B \approx A \oplus C$, and B is a split extension.

10.8 If T is a covariant functor and (*) is split, then $0 \to T(A) \to T(B) \to T(C) \to 0$ is a split short exact sequence (similarly for contravariant functors).

Definition A covariant functor T is **left exact** in case

(*) $$0 \to A \xrightarrow{\alpha} B \xrightarrow{\beta} C \to 0$$

exact implies exactness of

$$0 \to T(A) \to T(B) \to T(C);$$

a contravariant functor T is **left exact** in case exactness of (*) implies exactness of

$$0 \to T(C) \to T(B) \to T(A).$$

THEOREM 10.3 $S = \text{Hom}(\ ,K)$ is a left exact functor.

Proof   Let $A \xrightarrow{\alpha} B \xrightarrow{\beta} C \to 0$ be exact. Since S is contravariant, we get the sequence

$$0 \longrightarrow S(C) \xrightarrow{S(\beta)} S(B) \xrightarrow{S(\alpha)} S(A)$$

i.e.,

$$0 \longrightarrow \text{Hom}(C,K) \xrightarrow{S(\beta)} \text{Hom}(B,K) \xrightarrow{S(\alpha)} \text{Hom}(A,K),$$

which we claim is exact. It must be shown that $S(\beta)$ is one-to-one and that image $S(\beta) = $ kernel $S(\alpha)$.

(i)   Kernel $S(\beta) = 0$. Suppose $f: C \to K$ and $S(\beta)f = 0$, i.e., $f\beta = 0$. Then f annihilates image $\beta = C$, since β is onto, and so $f = 0$.

(ii)   Image $S(\beta) \subset$ kernel $S(\alpha)$. If $f: C \to K$, then $S(\alpha)S(\beta)(f) = S(\alpha)(f\beta) = f(\beta\alpha) = 0$, since $\beta\alpha = 0$.

(iii)   Kernel $S(\alpha) \subset$ image $S(\beta)$. Suppose $S(\alpha)(g) = 0$, where $g: B \to K$; thus $g\alpha = 0$. Define $g_\#: C \to K$ by $g_\#(c) = g(b)$ where $\beta(b) = c$. Now $g_\#$ is well defined, for if $\beta(b') = c$, then $b - b' \in$ kernel $\beta = $ image α, so that $b - b' = \alpha(a)$ for some $a \in A$. Therefore $g(b - b') = g\alpha(a) = 0$, so that $g(b) = g(b')$ and $g_\#$ is well defined. But $S(\beta)(g_\#) = g_\#\beta = g$, for if $b \in B$ and $c = \beta(b)$, then $g_\#\beta(b) = g_\#(c) = g(b)$. ∎

THEOREM 10.4 $T = \text{Hom}(G, \ )$ is a left exact functor.

Proof   Similar to the proof given above. ∎

The answer to the question of when "$\to 0$" can be tagged on the end of the functored sequence is given below.

THEOREM 10.5   A group G is free if and only if, whenever $0 \to A \xrightarrow{\alpha} B \xrightarrow{\beta} C \to 0$ is exact, the sequence

$$0 \longrightarrow \text{Hom}(G,A) \xrightarrow{T(\alpha)} \text{Hom}(G,B) \xrightarrow{T(\beta)} \text{Hom}(G,C) \longrightarrow 0$$

is exact.

Proof   Note that the critical assumption is that $T(\beta)$ is onto. Suppose G is free; consider the diagram above, where $f \in \text{Hom}(G,C)$. By Theorem 9.19, G has the projective property, so that there is a map $g: G \to B$ with $\beta g = f$. But $\beta g = T(\beta)(g)$, so that $f \in \text{image } T(\beta)$, as desired.

If $T(\beta)$ is onto, then every $f: G \to C$ is of the form $T(\beta)(g)$ for some $g \in \text{Hom}(G,B)$, i.e., $f = g\beta$. Since we are assuming $T(\beta)$ is onto for every exact sequence $A \to B \to C \to 0$, G has the projective property. Therefore, G is free, by Exercise 9.39. ∎

THEOREM 10.6   A group K is divisible if and only if whenever $0 \to A \xrightarrow{\alpha} B \xrightarrow{\beta} C \to 0$ is exact, the sequence

$$0 \to \text{Hom}(C,K) \to \text{Hom}(B,K) \to \text{Hom}(A,K) \to 0$$

is exact.

Proof   Left to the reader. ∎

THEOREM 10.7   Let $\{A_j\}$ be a family of groups; for any group K,

$$\text{Hom}(\textstyle\sum A_j, K) \approx \Pi \text{Hom}(A_j, K).$$

Proof   For each j, let $i_j: A_j \to \sum A_j$ be the inclusion. Define a map $\theta: \text{Hom}(\sum A_j, K) \to \Pi \text{Hom}(A_j, K)$ by $f \to \langle fi_j \rangle$. Define a map ψ in the reverse direction by $\langle f_j \rangle \to f$, where f is the unique map of $\sum A_j$ into K (Exercise 9.9) such that $fi_j = f_j$ for all j. A mechanical check shows that θ and ψ are inverse. ∎

We now have an example of a functor that does not preserve infinite direct sums.

THEOREM 10.8   Let $\{A_j\}$ be a family of groups; for any group G,

$$\text{Hom}(G, \Pi A_j) \approx \Pi \text{Hom}(G, A_j).$$

Proof   For each j, let $p_j: \Pi A_j \to A_j$ be the jth projection. An argument dual to the argument given above, using Exercise 9.11, shows that $\theta: \text{Hom}(G, \Pi A_j) \to \Pi \text{Hom}(G, A_j)$, defined by $f \to \langle p_j f \rangle$, is an isomorphism. ∎

THEOREM 10.9   Let $\mu: A \to A$ be multiplication by m, i.e., $\mu(a) = ma$ for all $a \in A$. If T is a functor, then $T(\mu): T(A) \to T(A)$ is also multiplication by m.

Proof   If we let $\alpha = 1:A$, then $\mu = \alpha + \cdots + \alpha$ (m times). Since T is a functor, $T(\mu) = T(\alpha) + \cdots + T(\alpha)$ (m times), and $T(\alpha) = T(1:A) = 1:T(A)$. Therefore, $T(\mu)$ is also multiplication by m. ∎

We now present some sample computations to illustrate how these theorems may be used.

Examples   1   For any group G, $\mathrm{Hom}(G,Q)$ is a vector space over Q.

A group H is torsion-free if and only if every nonzero multiplication $\mu: H \to H$ is one-to-one; a group H is divisible if and only if every nonzero multiplication $\mu: H \to H$ is onto. Thus, a group is torsion-free and divisible, i.e., a vector space over Q, if and only if every nonzero multiplication is an automorphism.

If $\mu: Q \to Q$ is multiplication by $m \neq 0$, then μ is an isomorphism. If T is the functor $\mathrm{Hom}(G, \ )$, then $T(\mu)$ is an isomorphism (Exercise 10.3) which is also multiplication by m. Therefore, $T(G) = \mathrm{Hom}(G,Q)$ is torsion-free and divisible and hence is a vector space over Q.

2   For any group G, $\mathrm{Hom}(Z,G) \approx G$.
The map $\theta: \mathrm{Hom}(Z,G) \to G$, defined by $f \to f(1)$, is an isomorphism.

3   For any group G, $\mathrm{Hom}(\sigma(n),G) \approx G[n]$.
Consider the exact sequence

$$0 \to Z \xrightarrow{\mu} Z \to \sigma(n) \to 0$$

where μ is multiplication by n. If we apply the functor $S = \mathrm{Hom}(\ ,G)$ to this sequence, then we obtain the exact sequence

$$0 \longrightarrow \mathrm{Hom}(\sigma(n),G) \to \mathrm{Hom}(Z,G) \xrightarrow{S(\mu)} \mathrm{Hom}(Z,G),$$

so that $\mathrm{Hom}(\sigma(n),G) = \mathrm{kernel}\ S(\mu)$. Since $\mathrm{Hom}(Z,G) \approx G$ and $S(\mu)$ is multiplication by n, $\mathrm{Hom}(\sigma(n),G) \approx G[n]$.

4   For any group G, let $G^* = \mathrm{Hom}(G,T)$, where T is the circle group. G^* is called the **character group** of G. If

$$0 \to A \to B \to C \to 0$$

is exact, then so is

$$0 \to C^* \to B^* \to A^* \to 0.$$

We are applying the functor $\text{Hom}(\ ,T)$, and T is a divisible group. Exactness of the sequence of character groups thus follows from Theorem 10.6.

Exercises   10.9   Show that $\text{Hom}(A,B) = 0$ in each of the following cases:
(a) A is torsion, B is torsion-free.
(b) A is divisible, B is reduced.
(c) A is p-primary, B is q-primary, $p \neq q$.
10.10   Prove that $\text{Hom}(G,T) = 0$ if and only if $G = 0$.
10.11   If G is finite, prove that $G \approx G^*$, where G^* is the character group of G.
*10.12   If S is a subgroup of the finite group G, set

$$S^\circ = \{f \in G^* : f(s) = 0 \qquad \text{for all } s \in S\}.$$

Prove that S° is a subgroup of G^*, and that $S^\circ \approx (G/S)^*$.
*10.13   Let G be finite of order n, and let k divide n. Prove that G has the same number of subgroups of order k as of subgroups of index k. (*Hint:* Prove that $S \to S^\circ$ is a one-to-one correspondence.)
10.14   Use character groups to give an alternative proof of Exercise 4.24.
10.15   We now present counterexamples showing that Theorems 10.7 and 10.8 cannot be extended. Let p_i denote the ith prime.
(a)   If $A_i = \sigma(p_i)$, then $\text{Hom}(\Pi A_i, Q) \neq 0$, but for each i, $\text{Hom}(A_i, Q) = 0$. Conclude that $\text{Hom}(\Pi A_i, Q)$ is isomorphic to neither $\Pi \text{Hom}(A_i, Q)$ nor $\sum \text{Hom}(A_i, Q)$.
(b)   Let $A_i = \sigma(p_i)$ and $G = \sum A_i$. Then $\text{Hom}(G, \sum A_i) \approx \Pi \text{Hom}(A_j, \sum A_i) \approx \Pi (\sum A_i)[p_j]$ (by Example 3) $\approx \Pi A_j$. On the other hand, $\text{Hom}(G, A_i) \approx \text{Hom}(A_i, A_i) \approx A_i$, so that $\sum \text{Hom}(G, A_i) \approx \sum A_i$. Conclude that $\text{Hom}(G, \sum A_i)$ and $\sum \text{Hom}(G, A_i)$ are not isomorphic.
(c)   If $G = Z$ and $A_i = \sigma(p_i)$, show that $\text{Hom}(G, \sum A_i)$ and $\Pi \text{Hom}(G, A_i)$ are not isomorphic.

Definition of Ext

We wish to consider all abelian extensions B of a group A by a group C, and so we recall the following definition from Chapter 7.

Definition   An **(abelian) factor set** is a function $f: C \times C \to A$ such that, for all $x, y, z \in C$:

(i) $f(y,z) - f(x + y,z) + f(x,y + z) - f(x,y) = 0$;
(ii) $f(0,y) = 0 = f(x,0)$;
(iii) $f(x,y) = f(y,x)$.

The main reason we used both additive and multiplicative notations in our previous discussion of extensions was that then the quotient could operate nontrivially on the kernel: If $c \in C$, ca was a convenient notation for the element $l(c) + a - l(c)$. Since we are now considering only abelian extensions, as is ensured by condition (iii), $ca = a$ always; consequently, there is no need for separate notations. Furthermore, there is no longer a need to keep track of $\theta: C \to \operatorname{Aut}(A)$, for θ must be the trivial map here.

Definition $Z(C,A)$ is the additive group of all abelian factor sets.

We say that a function $g: C \times C \to A$ is a **coboundary** if there is a function $\alpha: C \to A$ with $\alpha(0) = 0$ for which

$$g(x,y) = \alpha(y) - \alpha(x + y) + \alpha(x).$$

Definition $B(C,A)$ is the set of all coboundaries.

As in Chapter 7, the reader may prove that $B(C,A)$ is a subgroup of $Z(C,A)$.

Definition $\operatorname{Ext}(C,A) = Z(C,A)/B(C,A)$.

When all groups under discussion are abelian, one uses the notation $\operatorname{Ext}(C,A)$ rather than $H^2(C,A)$. We now recall Exercise 7.31, which says that two extensions B and B' of A by C are equivalent in case there is a commutative diagram with exact rows:

$$0 \to A \to B \to C \to 0$$
$$\downarrow \quad \downarrow \quad \downarrow$$
$$0 \to A \to B' \to C \to 0$$

where the outer downward maps are identities.

THEOREM 10.10 The set of equivalence classes of abelian extensions of A by C, $e(C,A)$, is a group isomorphic to $\text{Ext}(C,A)$; the zero element is the class of split extensions.

Proof We have only restated Theorem 7.11. ∎

COROLLARY 10.11 $\text{Ext}(C,A) = 0$ if and only if every short exact sequence $0 \to A \to B \to C \to 0$ splits.

COROLLARY 10.12 If D is divisible, then $\text{Ext}(A,D) = 0$ for every group A; if F is free abelian, then $\text{Ext}(F,A) = 0$ for every group A.

Proof If $0 \to D \to B \to C \to 0$ is exact, then D is a direct summand of B, by Corollary 9.23, so that this sequence splits. The second assertion follows from Corollary 9.20. ∎

Exercises 10.16 If C is torsion-free and A is of bounded order, then $\text{Ext}(C,A) = 0$.
10.17 If R denotes the additive group of real numbers, then $\text{Ext}(R, \sum \sigma(p)) \neq 0$. (*Hint:* Use Exercise 9.14).
10.18 Prove that $\text{Ext}(\sigma(p), \sigma(p)) \neq 0$.
10.19 If C is p-primary and A is q-primary, where $p \neq q$, then $\text{Ext}(C,A) = 0$.

Pull-Backs and Push-Outs

Let us give an explicit construction of the sum of two (classes of) extensions in $e(C,A)$. Rather than say that B is an extension of A by C, we now define an extension as a short exact sequence

$$0 \to A \to B \to C \to 0.$$

Suppose now that we have two extensions ($i = 1,2$):

$$0 \to A \xrightarrow{\lambda_i} B_i \xrightarrow{\pi_i} C \to 0.$$

Suppose further that $\{l_i(c)\}$ are choices of liftings, and $f_i: C \times C \to A$ are the corresponding factor sets. What is the extension of A by C determined by the factor set $f_1 + f_2$?

Now every $b_i \in B_i$ has the unique expression:

$$b_i = a + l_i(c), \qquad a \in A, c \in C,$$

and we add according to the rule:

$$[a + l_i(c)] + [a' + l_i(c')] = a + a' + l_i(c + c') + f_i(c,c').$$

Let H be the subset of $B_1 \oplus B_2$ consisting of all elements (b_1,b_2) such that $\pi_1(b_1) = \pi_2(b_2)$. The reader may verify that H is a subgroup and that the following sequence is exact:

$$0 \to A \oplus A \xrightarrow{\lambda} H \xrightarrow{\mu} C \to 0$$

where $\lambda(a,a') = (\lambda_1 a, \lambda_2 a')$ and $\mu(b_1,b_2) = \pi_1(b_1) = \pi_2(b_2)$. If we define a choice of liftings $l(c)$ in H by $l(c) = (l_1(c), l_2(c))$, then the usual computation defines a factor set $F: C \times C \to A \oplus A$ by $F(c,c') = (f_1(c,c'), f_2(c,c'))$. We must still produce an extension with a factor set that is the sum of the two coordinates.

Define $\nabla: A \oplus A \to A$ by $\nabla(a, a') = a + a'$, and let S be the subgroup of $A \oplus H$ consisting of all elements of the form

$$(\nabla(a,a'), -\lambda(a,a')).$$

We shall prove that $(A \oplus H)/S$ is an extension of A by C; moreover, with respect to the choice of liftings $\{l(c) + S\}$, the factor set of this extension is $f_1 + f_2$.

The complete construction thus consists of taking a subgroup of a direct sum and then taking a quotient of another direct sum. In the language of the preceding chapter, we perform dual constructions. Rather than supply more details now, we proceed to a systematic account of this construction.

Who would expect that a lemma about 10 groups and 13 homomorphisms could be of any use? Here is the "Five Lemma"; the method of proof is called "diagram-chasing."

LEMMA 10.13 (*The Five Lemma*)   Consider the commutative diagram with exact rows:

$$A_1 \xrightarrow{f_1} A_2 \xrightarrow{f_2} A_3 \xrightarrow{f_3} A_4 \xrightarrow{f_4} A_5$$

$$\downarrow{\alpha_1} \quad \downarrow{\alpha_2} \quad \downarrow{\alpha_3} \quad \downarrow{\alpha_4} \quad \downarrow{\alpha_5}$$

$$B_1 \xrightarrow[g_1]{} B_2 \xrightarrow[g_2]{} B_3 \xrightarrow[g_3]{} B_4 \xrightarrow[g_4]{} B_5$$

(i) If α_2 and α_4 are onto and α_5 is one-to-one, then α_3 is onto.

(ii) If α_2 and α_4 are one-to-one and α_1 is onto, then α_3 is one-to-one.

In particular, if α_1, α_2, α_4, and α_5 are isomorphisms, so is α_3.

Proof   We shall only prove (i), leaving the proof of the dual statement (ii) to the reader.

Remark   The way to understand our proof is to chase elements around the diagram without pausing to give names to everything; we approximate this by using transparent notation, i.e., b_2 denotes an element of B_2, etc.

If $b_3 \in B_3$, we must find a_3 with $\alpha_3(a_3) = b_3$. Now $b_3 \to b_4 = g_3(b_3)$; since α_4 is onto, we may lift b_4 to a_4. Commutativity gives $\alpha_5 f_4(a_4) = g_4\alpha_4(a_4) = g_4(b_4) = g_4g_3(b_3)$, and this is 0 because the bottom row is exact. Since $\alpha_5 f_4(a_4) = 0$ and α_5 is one-to-one, $a_4 \in$ kernel $f_4 =$ image f_3. Hence, there is $a_3 \in A_3$ with $f_3(a_3) = a_4$. Using commutativity in the next to last square, $g_3\alpha_3(a_3) = \alpha_4 f_3(a_3) = \alpha_4(a_4) = b_4 = g_3(b_3)$. Conclusion: $b_3 - \alpha_3(a_3)$ is in kernel $g_3 =$ image g_2. Therefore, $b_3 - \alpha_3(a_3) = g_2(b_2)$ for some b_2. Since α_2 is onto, we may lift b_2 to a_2. Using commutativity once more, $\alpha_3 f_2(a_2) = g_2\alpha_2(a_2) = g_2(b_2) = b_3 - \alpha_3(a_3)$. Thus, $b_3 = \alpha_3(f_2(a_2) + a_3)$, and α_3 is onto. ∎

COROLLARY 10.14   If B and B' are extensions of A by C, then B is equivalent to B' if and only if there is a commutative diagram with exact rows:

$$0 \to A \to B \to C \to 0$$

$$\downarrow{1:A} \quad \downarrow{\gamma} \quad \downarrow{1:C}$$

$$0 \to A \to B' \to C \to 0$$

Proof   The five lemma tells us that γ is automatically an iso-morphism. ∎

A weaker form of the five lemma says that if the four outer maps are isomorphisms, and if there is a middle map α_3 such that all commutes, then α_3 is an isomorphism. We remark that a map α_3 need not exist, for consider the diagram with exact rows:

$$0 \to \sigma(p) \to \sigma(p) \oplus \sigma(p) \to \sigma(p) \to 0$$
$$\downarrow \qquad\qquad\qquad \downarrow$$
$$0 \to \sigma(p) \longrightarrow \sigma(p^2) \longrightarrow \sigma(p) \to 0$$

where the outer maps are identities. One cannot insert a homo-morphism in the middle so that the resulting diagram commutes, lest it be an isomorphism between the two nonisomorphic middle groups.

Exercises   10.20   Consider the commutative diagram with exact rows:

$$A_1 \to A_2 \to A_3 \to 0$$
$$\alpha_1 \downarrow \quad \alpha_2 \downarrow$$
$$B_1 \to B_2 \to B_3 \to 0$$

Prove there is a homomorphism from A_3 to B_3 making the augmented diagram commute; this map is an isomorphism if α_1 and α_2 are.

10.21   Consider the diagram

$$0 \to R \to F \to C \to 0$$
$$\downarrow {\scriptstyle 1:C}$$
$$E \to B \to C \to 0$$

where the rows are exact and F is free. There exist maps $\alpha \colon F \to B$ and $\beta \colon R \to E$ such that the resulting diagram commutes.

10.22   Consider the diagram

$$0 \to A \to B \to E$$
$$\scriptstyle 1:A \downarrow$$
$$0 \to A \to D \to D' \to 0$$

where the rows are exact and D is divisible. There exist maps $\alpha: B \to D$ and $\beta: E \to D'$ such that the resulting diagram commutes.

Definition   Consider the extensions

$$E:\quad 0 \to A \xrightarrow{\lambda} B \xrightarrow{\mu} C \to 0$$

and

$$E':\quad 0 \to A' \xrightarrow{\lambda'} B' \xrightarrow{\mu'} C' \to 0;$$

a **map from E to E'** is an ordered triple (α,β,γ) of homomorphisms such that the following diagram commutes:

$$
\begin{array}{ccccccccc}
E: & 0 \to & A & \xrightarrow{\lambda} & B & \xrightarrow{\mu} & C & \to 0 \\
 & & \downarrow{\scriptstyle\alpha} & & \downarrow{\scriptstyle\beta} & & \downarrow{\scriptstyle\gamma} & \\
E': & 0 \to & A' & \xrightarrow{\lambda'} & B' & \xrightarrow{\mu'} & C' & \to 0.
\end{array}
$$

Our notation is $(\alpha,\beta,\gamma): E \to E'$.

One composes maps of extensions "coordinatewise." The definition of equivalence of extensions E and E' is that there is a map $(1:A, \beta, 1:C): E \to E'$, and one may prove again (with the five lemma) that this relation is an equivalence relation. The equivalence class of an extension E is denoted $[E]$.

There are two dual operations on extensions. We now prepare the first one.

By a **solution** of the diagram

$$(*)$$

$$
\begin{array}{c}
C' \\
\downarrow{\scriptstyle\gamma} \\
B \xrightarrow{\mu} C
\end{array}
$$

we mean a group B' and maps μ' and β such that

$$
\begin{array}{ccc}
B' & \xrightarrow{\mu'} & C' \\
\downarrow{\scriptstyle\beta} & & \downarrow{\scriptstyle\gamma} \\
B & \xrightarrow{\mu} & C
\end{array}
$$

commutes.

A solution of a diagram need not be unique; for example, given the preceding solution, one can construct another solution with upper left corner $B' \oplus X$, where X is any given group.

Definition   A solution of the diagram (*) is a **pull-back** in case, given any other solution (B'',μ'',β') of (*), there is a map $\theta \colon B'' \to B'$ such that the following diagram commutes:

(**)

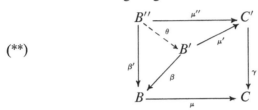

LEMMA 10.15   A pull-back exists for the diagram (*).

Proof   Let B' be the subgroup of $B \oplus C'$ consisting of all (b,c') such that $\mu b = \gamma c'$, and define μ' and β as projections. It is trivial to verify that we have defined a solution of (*).

Suppose now that we have a second solution (diagram (**)). Define $\theta \colon B'' \to B'$ as follows: If $x \in B''$, then $\theta x = (\beta'x, \mu''x)$. One checks quickly that (**) commutes. ∎

THEOREM 10.16   Let E be an extension of A by C and let $\gamma \colon C' \to C$ be a homomorphism. There is an extension E' of A by C' and a map $(1 \colon A, \beta, \gamma) \colon E' \to E$.

Proof   We are given the following diagram, which we must complete:

$$
\begin{array}{ccc}
A & & C' \\
{\scriptstyle 1:A}\downarrow & & \downarrow{\scriptstyle \gamma} \\
0 \to A \xrightarrow{\lambda} B & \xrightarrow{\mu} & C \to 0
\end{array}
$$

Let (B',μ',β) be the pull-back obtained in Lemma 10.15, and define $\lambda' \colon A \to B'$ by $\lambda'a = (\lambda a,0)$. It is easy to check that

$$E': 0 \to A \xrightarrow{\lambda'} B' \xrightarrow{\mu'} C' \to 0$$

is an extension and that $(1:A,\beta,\gamma): E' \to E$. ∎

The extension E' just constructed is denoted $E\gamma$.

Notation   If $\gamma: C' \to C$ is a function, then we define $\gamma \times \gamma: C' \times C' \to C \times C$ by $\gamma \times \gamma(c_1',c_2') = (\gamma c_1', \gamma c_2')$.

If $\lambda: A \to B$ and $\lambda': A' \to B'$ are homomorphisms, we define $\lambda \oplus \lambda': A \oplus A' \to B \oplus B'$ by $\lambda \oplus \lambda'(a,a') = (\lambda a, \lambda' a')$.

It is useful to do a bit of bookkeeping.

LEMMA 10.17   Let E be an extension of A by C, and let $\gamma: C' \to C$ be a homomorphism. If $f: C \times C \to A$ is a factor set of E, then $f(\gamma \times \gamma)$ is a factor set of $E\gamma$.

Proof   We use the notation of the preceding theorem. Let $\{l(c)\}$ be a choice of liftings determining f. Define a set of liftings $\{L(c')\}$ in B' by $L(c') = (l(\gamma c'), c')$. The reader may now compute that the corresponding factor set is $F = f(\gamma \times \gamma)$, i.e., $F(c_1', c_2') = f(\gamma c_1', \gamma c_2')$. ∎

COROLLARY 10.18   Let E and E'' be extensions of A by C, and let $\gamma: C' \to C$. If $[E] = [E'']$, then $[E\gamma] = [E''\gamma]$.

Proof   Let f and f'' be factor sets of E and E'', respectively; then $f - f'' \in B(C,A)$. By Lemma 10.17, $f(\gamma \times \gamma)$ and $f''(\gamma \times \gamma)$ are factor sets of $E\gamma$ and $E''\gamma$, respectively, and the reader may check that $f(\gamma \times \gamma) - f''(\gamma \times \gamma) \in B(C',A)$. Hence, $[E\gamma] = [E''\gamma]$. ∎

COROLLARY 10.19   Let E be an extension of A by C, and let $\gamma: C' \to C$ and $\gamma_1: C'' \to C'$ be homomorphisms. Then $[(E\gamma)\gamma_1] = [E(\gamma\gamma_1)]$.

Proof   If f is a factor set of E, then $f(\gamma \times \gamma) \circ \gamma_1 \times \gamma_1$ is a factor set of $(E\gamma)\gamma_1$ and $f \circ (\gamma \times \gamma \circ \gamma_1 \times \gamma_1)$ is a factor set of $E(\gamma\gamma_1)$. Since composition of functions is associative, $[(E\gamma)\gamma_1] = [E(\gamma\gamma_1)]$. ∎

We now prepare our second construction. By a **solution** of the diagram

$$A \xrightarrow{\lambda} B$$

(*')

$$\alpha \downarrow$$

$$A'$$

we mean a group B' and maps λ' and β such that

$$
\begin{array}{ccc}
A & \xrightarrow{\lambda} & B \\
\alpha \downarrow & & \downarrow \beta \\
A' & \xrightarrow{\lambda'} & B'
\end{array}
$$

commutes.

Definition   A solution of the diagram (*') is a **push-out** in case, given any other solution (B'',λ'',β') of (*'), there is a map $\theta \colon B' \to B''$ such that the following diagram commutes:

(**')

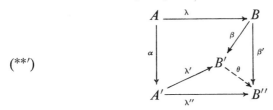

LEMMA 10.20   A push-out exists for the diagram (*').

Proof   Since the dual of a subgroup is a quotient, one should expect the push-out to be quotient of $A' \oplus B$. If S is the subgroup of $A' \oplus B$ consisting of all $(\alpha a, -\lambda a)$, where $a \in A$, then define $B' = (A' \oplus B)/S$. Define $\lambda' \colon A' \to B'$ by $\lambda'a' = (a',0) + S$; define $\beta \colon B \to B'$ by $\beta b = (0,b) + S$. It is a trivial matter to verify that we have defined a solution of (*').

Suppose now that we have a second solution (diagram (**')). Define $\theta \colon B' \to B''$ by $\theta((a',b) + S) = \lambda''a' + \beta'b$. One checks easily that θ is well defined and that (**') commutes. ∎

THEOREM 10.21   Let E be an extension of A by C, and let $\alpha \colon A \to A'$ be a homomorphism. There is an extension E' of A' by C and a map $(\alpha,\beta,1\colon C)\colon E \to E'$.

Proof   We are given the following diagram to complete:

$$0 \to A \xrightarrow{\lambda} B \xrightarrow{\mu} C \to 0$$
$$\downarrow{\scriptstyle \alpha} \qquad\quad \downarrow{\scriptstyle 1:C}$$
$$A' \qquad\quad C$$

Let (B', λ', β) be a push-out, and define $\mu'\colon B' \to C$ by $\mu'((a',b)) + S) = \mu b$. It is a simple matter to verify that μ' is well defined,

$$E'\colon 0 \to A' \xrightarrow{\lambda'} B' \xrightarrow{\mu'} C' \to 0$$

is an extension, and $(\alpha, \beta, 1\colon C)\colon E \to E'$. ∎

We denote the extension E' just constructed by αE.

LEMMA 10.22   Let E be an extension of A by C, and let $\alpha\colon A \to A'$ be a homomorphism. If $f\colon C \times C \to A$ is a factor set of E, then αf is a factor set of αE.

Proof   We use the notation of Theorem 10.21. If $\{l(c)\}$ is a choice of liftings in B determining f, choose a set of liftings $\{L(c)\}$ in B' by $L(c) = (0, l(c)) + S$. Now the factor set F determined by this choice is $F(c_1, c_2) = L(c_1) + L(c_2) - L(c_1 + c_2) = (0, f(c_1, c_2)) + S = (\alpha f(c_1, c_2), 0) + S = \lambda' \alpha f(c_1, c_2)$. We are done, for λ' is only the inclusion map. ∎

COROLLARY 10.23   If $[E] = [E'']$, then $[\alpha E] = [\alpha E'']$.

COROLLARY 10.24   If E is an extension of A by C, and if $\alpha\colon A \to A'$ and $\alpha_1\colon A' \to A''$ are homomorphisms, then $[\alpha_1(\alpha E)] = [(\alpha_1 \alpha)E]$.

COROLLARY 10.25   Let E be an extension of A by C and let $\alpha\colon A \to A'$ and $\gamma\colon C' \to C$ be homomorphisms. Then $[(\alpha E)\gamma] = [\alpha(E\gamma)]$.

Proof   If f is a factor set of E, then $(\alpha f)\gamma \times \gamma$ is a factor set of $(\alpha E)\gamma$ and $\alpha(f(\gamma \times \gamma))$ is a factor set of $\alpha(E\gamma)$. ∎

We have demonstrated that homomorphisms operate on extensions and that all possible associativity laws hold.

Definition   Consider the extensions

$$E: 0 \rightarrow A \xrightarrow{\lambda} B \xrightarrow{\mu} C \rightarrow 0$$

and

$$E': 0 \rightarrow A' \xrightarrow{\lambda'} B' \xrightarrow{\mu'} C' \rightarrow 0.$$

Their **direct sum** is the extension

$$E \oplus E': 0 \rightarrow A \oplus A' \xrightarrow{\lambda \oplus \lambda'} B \oplus B' \xrightarrow{\mu \oplus \mu'} C \oplus C' \rightarrow 0$$

Notation   The **diagonal map** $\triangle: C \rightarrow C \oplus C$ is defined by $\triangle(c) = (c,c)$; the **codiagonal map** $\triangledown: A \oplus A \rightarrow A$ is defined by $\triangledown(a,a') = a + a'$.

Definition   If E and E' are extensions of A by C, their sum $E + E'$ is the extension $\triangledown(E \oplus E')\triangle$.

The reader should observe that $E + E'$ is an extension of A by C (whose equivalence class is well defined, by Corollary 10.25).

Exercises   10.23   If E and E' are extensions with factor sets f and f' respectively, then $f \oplus f'$ is a factor set of $E \oplus E'$.
  10.24   If $[E] = [E']$ and $[E_0] = [E_0']$, then $[E \oplus E_0] = [E' \oplus E_0']$.
  10.25   Let E be an extension of A by C, E' an extension of A' by C', and $\gamma: C_1 \rightarrow C$, $\gamma': C_2 \rightarrow C'$ homomorphisms. Then $[(E \oplus E')(\gamma \oplus \gamma')] = [E\gamma \oplus E'\gamma']$. A similar equation holds on the left.
  10.26   If $[E] = [E']$ and $[E_0] = [E_0']$, then $[E + E_0] = [E' + E_0']$.
  10.27 $[E(\gamma + \gamma_1)] = [E\gamma + E\gamma_1]$; similarly on the left.
  10.28 $[(E + E')\gamma] = [E\gamma + E'\gamma]$; similarly on the left.

The following result shows that our constructions do give an extension corresponding to the sum of two factor sets.

LEMMA 10.26   If f is a factor set, let E_f be an extension it determines (so that $\varphi(f + B(C,A)) = [E_f]$ defines the one-to-one correspondence of Theorem 10.10). Then $[E_{f+f'}] = [E_f + E_{f'}]$.

Proof By definition, $E_{f+f'}$ has $f + f'$ as a factor set; $E_f + E_{f'}$ has $\nabla(f \oplus f')\triangle$ as a factor set. But these are the same:

$$
\begin{aligned}
\nabla(f \oplus f')\triangle(x,y) &= \nabla(f \oplus f')(x,y,x,y) \\
&= \nabla(f(x,y), f'(x,y)) \\
&= f(x,y) + f'(x,y) \\
&= (f + f')(x,y). \quad \blacksquare
\end{aligned}
$$

Definition If $[E]$ and $[E'] \in e(C,A)$, their **Baer sum** is $[E] + [E'] = [E + E']$.

By Exercise 10.26, the Baer sum is a well defined binary operation on $e(C,A)$.

THEOREM 10.27 $e(C,A)$ is an abelian group under Baer sum, and φ: $\mathrm{Ext}(C,A) \to e(C,A)$ defined by $\varphi(f + B(C,A)) = [E_f]$ is an isomorphism.

Proof We have known since Chapter 7 that φ is a one-to-one correspondence. Lemma 10.26 and Exercise 1.16 complete the proof. $\blacksquare$

The Ext Functors

We had an ulterior motive in examining the addition of extensions, for we are now in a position to prove that Ext defines functors that are closely related to the Hom functors.

THEOREM 10.28 If G is a fixed group, then $\mathrm{Ext}(G, \ )$ is a covariant functor.

Proof If α: $A \to A'$, we define a homomorphism

$$\alpha_*: \mathrm{Ext}(G,A) \to \mathrm{Ext}(G,A') \text{ by } \alpha_*(f + B(G,A)) = \alpha f + B(G,A').$$

It is mechanical to prove that α_* is a well defined homomorphism, and all the axioms of the definition of functor are satisfied. $\blacksquare$

THEOREM 10.29   If K is a fixed group, then Ext(,K) is a contravariant functor.

Proof   If $\alpha: A \to A'$, define $\alpha^*: \text{Ext}(A',K) \to \text{Ext}(A,K)$ by $\alpha^*(f + B(A',K)) = f(\alpha \times \alpha) + B(A,K)$. ∎

We have another way of looking at extensions, $e(C,A)$, and this also gives rise to functors. If $\alpha: A \to A'$, define a function $\alpha_\#: e(C,A) \to e(C,A')$ by

$$\alpha_\#([E]) = [\alpha E];$$

if $\gamma: C \to C'$, define a function $\gamma^\#: e(C',A) \to e(C,A)$ by

$$\gamma^\#([E]) = [E\gamma].$$

The following lemma will imply that these functions are homomorphisms.

LEMMA 10.30[1]   If $\alpha: A \to A'$, then the following diagram commutes for every G:

$$\begin{array}{ccc} \text{Ext}(G,A) & \xrightarrow{\alpha_*} & \text{Ext}(G,A') \\ {\scriptstyle\varphi}\downarrow & & \downarrow{\scriptstyle\varphi} \\ e(G,A) & \xrightarrow{\alpha_\#} & e(G,A') \end{array}$$

A dual theorem holds if we fix the second variable.

Proof   We must show that $\varphi\alpha_* = \alpha_\#\varphi$. If $f \in Z(G,A)$, then $\varphi\alpha_*(f + B) = \varphi(\alpha f + B') = [E_{\alpha f}]$, i.e., the class of an extension with factor set αf. On the other hand, $\alpha_\#\varphi(f + B) = \alpha_\#[E_f] = [\alpha E_f]$. By Lemma 10.22, αf is a factor set of αE_f, and so $[\alpha E_f] = [E_{\alpha f}]$. ∎

THEOREM 10.31   The functions $\alpha_\#$ and $\gamma^\#$ are homomorphisms.

Proof   By the lemma, $\alpha_\# = \varphi\alpha_*\varphi^{-1}$, and so is the composite of homomorphisms. ∎

We now connect Hom to Ext.

[1] This lemma says the functors Ext(G,) and $e(G,$) are **naturally equivalent.**

Definition   Let f be a factor set of the extension

$$E: 0 \to A \xrightarrow{\lambda} B \xrightarrow{\mu} C \to 0.$$

If G is a group, we define the **connecting homomorphisms**:

∂: $\mathrm{Hom}(G,C) \to \mathrm{Ext}(G,A)$ by $\partial(h) = f(h \times h) + B(G,A)$;

δ: $\mathrm{Hom}(A,G) \to \mathrm{Ext}(C,G)$ by $\delta(h') = h'f + B(C,G)$.

Exercise   10.29   Define $\partial_\#$: $\mathrm{Hom}(G,C) \to e(G,A)$ by $\partial_\#(h) = [Eh]$, and $\delta^\#$: $\mathrm{Hom}(A,G) \to e(C,G)$ by $\delta^\#(h') = [h'E]$. Prove the following diagrams commute:

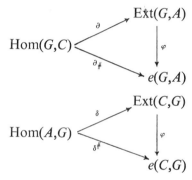

Two lemmas are needed before the main tool for calculating Ext can be presented. The proofs are dual, so that the second proof is left as an exercise.

LEMMA 10.32   If $0 \to A \xrightarrow{\lambda} B \xrightarrow{\mu} C \to 0$ is exact, then, for every group G, the map $\lambda^\#$: $e(B,G) \to e(A,G)$ is onto.

Proof   Let $0 \to G \xrightarrow{\alpha} E \xrightarrow{\beta} A \to 0$ represent an element of $e(A,G)$. We now hook this sequence to our given sequence to get the following exact sequence:

$$0 \to G \xrightarrow{\alpha} E \xrightarrow{\lambda\beta} B \xrightarrow{\mu} C \to 0.$$

There exists an exact sequence

$$0 \to R \to F \to C \to 0,$$

where F is free. By Exercise 10.21 there are maps such that the following diagram commutes:

$$
\begin{array}{ccccccccc}
0 & \to & R & \to & F & \to & C & \to & 0 \\
& & \downarrow{\scriptstyle\gamma} & & \downarrow{\scriptstyle\epsilon} & & \downarrow{\scriptstyle 1:C} & & \\
0 & \to & G & \xrightarrow{\lambda\beta} & E & \to & B & \to & C & \to & 0
\end{array}
$$

If we focus on the first square in this diagram, then we see that $(B,\lambda\beta,\epsilon)$ is a solution of the diagram

$$
\begin{array}{ccc}
R & \to & F \\
\downarrow & & \\
E & &
\end{array}
$$

If (E',τ,σ) is the push-out for this diagram, then there is a map $\theta: E' \to B$ with

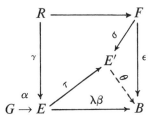

commuting. The reader may now verify that

$$0 \to G \xrightarrow{\tau\alpha} E' \xrightarrow{\theta} B \to 0$$

is an extension, and that

$$
\begin{array}{ccccccccc}
0 & \to & G & \to & E & \to & A & \to & 0 \\
& & \downarrow{\scriptstyle 1:G} & & \downarrow{\scriptstyle\tau} & & \downarrow{\scriptstyle\lambda} & & \\
0 & \to & G & \to & E' & \to & B & \to & 0
\end{array}
$$

commutes. In other words, $\lambda^{\#}$ sends the class of the bottom extension into the class of the top extension. ∎

LEMMA 10.33 If $0 \to A \xrightarrow{\lambda} B \xrightarrow{\mu} C \to 0$ is exact, then, for every group G, the map $\mu_{\#}: e(G,B) \to e(G,C)$ is onto.

Proof Dual to the preceding proof, using pull-backs instead of push-outs and Exercise 10.22 instead of Exercise 10.21. ∎

THEOREM 10.34 Let $0 \to A \xrightarrow{\lambda} B \xrightarrow{\mu} C \to 0$ be exact. For any group G, the following two sequences are exact:

(i) $0 \longrightarrow \mathrm{Hom}(G,A) \xrightarrow{T(\lambda)} \mathrm{Hom}(G,B) \xrightarrow{T(\mu)} \mathrm{Hom}(G,C) \xrightarrow{\partial}$
$\mathrm{Ext}(G,A) \xrightarrow{\lambda^*} \mathrm{Ext}(G,B) \xrightarrow{\mu^*} \mathrm{Ext}(G,C) \longrightarrow 0;$

(ii) $0 \longrightarrow \mathrm{Hom}(C,G) \xrightarrow{S(\mu)} \mathrm{Hom}(B,G) \xrightarrow{S(\lambda)} \mathrm{Hom}(A,G) \xrightarrow{\delta}$
$\mathrm{Ext}(C,G) \xrightarrow{\mu^*} \mathrm{Ext}(B,G) \xrightarrow{\lambda^*} \mathrm{Ext}(A,G) \longrightarrow 0.$

Proof The difficult portions are the proofs that μ_* and λ^* are onto, and they follow easily from Lemmas 10.32 and 10.33 and Lemma 10.30.
The other steps of the proof are utterly uninspiring, proceeding inexorably in the manner of the proof of Theorem 10.3. ∎

The groups Ext thus repair the exactness we may have lost by applying Hom. Consider the question: If A is a subgroup of B, when can a homomorphism $h: A \to G$ be extended to a homomorphism of B into G? The exact sequence answers this question. Let $0 \to A \xrightarrow{i} B \to B/A \to 0$ be exact (where i is the inclusion). Then we have exactness of

$$\mathrm{Hom}(B,G) \xrightarrow{S(i)} \mathrm{Hom}(A,G) \xrightarrow{\delta} \mathrm{Ext}(B/A,G).$$

Definition The element $\delta(h)$ is the **obstruction** of h.

COROLLARY 10.35 Let A be a subgroup of B and $h: A \to G$ a homomorphism. Then h can be extended to B if and only if its obstruction is 0.

Proof If h can be extended to B, there is a map $h': B \to G$ such that $h'i = h$. Hence, $h \in$ image $S(i) =$ kernel δ, so that $\delta(h) = 0$.

If $\delta(h) = 0$, then $h \in$ kernel $\delta = $ image $S(i)$, so that there is an $h' \in \text{Hom}(B,G)$ with $S(i)(h') = h$, i.e., $h'i = h$, as desired. ∎

COROLLARY 10.36   If $\text{Ext}(B/A,G) = 0$, every map $h: A \to G$ can be extended to B.

We now prove that Ext behaves very much like Hom.

THEOREM 10.37   Let $\{A_i\}$ be a family of groups. For any K,

$$\text{Ext}(\textstyle\sum A_i, K) \approx \Pi \text{Ext}(A_i, K).$$

Proof   For each i, let $0 \to R_i \to F_i \to A_i \to 0$ be exact, where F_i is free. Consider the commutative diagram with exact rows:

$$\text{Hom}(\textstyle\sum F_i, K) \to \text{Hom}(\textstyle\sum R_i, K) \to \text{Ext}(\textstyle\sum A_i, K) \to \text{Ext}(\textstyle\sum F_i, K)$$
$$\downarrow \qquad\qquad\qquad \downarrow$$
$$\Pi \, \text{Hom}(F_i, K) \to \Pi \, \text{Hom}(R_i, K) \to \Pi \, \text{Ext}(A_i, K) \to \Pi \, \text{Ext}(F_i, K)$$

where the downward maps are the isomorphisms of Theorem 10.7. By Corollary 10.12 the terms on the far right are 0, so that Exercise 10.20 yields the desired result. ∎

THEOREM 10.38   Let $\{A_i\}$ be any family of groups. For any G,

$$\text{Ext}(G, \Pi A_i) \approx \Pi \text{Ext}(G, A_i).$$

Proof   Left to the reader. ∎

THEOREM 10.39   For any group A, $\text{Ext}(\sigma(n), A) \approx A/nA$.

Proof   Consider the exact sequence

$$0 \to Z \xrightarrow{\mu} Z \to \sigma(n) \to 0$$

where μ is multiplication by n. We now have exactness of

$$\text{Hom}(Z,A) \xrightarrow{S(\mu)} \text{Hom}(Z,A) \to \text{Ext}(\sigma(n),A) \to \text{Ext}(Z,A) = 0.$$

Now $\text{Hom}(Z,A) \approx A$ and $S(\mu)$ is multiplication by n, so that our result follows. ∎

It follows from Theorem 10.39 that $\text{Ext}(\sigma(p), \sigma(p)) \approx \sigma(p)$, where p is a prime, so that this Ext has p elements. On the other hand, if

$0 \to \sigma(p) \to E \to \sigma(p) \to 0$ is exact, then E has order p^2 so that $E \approx \sigma(p^2)$ or $E \approx \sigma(p) \oplus \sigma(p)$. Therefore, if p is an odd prime, we have an example of inequivalent extensions of A by C with isomorphic middle terms.

The number of nonisomorphic middle groups B (where $0 \to A \to B \to C \to 0$ is exact) is at most $|\text{Ext}(C,A)|$. Our example above shows that this inequality can be strict.

Examples 5 For any group G, $\text{Ext}(V,G)$ is torsion-free and divisible when V is a vector space over Q.

By Theorem 10.9, the functor $\text{Ext}(\ ,G)$ takes a multiplication into a multiplication. The remainder of the proof is as the similar proof for Hom on page 212.

6 If A is torsion-free, then $\text{Ext}(A,G)$ is divisible for every group G.

Since A is torsion-free, A can be imbedded in a vector space V over Q (Exercise 9.59). Therefore, we have an exact sequence

$$0 \to A \to V \to V/A \to 0,$$

which gives another exact sequence

$$\cdots \to \text{Ext}(V,G) \to \text{Ext}(A,G) \to 0.$$

Since V is a vector space over Q, our first example shows that $\text{Ext}(V,G)$ is divisible. Hence, $\text{Ext}(A,G)$ is divisible, being a quotient of a divisible group.

7 If $mG = 0$, then $\text{Ext}(A,G) = 0$ for every torsion-free group A.

If $\mu: G \to G$ is multiplication by m, then $\mu_*: \text{Ext}(A,G) \to \text{Ext}(A,G)$ is also multiplication by m. Since $mG = 0$, μ is the zero map, so that μ_* is also the zero map. Therefore

$$\mu_* \, \text{Ext}(A,G) = m \, \text{Ext}(A,G) = 0.$$

On the other hand, we have just seen that $\text{Ext}(A,G)$ is divisible, for A is torsion-free. It follows that $\text{Ext}(A,G) = 0$.

We have given a proof by homological algebra of Corollary 9.35: If B is a group with tB of bounded order, then tB is a direct summand of B. The group B/tB is torsion-free, and by Corollary 10.11, $\text{Ext}(B/tB,tB) = 0$ implies that the sequence

$$0 \to tB \to B \to B/tB \to 0$$

splits.

Exercises 10.30 Prove that $\text{Ext}(Q,Z) \neq 0$. Conclude that there exists an indecomposable torsion-free group of rank 2. It is known that there exist indecomposable torsion-free groups of any rank.
10.31 Prove that

$$\text{Ext}\left(Q, \sum_{n=1}^{\infty} \sigma(p^n) \right) \neq 0.$$

Conclude that there exists a (countable) group G whose torsion subgroup $tG \approx \sum \sigma(p^n)$ and such that tG is not a summand of G.
10.32 Let $0 \to R \to F \to A \to 0$ be exact, where F is free. Prove that $\text{Ext}(A,G) \approx \text{Hom}(R,G)/\text{image Hom}(F,G)$. (This is often taken as the definition of $\text{Ext}(A,G)$.)
10.33 Prove that $\text{Ext}(A,G) = 0$ for every torsion-free group A if and only if $\text{Ext}(Q,G) = 0$.
*10.34 (*Nunke*) If $\text{Hom}(A,Z) = 0$ and $\text{Ext}(A,Z) = 0$, then $A = 0$.
*10.35 If A is a torsion-free group of rank 1 such that $\text{Ext}(A,Z) = 0$, then $A \approx Z$.
*10.36 A group G is divisible if and only if $\text{Ext}(Q/Z,G) = 0$.
*10.37 If G is a torsion group with character group G^*, then $G^* \approx \text{Ext}(G,Z)$.

If K is an abelian group and G is a not necessarily abelian extension of K by a group Q, then we remarked in Chapter 7 that K is a module over a ring ZQ. The constructions of this chapter involved Z-modules (abelian groups); the more general theory involves ZQ-modules. The main tool of the general theory is the existence of a sequence of functors $\text{Ext}^n(\ , \ )$ and a long exact sequence beginning with a triple of Hom, then a triple of Ext^1, a triple of Ext^2, etc. If one considers the group Z as a ZQ-module (by defining scalar multiplication suitably), then $H_\theta^2(Q,K) \approx \text{Ext}^2(Z,K)$. We refer the reader to the book of S. MacLane, *Homology* (see Bibliography), for further details.

Chapter II

Free Groups and
Free Products

Generators and Relations

In this chapter, we shall consider several special classes of infinite groups.

Recall first that a free abelian group F on generators X has the following basic[1] property: If G is an arbitrary abelian group, then any function $f: X \to G$ may be extended to a homomorphism of F into G. An immediate consequence of this property is Corollary 9.18: Every abelian group is a quotient of a free abelian group. The significance of this remark is that we now have a convenient way of describing abelian groups.

Definition   An abelian group G has **generators** $X = \{x_k\}$ **and relations** $\{r_j = 0\}$ in case $G \approx F/R$, where F is free abelian on X, and R is the subgroup generated by $\{r_j\}$.

In each of the following examples, we present *abelian* groups by generators and relations.

Examples   **1** $G = \sigma(6)$ has generator x and relation $6x = 0$.

2 $G = \sigma(6)$ has generators $\{x,y\}$ and relations $\{2x = 0, 3y = 0\}$.

3 $G = \sigma(p^\infty)$ has generators

$$\{a_1, a_2, \cdots, a_n, \cdots\}$$

---

[1] A pun is intended; if V is a vector space with basis X, and if W is another vector space, then any function $f: X \to W$ has an extension to a linear transformation of V into W.

and relations

$$\{pa_1 = 0, \; pa_n = a_{n-1} \quad \text{if } n > 1\}.$$

4 If G is free abelian on $\{x_k\}$, then G has generators $\{x_k\}$ and no relations; (recall that $\{0\}$ is the subgroup generated by the empty set). The etymology of the term *free* is apparent now.

We have seen that we can describe an existing group by generators and relations. We can also use generators and relations to construct a group having prescribed properties. For example, is there a reduced p-primary abelian group G such that

$$\bigcap_{n=1}^{\infty} p^n G \neq \{0\}?$$

Construct such a group G as the abelian group with generators

$$a, \, b_1, \, b_2, \, \cdots, \, b_n, \, \cdots$$

and relations

$$pa = 0 \quad \text{and} \quad p^n b_n = a, \quad \text{for all } n.$$

It is easy to see that G is a p-primary abelian group and that $a \in p^n G$ for all n. We shall prove that $a \neq 0$, leaving to the reader the proof that G is reduced.

Let F be the free abelian group on generators

$$a, \, b_1, \, b_2, \, \cdots, \, b_n, \, \cdots,$$

and let R be the subgroup of F generated by

$$\{pa, \, p^n b_n - a, \quad n \geq 1\}.$$

We must prove that $a \notin R$. If, on the contrary, $a \in R$, then

$$a = mpa + \sum m_n(p^n b_n - a)$$

for integers m and m_n. Collecting terms gives

$$(1 - mp + \sum m_n)a = \sum m_n p^n b_n.$$

Since $\{a, b_1, b_2, \cdots\}$ is a free set of generators, each $m_n p^n = 0$ and $1 - mp + \sum m_n = 0$. From these equations, it follows that each $m_n = 0$, and so $1 = mp$, a contradiction.

The reader should note that an abelian group G defined by generators and relations is the largest such group in the sense that any other group generated by elements subject to these defining relations is a quotient of G. For example, let G be the abelian group with generators $\{x,y\}$ and relations $\{2x = 0, 4y = 0\}$. The reader may check that

$$G = \sigma(2) \oplus \sigma(4).$$

On the other hand, if $H = \sigma(2) \oplus \sigma(2)$, then H is also generated by two elements that satisfy the defining relations of G (of course they satisfy an additional relation as well).

We wish to extend the idea of generators and relations from abelian groups to arbitrary groups. In order to do this, we need the nonabelian analog of free abelian groups, and so we abstract the basic property of a free set of generators.

Definition   Let X be a set and F a group containing X; F is **free on** X if, for every group G, every function $f: X \to G$ has a unique extension to a homomorphism of F into G.

$$\begin{array}{ccc} F & & \\ \uparrow & \searrow & \\ X & \xrightarrow[f]{} & G \end{array}$$

We shall prove later that the uniqueness of the extension is equivalent to saying that the set X generates F.

Our first question is whether there are any free groups.

THEOREM 11.1   If X is a set, then there exists a group F that is free on X.

Proof   Let X' be a set disjoint from X and in one-to-one correspondence with it; we denote this correspondence

$$x \leftrightarrow x^{-1}.$$

Let X'' be a set disjoint from $X \cup X'$ that contains only one element and which we denote "1." We call $X \cup X' \cup X''$ the *alphabet*, and we call its elements *letters*. Let S be the set of all sequences of letters. A *word* in X is a sequence:

$$w = (a_1, a_2, \cdots) \in S,$$

such that all coordinates are 1 from some point on, i.e., there is an integer k such that $a_n = 1$ for all $n \geq k$. In particular, the constant sequence

$$(1, 1, 1, \cdots)$$

is a word; it is called the *empty word*, and is denoted 1. A *reduced word in X* is a word in X that satisfies the extra conditions:

(i) x and x^{-1} are never adjacent.

(ii) If $a_m = 1$ for some m, then $a_n = 1$ for all $n > m$.

In particular, the empty word is a reduced word. Since words contain only a finite number of letters before they become constant, we use the more economical (and suggestive) notation:

$$w = x_1^{\epsilon_1} x_2^{\epsilon_2} \cdots x_n^{\epsilon_n},$$

where $\epsilon_i = \pm 1$ (we agree that x^1 may denote x). Observe that this spelling of a reduced word is unique, for this is the definition of equality in the set of sequences S.

The idea of the construction of the free group F is just this: The elements of F are the reduced words and the binary operation is juxtaposition. Unfortunately, the juxtaposition of two reduced words need not be reduced. This tiny fact incurs tedious case analyses in verifying associativity, so that we use a device to bypass the tedium.

Let W be the set of reduced words in X. For each $x \in X$, consider the two functions mapping W into itself, $|x|$ and $|x^{-1}|$, defined as follows:

$$|x^\epsilon|(x_1^{\epsilon_1} \cdots x_n^{\epsilon_n}) = \begin{cases} x^\epsilon x_1^{\epsilon_1} \cdots x_n^{\epsilon_n} & \text{if } x^\epsilon \neq x_1^{-\epsilon_1}; \\ x_2^{\epsilon_2} \cdots x_n^{\epsilon_n} & \text{if } x^\epsilon = x_1^{-\epsilon_1}, \end{cases}$$

where $\epsilon = \pm 1$.

Since $|x| \, |x^{-1}|$ and $|x^{-1}| \, |x|$ are each equal to the identity on W, each $|x|$ is a permutation of W (with inverse $|x^{-1}|$). Let S_W be the group of all permutations of W, and let F_0 be the subgroup of S_W generated by $X_0 = \{|x| : x \in X\}$. We claim that F_0 is free on X_0.

An arbitrary element (other than the identity) of F_0 has a factorization $|x_1^{\epsilon_1}| \cdots |x_n^{\epsilon_n}|$, where $\epsilon_i = \pm 1$ and $|x^\epsilon|$ and $|x^{-\epsilon}|$ are never adjacent (otherwise we may cancel). Such a factorization is unique, for applying this function to the reduced word 1 yields the reduced word $x_1^{\epsilon_1} \cdots x_n^{\epsilon_n}$, and we have already noted that a reduced word has a unique spelling. Hence, two different factorizations are distinct permutations.

Suppose G is a group and $f\colon X_0 \to G$ is a function. Define $h\colon F_0 \to G$ by

$$h(|x_1^{\epsilon_1}| \cdots |x_n^{\epsilon_n}|) = f(|x_1|)^{\epsilon_1} \cdots f(|x_n|)^{\epsilon_n};$$

h is well defined, since the factorization of an element of F_0 into powers of $|x|$ is unique. Now if α and β are in F_0, then $\alpha = |x_1^{\epsilon_1}| \cdots |x_n^{\epsilon_n}|$ and $\beta = |y_1^{\eta_1}| \cdots |y_m^{\eta_m}|$; thus, after possible cancellations,

$$\alpha\beta = |x_1^{\epsilon_1}| \cdots |x_s^{\epsilon_s}| \, |y_t^{\eta_t}| \cdots |y_m^{\eta_m}| \qquad s \le n, \ 1 \le t;$$

(our notation is careless, for we do not wish to overlook the cases in which all the $|x|$ are cancelled by $|y|$ or all the $|y|$ are cancelled by $|x|$). Since cancellation in F_0 implies cancellation in the group G, we have $h(\alpha\beta) = h(\alpha)h(\beta)$. Thus, h is a homomorphism; it is uniquely determined by f because X_0 generates F_0. Therefore, F_0 is free on X_0.

By Exercise 1.16, the set of reduced words in X under juxtaposition is a group isomorphic to F_0, and it is free on X. ∎

COROLLARY 11.2 Every group G is a quotient of a free group.

Proof Consider G as a set, and let F be free on G.

$$\begin{array}{ccc} F & & \\ \uparrow & \diagdown & \\ G & \xrightarrow{f} & G \end{array}$$

If $f\colon G \to G$ is the identity map, then there is a homomorphism $h\colon F \to G$ extending f; h is onto because f is onto. ∎

Definition A group G is defined by **generators** $X = \{x_k\}$ **and relations** $\triangle = \{r_j = 1\}$ in case F is free on X, R is the *normal* subgroup of F generated by $\{r_j\}$, and $G \approx F/R$. We also say that $(X|\triangle)$ is a **presentation** of G.

Examples **5** $G = \sigma(6)$ has generators x and y and relations $x^2 = 1$, $y^3 = 1$, and $x^{-1}y^{-1}xy = 1$.

6 The quaternions have generators a and b and relations $a^4 = 1$, $b^2 = a^2$, and $b^{-1}ab = a^{-1}$.

7   The dihedral group D_n has generators s and t and relations $s^n = 1$, $t^2 = 1$, and $tst = s^{-1}$; (compare D_3 with $\sigma(6)$).

8   A free group on $\{x_k\}$ has generators $\{x_k\}$ and no relations.

Exercises   11.1   Prove the existence of the following groups:

(a)   The generalized quaternion groups Q_n.

(b)   The groups of order p^3 described in Exercise 5.30.

11.2   A free group on no generators has one element; a free group on one generator is infinite cyclic; a free group on more than one generator is a centerless group in which every element (save the identity) has infinite order.

11.3   The group G with the presentation

$$(x, y \,|\, x^2 = 1, y^3 = 1)$$

is infinite.

11.4   Let F be free and K an arbitrary group; every extension of K by F is split.

11.5   If X is a set, there exists a free semigroup on X; every semigroup is a homomorphic image of a free semigroup. Conclude that an arbitrary semigroup can be described by a presentation giving generators and relations. (This existence proof is much simpler than that of a free group, for there is no cancellation here.)

11.6   An endomorphism $\varphi: G \to G$ is a **retraction** if $\varphi \circ \varphi = \varphi$. If φ is a retraction of G having kernel K and image L, then $G = KL$, $K \cap L = \{1\}$, and K is the normal subgroup of G generated by all elements $g\varphi(g^{-1})$, where $g \in G$. (Therefore, G is a semidirect product).

11.7   Let F be free on $\{x_k\}$ and let F' denote the commutator subgroup of F; F/F' is free abelian on $\{F'x_k\}$, a set having the same number of elements as $\{x_k\}$.

11.8   Let $X = \{x_k\}$ and let $Y \subset X$. If F is free on X and H is the normal subgroup generated by Y, then F/H is free.

Now that we know the existence of free groups, let us examine their uniqueness.

THEOREM 11.3   Let X and Y be nonempty sets, F free on X, and G free on Y. Then $F \approx G$ if and only if X and Y have the same number of elements.

Proof   If $F \approx G$, then $F_1 \approx G_1$ (where $F_1 = F/F'$ and $G_1 = G/G'$). By Exercise 11.7, F_1 is free abelian on the cosets of X and G_1 is free abelian on the cosets of Y. By Theorem 9.16, X and Y have the same number of elements.

Suppose $f: X \to Y$ is a one-to-one correspondence. Consider the diagram

$$F \overset{\alpha}{\dashrightarrow} G$$
$$\uparrow {\scriptstyle f} \uparrow$$
$$X \underset{f^{-1}}{\overset{}{\rightleftarrows}} Y$$

Since F is free on X, there is a homomorphism $\alpha: F \to G$ extending f; since G is free on Y, there is a homomorphism $\beta: G \to F$ extending f^{-1}. The composite $\alpha\beta: G \to G$ is a homomorphism fixing Y pointwise, and so is the identity (by the uniqueness of the extension $\alpha\beta$). Similarly, $\beta\alpha: F \to F$ is the identity, so that $\alpha: F \to G$ is an isomorphism. ∎

Definition   If F is a free group, the **rank** of F, $r(F)$, is the number of elements in a free set of generators. (We shall only consider F having rank 0, 1, 2, $\cdots$, and infinity.)

COROLLARY 11.4   If F is free on X, then F is generated by X.
Proof   Let Y be a set having the same number of elements as X. If G is the free group on Y (as constructed in Theorem 11.1) then Y generates G. By Theorem 11.3, there is an isomorphism $\beta: G \to F$ that takes Y onto X; therefore, X generates F.

The Subgroup Theorem

Definition   If S is a subgroup of G, a **right transversal of S in G** (**complete set of representatives**) is a subset of G consisting of precisely one element from each right coset of S in G.

Definition   If F is free on X, we define $l(1) = 0$; $l(y) = n$ if $y = x_1^{\epsilon_1} \cdots x_n^{\epsilon_n}$, where $x_i \in X$, $\epsilon_i = \pm 1$, and this product is a reduced word in X; $l(y)$ is the **length** of y.

THEOREM 11.5 (*Nielsen-Schreier*)   Every subgroup S of a free group F is itself free.

Let us first give an outline of the proof. The only way to prove that S is free is to exhibit a free set of generators for it. Since all we know about S is that it lies in F, it is reasonable to consider the cosets of S in F, and hence transversals of S in F. Consideration of any fixed transversal allows us to exhibit elements $t_{b,x}$ of S (that later will be seen to generate S). After examining relations among these elements (equations (**i**) and (**ii**) below), one can give a presentation of S (Corollary 11.7). This presentation is greatly simplified by using a special kind of transversal, and it can then be shown that a free set of generators for S consists of certain $t_{b,x}$.

Proof[2]   Let F be free on X, and let $\{\overline{Sb}\}$ (where $\overline{Sb}$ denotes an element of Sb) be a transversal of S in F subject only to the condition $\overline{S} = 1$. For every $x \in X$, $(\overline{Sb})x$ and $\overline{Sbx}$ both lie in Sbx, so that the element $t_{b,x}$ defined by

$$t_{b,x} = (\overline{Sb})x(\overline{Sbx})^{-1}$$

lies in S. Let Y be free on $\{y_{b,x}\}$, where $\{y_{b,x}\}$ is a set in one-to-one correspondence with $\{t_{b,x}\}$.

[2] This proof is due to A. J. Weir, "The Reidemeister-Schreier and Kuros subgroup theorems," *Mathematika*, 3 (1956), pp. 47–55.

LEMMA 11.6   Let $\alpha: Y \to S$ be the homomorphism sending each $y_{b,x}$ into $t_{b,x}$. There is a homomorphism $\beta: S \to Y$ with $\alpha\beta = 1{:}S$.

Proof   We approximate β by constructing a family of functions (one for each coset Sb) mapping $F \to Y$. Our notation for each such function is $u \to u^{Sb}$, where $u \in F$. For fixed Sb, define $1^{Sb} = 1$, and if $x \in X$, define $x^{Sb} = \overline{Yb,x}$. We wish to extend the domain of these functions to all of F in such a way that they are related by the equations:

(i) $$(uv)^{Sb} = u^{Sb}v^{Sbu} \qquad u, v \in F.$$

Formula **(i)** applied to $(x^{-1}x)^{Sb}$ shows that $(x^{-1})^{Sb}$ must be defined to be $(y_{bx^{-1},x})^{-1}$. All the functions Sb have now been defined on words of length 1. Complete the definitions by induction: if $l(u) = m + 1$, then $u = x^\epsilon v$, where $\epsilon = \pm 1$ and $l(v) = m$. Define $u^{Sb} = (x^\epsilon)^{Sb}v^{Sbx^\epsilon}$. An induction on length shows that, for every $u \in F$,

(ii) $$\alpha(u^{Sb}) = (\overline{Sb})u(\overline{Sbu})^{-1}.$$

Consider the function $u \to u^S$ (i.e. $Sb = S$), and let β be the restriction of this function to S (i.e., $u \in S$). Equation **(i)** implies that β is a homomorphism, and equation **(ii)** implies that $\alpha\beta = 1{:}S$. ∎

It follows that $\varphi: Y \to Y$ defined by $\varphi = \beta\alpha$ is a retraction. Moreover, α is onto, so that S is generated by the $t_{b,x}$.

COROLLARY 11.7 $(\{y_{b,x}\}|\{b^S = 1\})$ is a presentation of S, where the b form a transversal of S in F.

Proof   By Exercise 11.6, S has a presentation

$$(\{y_{b,x}\}|\{y_{b,x} = \varphi(y_{b,x})\}).$$

Now

$$\varphi(y_{b,x}) = \beta\alpha(y_{b,x}) = \beta(t_{b,x}) = (bxu^{-1})^S,$$

where $u = \overline{Sbx}$, and by **(i)**,

$$(bxu^{-1})^S = b^Sx^{Sb}(u^{-1})^{Sbx} = b^Sy_{b,x}(u^{-1})^{Su}.$$

Since $1 = (u^{-1}u)^{Su} = (u^{-1})^{Su}u^S$, we have $(u^{-1})^{Su} = (u^S)^{-1}$. Therefore,

$$\varphi(y_{b,x}) = b^S y_{b,x}(u^S)^{-1}.$$

Let N be the normal subgroup of Y generated by $\{b^S : b$ is in the fixed transversal$\}$; let M be the normal subgroup of Y generated by $\{y_{b,x}^{-1}\varphi(y_{b,x})\}$. Now observe that $u^S \in N$, since u is an element of the transversal. Thus,

$$y_{b,x}^{-1}\varphi(y_{b,x}) = (y_{b,x}^{-1}b^S y_{b,x})(u^S)^{-1} \in N,$$

while

$$\begin{aligned}
b^S &= \varphi(y_{b,x})u^S y_{b,x}^{-1}\\
&= \varphi(y_{b,x})y_{b,x}^{-1}(y_{b,x}u^S y_{b,x}^{-1}) \in M.
\end{aligned}$$

It follows that $M = N$. $\blacksquare$

In order to simplify this presentation further, we shall choose a special transversal.

LEMMA 11.8   There exists a transversal B of S in F such that if $b = x_1^{\epsilon_1} \cdots x_n^{\epsilon_n} \in B$ is a reduced word in X, then $x_1^{\epsilon_1} \cdots x_k^{\epsilon_k} \in B$ for $1 \le k \le n$. (We call B a **Schreier transversal.**)

Proof   We define the length of a coset Sg as the minimum of the lengths of its elements, and we prove, by induction on this length, that the desired kind of representative exists for all cosets of length $\le n$. We begin by choosing $\overline{S} = 1$. Let Sz have length $n + 1$, and let $ux^\epsilon \in Sz$, where $\epsilon = \pm 1$ and $l(ux^\epsilon) = n + 1$. The coset Su has length n and so has a representative b such that any initial segment of b is also a representative. Choose bx^ϵ as a representative of $Sz = (Su)x^\epsilon = (Sb)x^\epsilon$. $\blacksquare$

The following lemma completes the proof of the Nielsen-Schreier theorem.

LEMMA 11.9   If $\{\overline{Sb}\}$ is a Schreier transversal of S in F, then S is free on the set of those $t_{b,x}$ that are distinct from 1.

Proof   Let $b = \overline{Sb}$; we shall show that the normal subgroup of Y generated by all b^S (call it N) is equal to the normal subgroup generated by all those $y_{b,x}$ with $t_{b,x} = 1$ (call it K). Corollary 11.7 and Exercise 11.8 will then complete the proof.

By Corollary 11.7, $K \subset N$, so that it suffices to prove the reverse inclusion. We shall show that each b^S is a word in the special $y_{b,x}$ by performing an induction on $l(b)$. If $l(b) = 0$, then $b = 1$, and all is well. If $l(b) > 0$, then $b = ux^\epsilon$, where $\epsilon = \pm 1$, $l(u) < l(b)$, and u is also a representative (for $\{\overline{Sb}\}$ is a Schreier transversal). By (i),

$$b^S = u^S(x^\epsilon)^{Su}.$$

By induction, u^S is a word in the special y. If $\epsilon = +1$, then $(x^\epsilon)^{Su} = x^{Su} = y_{u,x}$; since

$$\alpha(y_{u,x}) = (\overline{Su})x(\overline{Sux})^{-1} = ux(ux)^{-1} = 1,$$

$y_{u,x}$ is a special y. If $\epsilon = -1$, then $u = \overline{Sbx}$ and

$$(x^\epsilon)^{Su} = (x^{-1})^{Su} = (x^{-1})^{Sbx} = (y_{b,x})^{-1}$$

Therefore, α sends this element into $(t_{bx})^{-1}$, so that

$$\alpha(y_{b,x}^{-1}) = [(\overline{Sb})x(\overline{Sbx})^{-1}]^{-1} = (ux^{-1}xu^{-1})^{-1} = 1,$$

and $y_{b,x}$ is a special y. Thus, every b^S is a word in the special y. ∎

There are several other proofs of the subgroup theorem; we cite two of the most interesting. The first is due to Baer and Levi, *"Freie Produkte und ihre Untergruppen,"* Comp. Math (1936), and uses techniques of algebraic topology, specifically, fundamental groups of certain covering spaces. The second is due to P. J. Higgins, *Presentations of groupoids, with applications to groups*, Proc. Camb. Phil. Soc. (1963), and uses only the rudiments of graph theory. Given a presentation of a group G, then to any subgroup H of G one may associate a certain directed graph in such a way that paths of the graph correspond to words in the generators of G; if G is free, a free set of generators of H is essentially the complement of a maximal tree of the graph.

THEOREM 11.10   If F is a free group of finite rank n and S is a subgroup of finite index j, then S is a free group of rank $jn - j + 1$.[3]

Proof   Let $X = \{x_1, x_2, \cdots, x_n\}$ be a free set of generators of F and let $\{\overline{Sb}\}$ be a Schreier transversal of S in F. In the notation of

[3] In the geometric proofs of the subgroup theorem, this number is the number of edges of a graph less the number of its vertices.

the preceding theorem, there are just jn $t_{b,x}$. Therefore, by Lemma 11.9, S is a free group of rank $jn - k$, where k is the number of $t_{b,x}$ equal to 1.

To each right coset Sa other than S itself, we associate a pair $(b,x) = \varphi(Sa)$ (which will index a t). Suppose $\overline{Sa} = a = ux^\epsilon$, where $x \in X$, $\epsilon = \pm 1$, and ux^ϵ is a reduced word in X. We define

$$\varphi(Sa) = \begin{cases} (a,x) & \text{if } \epsilon = -1; \\ (u,x) & \text{if } \epsilon = +1. \end{cases}$$

Observe that if $\epsilon = -1$, $t_{a,x} = 1$, and if $\epsilon = +1$, then $t_{u,x} = 1$.

We claim that all these associated pairs are distinct, i.e., that φ is one-to-one. Suppose $\varphi(Sa) = \varphi(Sb)$. A glance at the definition of φ tells us that both $\overline{Sa}$ and $\overline{Sb}$ must have the same last letter, say, x. Hence, $\overline{Sa} = ux^\epsilon$ and $\overline{Sb} = bx^\eta$. If $\epsilon = -1 = \eta$, then $\varphi(Sa) = (a,x)$ and $\varphi(Sb) = (b,x)$ so that $a = b$ and $Sa = Sb$; if $\epsilon = +1 = \eta$, then $\varphi(Sa) = (u,x)$ and $\varphi(Sb) = (v,x)$ so that $u = v$, $a = b$ and $Sa = Sb$. Finally, if $\epsilon = -1$ and $\eta = +1$, then $\varphi(Sa) = (a,x)$, $\varphi(Sb) = (v,x)$, and $a = v$. Therefore, $\overline{Sb} = vx = ax = (ux^{-1})x = u$, so that the last letter of u is x. This contradicts the fact that $\overline{Sa} = ux^{-1}$ is a reduced word in X. We have thus exhibited $j - 1$ $t_{b,x}$ equal to 1.

Every (b,x) with $t_{b,x} = 1$ must arise from a coset of S via φ, for $t_{b,x} = 1$ merely says that $(\overline{Sb})x = \overline{Sbx}$. We conclude that S is a free group of rank $jn - (j - 1) = jn - j + 1$. ∎

THEOREM 11.11   Let F be free of rank 2; then F', the commutator subgroup of F, is free of infinite rank.

Proof   Let $\{x,y\}$ be a free set of generators of F. By Exercise 11.7, F/F' is a free abelian group generated by $F'x$ and $F'y$; hence, every right coset of F' in F has a unique representative of the form $x^m y^n$. The assignment $\overline{F'b} = x^m y^n$ is thus a well defined function that is clearly a Schreier transversal of F' in F.

If $n > 0$, then $\overline{Sy^n} = y^n$ while $\overline{Sy^n x} \neq y^n x$. Therefore, $(\overline{Sy^n})x(\overline{Sy^n x})^{-1} \neq 1$, so that there are infinitely many t distinct from 1. The theorem now follows from Lemma 11.9. ∎

It follows that, in contrast to abelian groups, a subgroup of a finitely generated group need not be finitely generated.

Exercises   11.9   If F is free of rank > 1, then F' is free of infinite rank.

11.10   Let G be a finite group that is not cyclic, and let $G \approx F/S$, where F is free of finite rank. Prove that rank $S >$ rank F.

11.11   Let F be free of rank 2. Does F have a proper normal subgroup H that is finitely generated?

11.12   A free group of rank > 1 is not solvable.

11.13   Exhibit infinitely many free sets of generators of a free group of rank 2.

11.14   Let F be free on $\{a,b\}$. Prove that F contains a subgroup that is free on infinitely many generators, one of which is b.

11.15   Let H be a group such that, for every group G, each extension of G by H is split. Prove that H is free. (This is the converse of Exercise 11.4.)

11.16   Let G be a finitely generated group containing a subgroup H of finite index. Prove that H is finitely generated.

*11.17   Let G be a group having n generators and k relations, where $n > k$; then G contains an element of infinite order. (*Hint:* Map a free group on n generators onto a free abelian group on n generators, and observe what happens to the relations; use Exercise 9.38.)

Free Products

We now generalize the notion of a free group to that of a free product. As with the definition of a free group, we shall define a free product as a group having a certain "universal mapping" property. Since it is not obvious that such a group exists, we shall then be obliged to construct one.

Definition   Let $\{A_\alpha\}$ be a family of groups. A **free product of the** A_α is a group P having the following properties:

(i) P contains an isomorphic copy of each A_α, i.e., for each α there is a homomorphism $i_\alpha \colon A_\alpha \to P$ that is one-to-one.

(ii)   For every group G and every family of homomorphisms $f_\alpha \colon A_\alpha \to G$, there is a unique homomorphism $\psi \colon P \to G$ extending each f_α, i.e., for each α, $\psi i_\alpha = f_\alpha$.

The diagrams are:

$$
\begin{array}{ccc}
P & \overset{\psi}{\dashrightarrow} & \\
{\scriptstyle i_\alpha}\uparrow & \searrow & \\
A_\alpha & \underset{f_\alpha}{\to} & G
\end{array}
$$

The reader should think of the maps i_α only as inclusion maps; indeed, no one will be harmed if he pretends the A_α are actually subgroups of P. The reader should compare this definition with the corresponding property of direct sums (Exercise 9.9).

Example 9   A free group is a free product of infinite cyclic groups.

THEOREM 11.12   If $\{A_\alpha\}$ is a family of groups, a free product of the A_α does exist.

Proof   This proof is so similar to the construction of a free group that we present only its highlights and leave the details to the reader.

Call $\bigcup A_\alpha$ the *alphabet*[4] and the elements of the alphabet *letters;* one may now form *words* with these letters. A word w is reduced if $w = 1$ or if $w = a_1 a_2 \cdots a_k$, where no $a_i = 1$ and no adjacent letters lie in the same A_α. The reader may now prove that the set of reduced words under juxtaposition is a free product of the A_α. ∎

THEOREM 11.13   Let $\{A_\alpha\}$ be a family of groups, and let G and H each be free products of the A_α. Then $G \approx H$.

Proof   Let $i_\alpha\colon A_\alpha \to G$ and $j_\alpha\colon A_\alpha \to H$ be the imbeddings, and let $h_\alpha\colon A_\alpha \to A_\alpha$ be the identity on A_α.

$$
\begin{array}{ccc}
G & \overset{\psi}{\dashrightarrow} & H \\
{\scriptstyle i_\alpha}\uparrow & & \uparrow{\scriptstyle j_\alpha} \\
A_\alpha & \underset{h_\alpha}{\to} & A_\alpha
\end{array}
$$

Then $f_\alpha = j_\alpha h_\alpha\colon A_\alpha \to H$, so that there is a map $\psi\colon G \to H$ extending each f_α. Similarly, if $g_\alpha = i_\alpha h_\alpha\colon A_\alpha \to G$, there is a map $\theta\colon H \to G$ extending each g_α. The composite

---

[4] We assume that the A_α are pairwise disjoint; this can always be arranged by "painting elements in distinct A_α different colors."

$$G \xrightarrow{\theta\psi} G$$
$$^{i_\alpha}\uparrow \quad_{h_\alpha} \quad \uparrow^{i_\alpha}$$
$$A_\alpha \xrightarrow{} A_\alpha$$

$\theta\psi \colon G \to G$ is such that $\theta\psi i_\alpha = i_\alpha$ for every α. Since the identity map $I \colon G \to G$ also has the property that $Ii_\alpha = i_\alpha$ for all α, the uniqueness part of the definition of free product implies that $\theta\psi = I$. Similarly, $\psi\theta$ is the identity on H, so that ψ is an isomorphism. ∎

Because of this theorem, we may speak of *the* free product of the A_α; it is denoted $*A_\alpha$. If there are only finitely many A_α, we also denote $*A_\alpha$ by $A_1 * A_2 * \cdots * A_n$.

Kurosch has proved that every subgroup of a free product is itself a free product. Unfortunately, the proof is too lengthy to present here; we refer the reader to either of the cited papers of A. J. Weir or P. J. Higgins (see page 245).

Exercises 11.18 The operation of free product is commutative and associative: For any groups A, B, C, one has $A * B \approx B * A$ and $(A * B) * C \approx A * (B * C)$.

11.19 If N is the normal subgroup of $A * B$ generated by A, then $(A * B)/N \approx B$ (cf. Exercise 11.8).

11.20 If G' is the commutator subgroup of $G = *A_\alpha$, then $G/G' \approx \sum (A_\alpha/A'_\alpha)$ (cf. Exercise 11.7).

11.21 If G and H have more than one element, then $G * H$ is an infinite, centerless group.

11.22 If A_α has a presentation $(X_\alpha | \triangle_\alpha)$, then $*A_\alpha$ has a presentation $(\bigcup X_\alpha | \bigcup \triangle_\alpha)$.

11.23 If G has a presentation$(x, y | x^2 = 1, y^3 = 1)$, then $G \approx \sigma(2) * \sigma(3)$.

11.24 Let M be the **modular group**, i.e., the multiplicative group of all 2×2 unimodular matrices over Z modulo the subgroup $\{\pm E\}$. Prove that $M \approx \sigma(2) * \sigma(3)$ (see Exercise 2.19).

11.25 If $G = \sigma(2) * \sigma(4)$, then $\sigma(2)$ and $\sigma(4)$ are each maximal 2-subgroups of G. Conclude that in an infinite group, sylow subgroups need not be isomorphic; a fortiori, they need not be conjugate.

11.26 If $f \colon G_1 \to G_2$ and $g \colon H_1 \to H_2$ are homomorphisms, there is a unique homomorphism $h \colon G_1 * H_1 \to G_2 * H_2$ such that $h|G_1 = f$ and $h|G_2 = g$.

Free Products
with Amalgamated Subgroups

Let B be a group and let $\{A_\alpha\}$ be a family of groups. For each α, let there be given a subgroup B_α of A_α and an isomorphism $\varphi_\alpha\colon B \to B_\alpha$.

Definition   The **free product of the** A_α **with amalgamated subgroup** B is the group

$$((*A_\alpha) * B)/N,$$

where N is the normal subgroup generated by all elements of the form $b\varphi_\alpha(b^{-1})$ where $b \in B$.

Exercise   11.27   Let A_α have a presentation $(X_\alpha|\triangle_\alpha)$ and let $\triangle$ be the set of equations $\varphi_\alpha(b)\varphi_\beta(b^{-1})$ (for all α, β and all $b \in B$). Prove that the free product with amalgamated subgroup has a presentation $(\bigcup X_\alpha|(\bigcup \triangle_\alpha) \cup \triangle)$.

It is clear that our construction identifies the various subgroups B_α with B via the isomorphisms φ_α; it is not clear whether other significant identifications are consequences of this amalgamation. For example, is it obvious that the free product with amalgamated subgroup is nontrivial?

For each α, choose a left transversal of B_α in A_α subject only to the condition that the representative of B_α be 1. Let $\bar{a}_\alpha$ denote the representative of $a_\alpha B_\alpha$, so that

$$a_\alpha = \bar{a}_\alpha b_\alpha \quad \text{for some } b_\alpha \in B_\alpha.$$

Observe that b_α is uniquely determined by a_α (once the transversal is chosen).

Definition   A **normal form** is an element of $(*A_\alpha) * B$, which has the form

$$\bar{a}_1\bar{a}_2 \cdots \bar{a}_n b,$$

where $b \in B, n \geq 0$, and adjacent $\bar{a}$ lie in distinct A_α.

In the special case that B (hence, all B_α) $= \{1\}$, every reduced word in the free product is a normal form.

THEOREM 11.14 (*Normal Form*)   Let B be a group and $\{A_\alpha\}$ be a family of groups; for each α, let B_α be a subgroup of A_α, and let $\varphi_\alpha: B \to B_\alpha$ be an isomorphism. If G is the corresponding free product with amalgamated subgroup, then every element in G has a unique representative that is a normal form.

Proof   Let N be the normal subgroup generated by all elements $b\varphi_\alpha(b^{-1})$. If w and w' are elements of $(*A_\alpha) * B$, then we shall write $w \equiv w'$ instead of "w and w' lie in the same coset of N." If $x \in G$, then x has a representative $a_1 a_2 \cdots a_n \in (*A_\alpha) * B$. Now the letters a_i either lie in B or in some A_{α_i}; in the latter case, $a_i = \bar{a}_i b_i$ for some $b_i \in B_{\alpha_i}$. But $b_i \equiv \varphi^{-1}_{\alpha_i}(b_i) \in B$, so that $a_i \equiv \bar{a}_i \varphi^{-1}_{\alpha_i}(b_i)$. Hence, $a_1 a_2 \cdots a_n$ lies in the same coset of N as a product of the $\bar{a}$ and b. Therefore, if we can commute a product $b\bar{a}$ into a product $\bar{a}'b'$, we can transform any product

$$b_1 \bar{a}_1 b_2 \bar{a}_2 \cdots b_n \bar{a}_n b_0$$

into a normal form by successively commuting the b from left to right.

Suppose, then, that we are given a product ba, where $b \in B$ and $a \in A_\alpha$. Define $b_1 = \varphi_\alpha(b)$ and $a' = b_1 a \in A_\alpha$. Now $a' = \bar{a}_1 b'_1$ for some $b'_1 \in B_\alpha$. Finally, define $b' = \varphi^{-1}_\alpha(b'_1)$. We claim that $ba \equiv \bar{a}_1 b'$:

$$\bar{a}_1 b' = \bar{a}_1 \varphi^{-1}_\alpha(b'_1) = a'(b'_1)^{-1} \varphi^{-1}_\alpha(b'_1) \equiv \bar{a}_1 b'_1$$

and

$$\bar{a}_1 b'_1 = a' = b_1 a = \varphi_\alpha(b)a = \varphi_\alpha(b)b^{-1}ba \equiv ba.$$

We have shown that every $x \in G$ is represented by a normal form. But we have done more; given any reduced word $a_1 a_2 \cdots a_n$ in $(*A_\alpha) * B$, the commuting process described above assigns a specific normal form to it. We denote this normal form $F(a_1 a_2 \cdots a_n)$.

It is conceivable that there are normal forms $\equiv a_1 a_2 \cdots a_n$ aside from $F(a_1 a_2 \cdots a_n)$. In order to prove the uniqueness of this normal form, we use the device of Theorem 11.1. Let M be the set of all normal forms; observe that two normal forms are equal if and only if they have the same spelling. If $a \in A_\alpha$, we define a function $|a|: M \to M$ by

$$|a|(\bar{a}_1\bar{a}_2 \cdots \bar{a}_n b) = F(a\bar{a}_1\bar{a}_2 \cdots \bar{a}_n b).$$

Clearly, $|1|$ is the identity function on M. Furthermore, consideration of the several cases (depending on possible cancellations) shows that if $a, a' \in A_\alpha$, then

$$|a| \circ |a'| = |aa'|.$$

Therefore, $|a^{-1}| = |a|^{-1}$, so that each $|a|$ is a permutation of M.

Let S_M be the group of all permutations of M. For each α, the map of A_α into S_M given by

$$a \to |a|$$

has been seen to be a homomorphism. If $a \neq 1$, then $|a|(1) = \bar{a}b$, so that $|a|$ is not the identity; hence, the homomorphism is one-to-one. Therefore, S_M contains an isomorphic copy of each A_α. Also, if $b \in B$, we may define

$$|b| = |\varphi_\alpha(b)|;$$

this is well defined. By the defining property of a free product, there is a homomorphism

$$\Phi \colon (*A_\alpha) * B \to S_M$$

which extends each of the homomorphisms on the factors. Since Φ sends every $b\varphi_\alpha(b_\alpha^{-1})$ into the identity, Φ induces a homomorphism

$$\Phi' \colon G \to S_M$$

by

$$\Phi'(x) = \Phi'(a_1a_2 \cdots a_n N) = \Phi(a_1a_2 \cdots a_n).$$

This says that if w and $w' \in (*A_\alpha) * B$ and $w \equiv w'$, then $\Phi(w) = \Phi(w')$. Therefore, if $\bar{a}_1\bar{a}_2 \cdots \bar{a}_n b$ is a normal form representing $x \in G$, then $\Phi'(x) = |\bar{a}_1| \, |\bar{a}_2| \, \cdots \, |\bar{a}_n| \, |b|$. If $\bar{a}_1\bar{a}_2 \cdots \bar{a}_n b$ and $\bar{a}_1'\bar{a}_2' \cdots \bar{a}_m' b'$ are distinct normal forms, then $|\bar{a}_1| \, |\bar{a}_2| \, \cdots \, |\bar{a}_n| \, |b|$ and $|\bar{a}_1'| \, |\bar{a}_2'| \, \cdots \, |\bar{a}_m'| \, |b'|$ are distinct permutations, for they assume distinct values at 1. Hence, x cannot be represented by two distinct normal forms. ∎

COROLLARY 11.15   Let G be isomorphic to the free product of groups $\{A_\alpha\}$ with amalgamated subgroup B. Then G contains subgroups $\{A_\alpha'\}$ and B' such that:

(i) $B \approx B'$ and, for all α, $A_\alpha \approx A'_\alpha$.
(ii) G is generated by $\{A'_\alpha\}$.
(iii) if $\alpha \neq \beta$, $A'_\alpha \cap A'_\beta = B'$.

Proof   Let H be the subset of all permutations of M (our notation is as in Theorem 11.14) of the form $|\bar{a}_1| \, |\bar{a}_2| \, \cdots \, |\bar{a}_n| \, |b|$; H is a subgroup of S_M, for it is the image of G under the homomorphism Φ'. Now Φ' is an isomorphism of G onto H, for if $\Phi'(x) = |1|$, then $x = 1$.

Our corollary is now easy. Let $B' = \{|b| : b \in B\}$, and let $A'_\alpha = \{|a| \, |b| : a \in A_\alpha, b \in B\}$. Finally, if $\alpha \neq \beta$, then $|\bar{a}_\alpha| \, |b| = ||\bar{a}_\beta| \, |b'|$ if and only if $\bar{a}_\alpha = 1 = \bar{a}_\beta$ and $b = b'$. ∎

We now apply this last construction to obtain some imbedding theorems.

THEOREM 11.16 (*Higman, Neumann, and Neumann*)
Let G be a group that contains isomorphic subgroups A and B; let $\varphi : A \to B$ be an isomorphism. There exists a group H containing G in which φ is induced by an inner automorphism, i.e., there is an element $t \in H$ with

$$\varphi(a) = t^{-1}at \quad \text{for all } a \in A.$$

Proof   Let $[u]$ and $[v]$ be disjoint infinite cyclic groups; let

$$K_1 = G * [u],$$
$$K_2 = G * [v],$$

and let L_1 be the subgroup of K_1 generated by G and $u^{-1}Au$. Now

$$L_1 = G * u^{-1}Au,$$

for there can be no equation

$$g_1 u^{-1}a_1 u g_2 u^{-1}a_2 u \cdots g_n u^{-1}a_n u = 1$$

in K_1; a fortiori, there can be no such equation in L_1. Similarly, the subgroup L_2 of K_2 generated by G and $v^{-1}Bv$ is a free product:

$$L_2 = G * v^{-1}Bv.$$

By Exercise 11.26, there is an isomorphism $\mu : L_1 \to L_2$ such that $\mu|G$ is the identity and $\mu(u^{-1}au) = v^{-1}\varphi(a)v$.

Let H be the free product of K_1 and K_2 in which we amalgamate L_1 and L_2 via the isomorphism μ. By Corollary 11.15, H contains a subgroup isomorphic to L_1 (and L_1 contains G).

Furthermore, for each $a \in A$,

$$u^{-1}au = v^{-1}\varphi(a)v.$$

If $t = uv^{-1}$, then $t \in H$, and for all $a \in A$,

$$t^{-1}at = \varphi(a). \quad \blacksquare$$

If G is a countable group, then G is a homomorphic image of a countable free group F of infinite rank:

$$F/R \approx G,$$

where R is a normal subgroup of F. Now we know that F can be imbedded in a free group F_1 on two generators (Theorem 11.11); were R normal in the larger group F_1, then G would be imbedded in F_1/R, a group on two generators. This proof is fictitious, but the theorem is true.

THEOREM 11.17 (*Higman, Neumann, and Neumann*)
Every countable group G can be imbedded in a group H that can be generated by two elements.

Proof[5]   Suppose that G is generated by $\{g_1, g_2, \cdots\}$. Let F_1 be the free group generated by $\{a, b\}$, and let U be a free subgroup of F_1 with infinitely many free generators, one of which is b (Exercise 11.14) and the others of which are $u_1, u_2, \cdots$.

The group

$$K = G * F_1$$

is generated by $\{a, b, g_1, g_2, \cdots\}$. If we now put

$$w_0 = b$$

and

$$w_i = g_i u_i, \quad i = 1, 2, \cdots,$$

then K is also generated by $\{a, b = w_0, w_1, w_2, \cdots\}$. Let W be the subgroup of K generated by the w. We claim that W is freely generated by the w, for if

[5] This proof is that of B. H. Neumann, *An Essay on Free Products of Groups*, Phil. Trans. Royal Soc. London, 246, (1954), pp. 503–554.

$$\pi: K \to F_1$$

is the homomorphism obtained by setting each element in G equal to 1, then π sends the w_i onto the free generators $\{u_0, u_1, \cdots\}$ of U.

Now let F_2 be a free group on $\{b',c\}$, and let V be a free subgroup of F_2 with infinitely many free generators, one of which is b':

$$v_0 = b', \quad v_1 = v_1(b',c), \quad v_2 = v_2(b',c), \quad \cdots.$$

This notation means that $v_1, v_2, \cdots$ are words in the letters b' and c. The groups W and V are isomorphic, for they are free groups with the same number of free generators. Choose an isomorphism $\varphi: W \to V$ such that

$$\varphi(w_i) = v_i, \quad i = 0, 1, 2, \cdots.$$

Let L be the free product of K and F_2 in which we amalgamate the subgroups W and V via the isomorphism φ; L is generated by $\{a, b', c, w_0, w_1, \cdots\}$. But in L, $b = b'$ and each $w_i = v_i$. Since $v_i = v_i(b',c)$, L is generated by $\{a,b,c\}$. Now L contains the isomorphic subgroups $F_1 = [a,b]$ and $F_2 = [b,c]$. By Theorem 11.16, we may adjoin an element t such that

$$t^{-1}F_1t = F_2;$$

we call the resulting group H. In particular,

$$t^{-1}at = b \quad \text{and} \quad t^{-1}bt = c.$$

Thus, H is generated by $\{a,b,c, \text{ and } t\}$; even more, H is generated by c and t. Thus, G is imbedded in H, a group that can be generated by two elements. ∎

Exercises   11.28   Let G be a countable group having n defining relations. Prove that G can be imbedded in a group H having two generators and only n defining relations.

*11.29   Let G be a group in which every element $\neq 1$ has infinite order. G can be imbedded in a group H, where H has only two conjugacy classes (cf. Exercise 3.24).

11.30   Prove that there exists a group G on two generators that contains an isomorphic copy of every countable abelian group.

Chapter 12

The Word Problem

Statement of the Problem; Turing Machines

Novikov and Boone have proved that there exists a group G with an unsolvable word problem; there is thus a sequence of elementary questions about G that no one machine can answer. This chapter is devoted to proving this remarkable result.

We begin by defining the class of groups we shall be interested in.

Definition   A group is **finitely presented** in case it has a presentation with only a finite number of generators and a finite number of relations. (B. H. Neumann has proved that there are finitely generated groups that are not finitely presented.)

Exercises   12.1   Every free group of finite rank is finitely presented.

12.2   Every finite group G is finitely presented. (*Hint:* If $|G| = n$, there is a presentation of G with n generators and n^2 relations, the latter being given by the multiplication table of G.)

12.3   Every finitely generated abelian group is finitely presented.

12.4   If G has a presentation with a finite number of relations, then G is a free product of a finitely presented group and a free group.

12.5   If each of G and H is finitely presented, then the same is true of $G \times H$ and $G * H$.

Let Q be a set of questions; a *decision process* for Q is a "uniform set of directions which, when applied to any of the questions in Q, produces the correct answer after a finite number of steps, never at any stage of the process leaving the user in doubt as to what to do next."[1]

Suppose G is a group having the presentation

$$G = (x_1, \cdots, x_n | r_1 = 1, \cdots, r_m = 1).$$

By means of this presentation, every (not necessarily reduced) word in the x represents an element of G. We say that the **word problem** for G is **solvable** in case there exists a decision process for the set of all questions of the form: Does the word w in the x represent the identity element of G?[2]

For the remainder of this chapter, *word* will mean *not necessarily reduced word*. Furthermore, we alter the definition of the *length* of a word w so that it will henceforth mean the number of x_i and x_i^{-1} occurring in the spelling of w. Thus, the empty word has length 0, but $x_1 x_1^{-1}$ has length 2.

In order to illustrate these ideas, we show that a free group

$$G = (x_1, \cdots, x_n | \phi)$$

has a solvable word problem. Here is a decision process:

1. If the length of w is 0 or 1, proceed to step 3. If the length of $w \geq 2$, underline the first adjacent pair of letters (if there is any) of the form $x_i x_i^{-1}$ or $x_i^{-1} x_i$; if there is no such pair, underline the final two letters. Proceed to step 2.

2. If the underlined pair has the form $x_i x_i^{-1}$ or $x_i^{-1} x_i$, erase it, and proceed to step 1; otherwise, proceed to step 3.

3. If the word is empty, write $w = 1$ and stop. If the word is not empty, write $w \neq 1$ and stop.

The reader should experiment a bit with this program until he is convinced it is a decision process.

Exercises   12.6   Sketch a proof that every finite group has a solvable word problem.

---

[1] W. W. Boone, "The Word Problem," *Annals of Math.* (1959), pp. 207–265.

[2] As we have posed it, the word problem for G depends on a particular finite presentation of G. It is true (though we shall not need the fact here) that if the word problem is solvable for some one finite presentation of G, then it is solvable for every finite presentation of G.

12.7 Sketch a proof that every finitely generated abelian group has a solvable word problem.

12.8 Sketch proofs that if each of G and H has a solvable word problem, then the same is true of their direct product $G \times H$ and their free product $G * H$.

Our proof of the Novikov-Boone theorem (Theorem 12.5) is not self-contained, for we shall quote a theorem of Post (exhibiting a specific semigroup with an unsolvable word problem) that we shall not prove. We shall then define a group G and show that solvability of the word problem for G contradicts Post's theorem. Nowhere in the reduction of the group problem to the semigroup problem is a technical definition of unsolvability used, so that the reader knowing only our intuitive description as given above should have no difficulty in following our discussion. We do, however, include a technical definition below. There are at least three good reasons for doing this: The word problem can be properly stated; a discussion of Post's theorem can be given; the generators and relations of Post's semigroup can be accounted for. A more thorough treatment of Turing machines (defined below) could account for the remaining generators and relations of the group G, but such a treatment is beyond the scope of this book.

Let us pose the word problem in a somewhat different setting. List all the words on $x_1, \cdots, x_n$ in the following effective way: first, the empty word; second, the words of length 1; next, the words of length 2, and so on. The words of length 1 are ordered so: $x_1, x_1^{-1}, \cdots, x_n, x_n^{-1}$; the words of length l are ordered lexicographically, i.e., as in a dictionary. All the words are now listed $w_1, w_2, \cdots, w_k, \cdots$ in such a way that, given a word w, one can compute its exact position in this list. From a finite presentation of a group G, we define a function f on the positive integers:

$$f(k) = \begin{cases} 1 & \text{if } w_k \text{ represents the identity of } G; \\ 2 & \text{otherwise.} \end{cases}$$

It is intuitively clear that the word problem for G is solvable if and only if the function f is computable, i.e., there is a complete set of directions for evaluating f. We shall give Turing's definition of computability[3] and begin with the concept of a Turing machine.

---

[3] Logicians have formulated several abstractions of the intuitive idea of computability, and all these abstractions are equivalent in the sense that a function is computable in one formulation if and only if it is computable in any of the other formulations.

Informally, a Turing machine can be pictured as a box with a tape running through it. The tape consists of a serial collection of squares, which is as long to the right and to the left as desired. The box is capable of printing a finite number of symbols s_0, s_1, $\cdots$, s_m and of being in a finite number of states q_0, q_1, $\cdots$, q_n. At any fixed moment, the box is in a state q_i and is "scanning" a particular square of the tape that bears a single symbol s_j (we may agree that s_0 means blank). The action of the machine is determined by its initial structure and by q_i and s_j; this action consists of either stopping or going into some state q_l after obeying one of the following instructions:

1. Erase the symbol s_j and print some symbol s_k.
2. Move one square to the right and scan this square.
3. Move one square to the left and scan this square.

The machine is now ready for its next move.

The machine is started in the first place by being given a tape, which may have some nonblank symbols printed on it (one to a square), and by being set to scan some one square while in a state q_1. The machine may eventually stop, or it may continue working indefinitely. We shall say that a function f is *computable* if there is a Turing machine that, whenever it begins with k printed on its tape, eventually prints $f(k)$ and then stops.

We proceed to a formal definition of a Turing machine. Let us first choose, once for all, two infinite lists of symbols:

$$s_0, s_1, s_2, \cdots \quad \text{and} \quad q_0, q_1, q_2, \cdots .$$

Definition A **quadruple** is a 4-tuple of one of the following three types:

1. $q_i s_j s_k q_l$.
2. $q_i s_j R q_l$.
3. $q_i s_j L q_l$.

Definition A **Turing machine** is a finite, nonempty set of quadruples such that no two quadruples have the same first two symbols.

The three kinds of quadruples correspond to the three kinds of moves in our informal description given above. For example, $q_i s_j R q_l$ may be interpreted as the instruction: "when scanning symbol s_j in state q_i, move right one square and enter state q_l."

A **positive** word is a word with no negative exponents. In particular, the empty word is positive. A **tape expression** is a positive word in the symbols s_j.

Definition An **instantaneous description** α is a positive word on symbols s_j and exactly one q_i (which is not at the right end).

As an example, the instantaneous description $s_2 s_0 q_1 s_5 s_2$ is to be interpreted as "the symbols on the tape are $s_2 s_0 s_5 s_2$ (*with blanks everywhere else*) and the machine is in state q_1 scanning s_5."

Definition Let T be a Turing machine, and let α, β be instantaneous descriptions. We write $\alpha \to \beta$ if there are tape expressions P and Q (possibly empty) such that one of the following conditions holds:

(i) $\left. \begin{aligned} \alpha &= P q_i s_j Q \\ \beta &= P q_l s_k Q \end{aligned} \right\}$ where $q_i s_j s_k q_l \in T$.

(ii) $\left. \begin{aligned} \alpha &= P q_i s_j s_k Q \\ \beta &= P s_j q_l s_k Q \end{aligned} \right\}$ where $q_i s_j R q_l \in T$.

(iii) $\left. \begin{aligned} \alpha &= P q_i s_j \\ \beta &= P s_j q_l s_0 \end{aligned} \right\}$ where $q_i s_j R q_l \in T$.

(iv) $\left. \begin{aligned} \alpha &= P s_k q_i s_j Q \\ \beta &= P q_l s_k s_j Q \end{aligned} \right\}$ where $q_i s_j L q_l \in T$.

(v) $\left. \begin{aligned} \alpha &= q_i s_j Q \\ \beta &= q_l s_0 s_k Q \end{aligned} \right\}$ where $q_i s_j L q_l \in T$.

The reader should interpret $\alpha \to \beta$ as a single move of the machine. Some further explanation is now needed to interpret moves described by (iii) or (v). The tape is finite but when the machine comes to an end of the tape, the tape is lengthened by adjoining a blank square. Since s_0 means "blank," the two rules (iii) and (v) thus correspond to the cases when the machine is scanning the last symbol or the first symbol in the tape expression.

The proviso in the definition of a Turing machine that no two quadruples have the same first two symbols may be interpreted to mean that there is never ambiguity about a machine's next move. Formally, $\alpha \to \beta$ and $\alpha \to \gamma$ implies $\beta = \gamma$.

Definition   Let T be a Turing machine. An instantaneous description α is **terminal** if there is no β with $\alpha \to \beta$. A **computation** of T is a finite sequence of instantaneous descriptions

$$\alpha_1, \alpha_2, \cdots, \alpha_t$$

where α_t is terminal and $\alpha_i \to \alpha_{i+1}$ for $i = 1, 2, \cdots, t - 1$.

Definition   Let f be a function on the positive integers; f is **computable** if there is a Turing machine such that, for any positive integer k, there is a computation starting with $q_1 s_1^k$ and ending with $q_0 s_1^{f(k)}$ (where s_1^k means a string of k s_1). The symbol q_0 thus denotes "stop."

Exercises   12.9   Prove that the function f defined by $f(k) = k + 1$, all k, is computable. (*Hint:* Consider the Turing machine whose quadruples are: $q_1 s_1 L q_1$, $q_1 s_0 s_1 q_2$, $q_2 s_1 s_1 q_0$.)

12.10   Prove that the function f defined by $f(k) = 2k$, all k, is computable.

Using this definition of computability, every example of a function that, on intuitive grounds, "ought to be" computable has been proved to be computable.

The discussion below, as far as the statement of Post's theorem, is again informal. Let us exhibit a function that is *not* computable, for this is the sort of function we seek in Post's theorem (and in the main theorem of this chapter). Given a Turing machine T, record the symbols s_i in the order in which T prints them; this record will probably have many repetitions. Call a Turing machine *irrational* if, starting with a blank tape and in state q_1, its record contains infinitely many entries equal to either s_1 or s_2 (it may print other symbols as well). Notice that an irrational machine never stops.

LEMMA   There exist infinitely many irrational Turing machines.

THEOREM   There is no decision process to determine whether or not an arbitrary Turing machine is irrational.

Sketch of proof   Since Turing machines are merely finite sets of quadruples based on our two fixed lists of s and q, we may effectively list all Turing machines: $T_1, T_2, \cdots, T_i, \cdots$. Assume there is a decision process D that determines whether or not each T_i is irrational. We shall reach a contradiction by a "Cantor diagonalization" argument.[4] Define a new decision process as follows:

1. Take the first T_i in the list not already dealt with, and apply D to it. If T_i is irrational, proceed to step 2; if T_i is not irrational, proceed to step 1.

2. Find the integer j, where T_i is the jth irrational machine in the list. Consider the subsequence of the record of T_i consisting of all the s_1 and s_2 printed by T_i; find which symbol is the jth term in this subsequence. If this symbol is s_1, write s_2; if this symbol is s_2, write s_1. Proceed to step 1.

A Turing machine M can be constructed to carry out this new decision process. Moreover, M can be chosen so that it starts with a blank tape and in state q_1, and further, so that it avoids printing either of the symbols s_1 or s_2 except as required to do so in step 2. Clearly, M is an irrational machine; in addition, M occurs in the original list that contains all Turing machines. If M is the jth irrational machine in the list, we reach a contradiction by considering the jth time s_1 or s_2 is printed by M. ∎

COROLLARY   The function f defined by

$$f(k) = \begin{cases} 1 & \text{if } T_k \text{ is irrational} \\ 2 & \text{otherwise} \end{cases}$$

is not computable.

Other undecidability results about Turing machines are known. In particular, there is a specific Turing machine T^* for which there is no decision process for determining whether or not T^* will enter state q_0 from an arbitrary starting position. Since q_0 means "stop," there is no decision process for determining whether or not an arbitrary instantaneous description is the first step of a computation of T^*.

Algebraic undecidability results can be obtained by observing that every Turing machine T gives a presentation of a semigroup[5]

$$\pi(T) = (X|\triangle);$$

[4] We allude to Cantor's proof that the set of real numbers is uncountable.
[5] In this context, one often calls a finitely presented semigroup a **Thue system**.

the set X of generators is the set of symbols s_j and q_i that occur in the quadruples of T; the defining relations $\triangle$ have the form $\alpha = \beta$, where $\alpha \to \beta$ is a *basic* single move of T; i.e., we delete the P and Q that occur in the definition of $\alpha \to \beta$. (The semigroup is a bit more complicated than this, for one must distinguish between the basic relations given by rules (ii) and (iii) as well as between those given by rules (iv) and (v).) In particular, the machine T^* described above defines a semigroup $\pi(T^*)$.

Definition   If X and Y are (not necessarily reduced) words, then $X \equiv Y$ means that X and Y have exactly the same spelling.

Definition   A word Σ on symbols $\{s_0, s_1, \cdots; q_0, q_1, \cdots\}$ is **special** if it positive and if it has the form

$$\Sigma \equiv Aq_iB,$$

where A and B are words in the s alone.

Note that special words correspond to instantaneous descriptions. We now quote our fundamental theorem from mathematical logic.

THEOREM 12.1 (*Post*)   There is a finitely presented semigroup

$$\pi(T^*) = (q_0, \cdots, q_N; s_0, \cdots, s_M | \Sigma_i = \Gamma_i, i \in I)$$

(where Σ_i and Γ_i are special words) that has an unsolvable word problem. Furthermore, for an arbitrary special word Σ, there is no decision process to determine whether or not $\Sigma = q_0$ in $\pi(T^*)$.

Sketch of proof   Suppose a group G has a presentation

$$G = (a_1, \cdots, a_m | A_1 = B_1, \cdots, A_n = B_n);$$

let U and V be words in the a. The elements of G corresponding to U and V are equal if and only if there is a finite sequence of elementary operations

$$U \equiv W_1 \to W_2 \to \cdots \to W_t \equiv V$$

transforming U into V, where $W_j \to W_{j+1}$ ($j = 1, 2, \cdots, t - 1$) denotes one of the following:

   (i)   *Cancellation:* replace a word of the form $Xa_ia_i^{-1}Y$ or $Xa_i^{-1}a_iY$ by XY.

(ii) *Insertion:* the converse process of (i).
(iii) *Substitution:* replace a word of the form XA_kY by XB_kY, or conversely.

If G is a semigroup, the only elementary operations are substitutions (for there are no inverses not specified by defining relations). One links the two concepts of decision process and equality of elements with the observation that single moves of the Turing machine T^* correspond to elementary operations in the semigroup $\pi(T^*)$. If there is a decision process, each of its instructions gives an elementary operation, and the sequence of instructions gives a transformation of one word into another. The full argument for Post's theorem is fairly short; proofs may be found in Post's original paper[6] or in textbooks in mathematical logic.[7] ∎

Britton's Lemma

The history of the word problem for groups is rather involved. It was first considered by M. Dehn (1912)[8] and A. Thue (1914). The solution was given by P. Novikov (1955) and, independently, by W. W. Boone (1954–1957). In 1959, Boone exhibited a much simpler group than any of those previously given, which he proved has an unsolvable word problem. Among the generators of Boone's group G are s_j, q_i, t, and k. The crucial lemma in Boone's proof is: If Σ is a special word, then

$$(\Sigma^{-1}t\Sigma)k = k(\Sigma^{-1}t\Sigma) \quad \text{in } G$$

if and only if $\Sigma = q_0$ in $\pi(T^*)$. Therefore, if there were a decision process to determine whether or not two words are equal in G, there would be a decision process to determine for an arbitrary special word Σ, whether or not $\Sigma = q_0$ in $\pi(T^*)$; by Post's theorem, G must have an unsolvable word problem. Boone proved the crucial lemma

---

[6] E. Post, "Recursive unsolvability of a problem of Thue," *J. Symbolic Logic* (1947), pp. 1–11.

[7] M. Davis, *Computability and Unsolvability*, McGraw-Hill, 1958; H. Hermes, *Aufzählbarkeit, Entscheidbarkeit, Berechenbarkeit*, Springer Verlag, 1961; S. Kleene, *Introduction to Metamathematics*, Van Nostrand, 1950.

[8] A complete bibliography can be found at the end of Boone's paper, "The Word Problem," *Annals of Math.* (1959), pp. 207–265.

with an intricate series of combinatorial arguments. In 1963, J. L. Britton[9] discovered a lemma exploiting free products with amalgamated subgroup, which considerably shortens Boone's proof. Britton's lemma amounts to saying that certain sequences of elementary operations can be performed without insertions. Hence, each application of Britton's lemma guarantees that certain elementary operations can take place in a semigroup.

Definition   Let W be a word on $a_1, \cdots, a_m$. We say that Y is a **subword** of W if $W \equiv XYZ$; a word W **involves** a_i if either a_i or a_i^{-1} is a subword of W.

If $H = (S|D)$ is a presentation of a group, we shall also denote that group by H. A word W on S determines an element of H, and we shall also denote that element by W. Finally, we write

$$X = Y \quad \text{in } H$$

if the words X and Y determine the same element of H.

Definition   Let $H = (S|D)$ and $H^* = (S^*|D^*)$ be presentations; we say that

$$H \leq H^*$$

in case $S \subset S^*$, $D \subset D^*$, and for every word W on S, $W = 1$ in H if and only if $W = 1$ in H^*.

Exercise   12.11   Let $H = (S|D)$ and $H^* = (S^*|D^*)$, where $S \subset S^*$ and $D \subset D^*$. There is a homomorphism $\varphi \colon H \to H^*$ which takes any word on S into "itself"; φ is an imbedding if and only if $H \leq H^*$.

LEMMA 12.2   Let $H = (S|D)$ and

$$H^* = (S, t|D, t^{-1}X_i t = X_i, i \in I)$$

be presentations, where the X_i are words on S; let W be a word on $\{S,t\}$ that involves t. If $W = 1$ in H^*, then W contains a subword of the form $t^{-1}Ct$ or tCt^{-1}, where

   (i) C is a word on S.
   (ii)   The group element of H determined by C lies in the subgroup of H generated by the X_i.

[9] J. L. Britton, "The Word Problem," *Annals of Math.* (1963), pp. 16–32.

Proof   Let X be the subgroup of H generated by the X_i, and let X' be another group isomorphic to X, say, by an isomorphism $\psi\colon X \to X'$. We claim that H^* is a free product with an amalgamated subgroup, and that $H \leq H^*$.

There is a presentation

$$X' = (x_i, i \in I | r_j = 1, j \in J),$$

where $x_i = \psi(X_i)$ and r_j is a word in the x. Let $[t]$ denote an infinite cyclic group with generator t, and set $Y = X' \times [t]$ (direct product). Finally, let A be the free product of H and Y in which we amalgamate X and X' via the isomorphism ψ. By Exercise 11.27, one presentation of A is

$$A = (S, t, x_i, i \in I | D, r_j = 1, j \in J, t^{-1}x_i t = x_i, x_i = X_i, i \in I).$$

But a second presentation is

$$A = (S, t | D, R_j = 1, j \in J, t^{-1}X_i t = X_i, i \in I),$$

where $\psi(R_j) = r_j$. Now each $R_j = 1$ in X, and hence $= 1$ in H. By Exercise 12.11, $R_j = 1$ in A. The relations $R_j = 1$ are thus superfluous in the second presentation of A, so that $A \approx H^*$. By Corollary 11.15, H is a subgroup of H^*, so that $H \leq H^*$.

We now prove the lemma. If W contains a subword tt^{-1} or $t^{-1}t$, we are done. Therefore, we may assume

$$W \equiv W_0 t^{e_1} W_1 \cdots t^{e_n} W_n,$$

where $n \geq 1$, each e_j is a nonzero integer, and the W_j are words on S of which only W_0 and W_n are allowed to be empty.

If $n = 1$, then $W \equiv W_0 t^{e_1} W_1$. Since $W = 1$ in H^*,

$$t^{e_1} = W_0^{-1} W_1^{-1} \in H \cap Y = X,$$

by Corollary 11.15. This is a contradiction, for X contains no nontrivial power of t as a consequence of the amalgamation. The case $n = 1$ is thus impossible, as the lemma predicts.

For the inductive step, we use the following statement, which follows easily from the normal form. Let P be the free product of groups G_α with amalgamated subgroup Q. If $y_1, \cdots, y_r$ are elements of P not in Q, where $y_i \in G_{\alpha_i}$ and $\alpha_i \neq \alpha_{i+1}$, then $z = y_1 y_2 \cdots y_r \notin Q$; in particular, $z \neq 1$. Applying this to the word W (which is 1 in H^*) we see that W_j lies in X for some j, $1 \leq j \leq n - 1$. If e_j and e_{j+1} have opposite signs, we are finished. Suppose e_j and e_{j+1} have the same sign. In H^*,

$$W \equiv \cdots t^{e_j} W_j t^{e_{j+1}} W_{j+1} \cdots = \cdots t^{e_j + e_{j+1}} W_j W_{j+1} \cdots .$$

The second word has one fewer occurrence of a power of t, and it satisfies all the inductive hypotheses. Therefore, it, and hence W, has a subword of the desired kind. ∎

Definition   Let $E = (S|D)$ be a presentation. We say that a second presentation E^* has a **basis** E and **stable letters** p_v, $(v \in V)$, if

$$E^* = (S, p_v, v \in V | D, p_{v_i}^{-1} A_i p_{v_i} = B_i, i \in I),^{10}$$

where A_i and B_i are words on S, and for each $v \in V$, p_v is involved in at least one of the new relations of E^*.

Sometimes the relations of E^* will appear in the following somewhat more complicated form: $F_i p_{v_i} G_i = H_i p_{v_i} K_i$, where F_i, G_i, H_i, and K_i are words on S. In this notation, $A_i \equiv H_i^{-1} F_i$ and $B_i \equiv K_i G_i^{-1}$.

Our condition on the index sets V and I is that for each $v \in V$, there is at least one $i \in I$ with $v_i = v$; let $J(v)$ be the set of all i for which $v_i = v$. Given E^* having a basis E, there are several subgroups of E that we must consider:

$$A = [A_i : i \in I] \qquad B = [B_i : i \in I]$$
$$A(v) = [A_i : i \in J(v)] \qquad B(v) = [B_i : i \in J(v)].$$

For each v, $A(v)$ is a subgroup of A and $B(v)$ is a subgroup of B. We shall keep to this notation for the remainder of the chapter so that all apparently wandering A_i, $B(v)$, etc., really have a home.

Definition   The **isomorphism condition** is that for each $v \in V$, there is an isomorphism $\varphi_v : A(v) \to B(v)$ under which $\varphi_v(A_i) = B_i$ for all $i \in J(v)$.

Observe that if there is an isomorphism $f : A \to B$ under which $f(A_i) = B_i$, then the isomorphism condition is satisfied. This fact will be used several times in the sequel.

LEMMA 12.3   Let E^* have a basis $E = (S|D)$ and stable letters p_v, $v \in V$. If the isomorphism condition holds, then $E \leqq E^*$.

---

[10] The index sets V and I will always be finite.

Proof   Since the isomorphism condition holds, there are isomor-phisms $\varphi_v \colon A(v) \to B(v)$, for each v, such that $\varphi_v(A_i) = B_i$ for all $i \in J(v)$. By iterated applications of the imbedding theorem of Higman, Neumann, and Neumann (Theorem 11.16), there exists a group E_0 containing E and elements p_v, $v \in V$, such that $p_v^{-1}A_i p_v = B_i$ whenever $v \in V$ and $i \in J(v)$. If we relabel, this amounts to saying that $p_{v_i}^{-1}A_i p_{v_i} = B_i$ for all $i \in I$. Clearly, we may assume that E_0 is generated by E and p_v, $v \in V$. A presentation of E_0 can thus be obtained from that of E^* by adding (a possibly empty set of) further defining relations. Therefore, E_0 is a homomorphic image of E^*. It follows that if W is a word on S and $W = 1$ in E^*, we must have $W = 1$ in E_0, and hence $W = 1$ in E_0's subgroup, E. Conversely, if $W = 1$ in E, it is trivial that $W = 1$ in E^*. We have shown that $E \leqq E^*$. $\blacksquare$

The next lemma generalizes Lemma 12.2.

LEMMA 12.4 (*Britton*)   Let E^* be a presentation with basis $E = (S|D)$ and stable letters $p_v, v \in V$; let W be a word involving at least one stable letter. If the isomorphism condition holds, and if $W = 1$ in E^*, then W contains a subword

$$p_v^{-1}Cp_v,$$

where C is equal in E to some word in the A_i, or

$$p_vCp_v^{-1},$$

where C is equal in E to some word in the B_i; in either case, C is a word on S.[11]

Proof   We first prove the lemma for the special case of one stable letter, p. Thus, the presentation we deal with is

$$E^* = (S,p|D,\, p^{-1}A_i p = B_i,\, i \in I).$$

We are done if W contains a subword of the form $p^{-1}p$ or pp^{-1}, so that we may assume

$$W \equiv W_0 p^{a_1} W_1 \cdots p^{a_n} W_n,$$

[11] We emphasize the fact that Britton's lemma is concerned with the exact spelling of a (not necessarily reduced) word W, not merely with the location of a group element corresponding to it.

where $n \geqq 1$, each A_i is a nonzero integer, and the W_i are words on S of which only W_0 and W_n may be empty.

We wish to use Lemma 12.2, but it does not apply because A_i and B_i may be distinct. Since the isomorphism condition holds, $E \leqq E^*$, by Lemma 12.3. Therefore, $E \leqq H$, where H (isomorphic to E^*) has the presentation

$$H = (S,q \mid D, q^{-1}A_i q = B_i, i \in I).$$

Consider now

$$H^* = (\{S,q\}, t \mid \{D, q^{-1}A_i q = B_i, i \in I\}, t^{-1}B_i t = B_i, i \in I)$$

and the word

$$U \equiv W_0(qt)^{a_1}W_1 \cdots (qt)^{a_n}W_n.$$

First of all, we claim that $U = 1$ in H^*. To see this, add the new generator p and the defining relation $p = qt$ to H^* to obtain a group K, where

$$K = (S,q,t,p \mid D, q^{-1}A_i q = B_i, p = qt, p^{-1}A_i p = B_i, i \in I).$$

Now $K \approx H^*$; furthermore, K contains all the generators and defining relations of E^*. Therefore, $W = 1$ in E^* implies $U = 1$ in H^*. Applying Lemma 12.2 to H, H^*, and U, one sees that U contains a subword $t^e C t^{-e}$ $(e = \pm 1)$, where the group element C is in B, the subgroup generated by the B_i. If $e = 1$, $C \equiv W_j$ for some j, $1 \leqq j \leqq n - 1$, and we are done. If $e = -1$, then $C \equiv q^{-1}W_j q$ for some j; therefore, $q^{-1}W_j q \in B$ and so $W_j \in qBq^{-1} = A$.

We now consider the general case. Denote the elements of the index set V by $1, 2, \cdots$. Let $D(v)$ consist of the defining relations $p_{v_i}^{-1}A_i p_{v_i} = B_i$ in E^* such that $i \in J(v)$. Since $W = 1$ in E^*, $W = 1$ in E_r for some r, where

$$E_r = (S, p_1, \cdots, p_r \mid D, D(1), \cdots, D(r)).$$

It is straightforward to show that $E \leqq E_1 \leqq E_2 \leqq \cdots$. Choose s maximal such that W involves p_s; the chain of inequalities implies that $W = 1$ in E_s. Since E_s has a basis E_{s-1} and stable letter p_s, it follows from the first portion of our proof that W contains a subword $p_s^e C p_s^{-e}$, where, for example, $e = 1$ and the group element C belongs to the subgroup of E_{s-1} (hence of E) generated by B_i, $i \in J(s)$.

If the word C is a word on S, we are done. On the other hand, if the word C involves some of $p_1, \cdots, p_{s-1}$, then there is a word C' over S (namely, a product of B_i) such that $C = C'$ in E_{s-1}. Thus, $CC'^{-1} = 1$ in E_{s-1}, and an induction on s implies that the word CC'^{-1}, and hence C and hence W, contains a subword of the required type. ∎

The Novikov-Boone Theorem

THEOREM 12.5 (*Novikov-Boone*) There exists a finitely presented group G having an unsolvable word problem.

Consider first the presentation of Post's semigroup:

$$\pi(T^*) = (s_0, s_1, \cdots, s_M, q_0, q_1, \cdots, q_N | \Sigma_i = \Gamma_i, i \in I).$$

We shall usually denote q_0 by q.
We now present the desired group G. It has generators:

$$s_b, q_a, k, t, x, y, l_i, r_i$$

and defining relations:

$$
\left.\left.\left.\left.
\begin{array}{l}
s_b y = y y s_b, \quad x s_b = s_b x x \\
s_b l_i = y l_i y s_b, \quad r_i s_b = s_b x r_i x \\
\Sigma_i = l_i \Gamma_i r_i \quad \blacksquare \\
t l_i = l_i t, \quad t y = y t
\end{array}
\right] G_1 \right] G_2 \right] G_3 \right] G_4
$$

$$
\begin{array}{c}
r_i k = k r_i, \quad x k = k x, \\
(q^{-1} t q) k = k (q^{-1} t q),
\end{array}
$$

where $b = 0, 1, \cdots M; a = 0, 1, \cdots, N; i \in I$.[12]
The subsets G_1, G_2, G_3, G_4 of the defining relations indicated here are for future reference.

The reduction to Post's theorem is accomplished by the following lemma.

---

[12] It has been announced by A. A. Fridman (1963) that if one deletes the last relation, then the resulting group has a solvable word problem.

LEMMA 12.6   Let Σ be a special word. Then

(1) $(\Sigma^{-1}t\Sigma)k = k(\Sigma^{-1}t\Sigma)$ in G

if and only if $\Sigma = q$ in $\pi(T^*)$.

Proof of Sufficiency in Lemma 12.6   Suppose that for the special word Σ, $\Sigma = q$ in $\pi(T^*)$. We first prove that $\Sigma = LqR$ in G, where L is a word in y, l_i and R is a word in x, r_i. There is a sequence of elementary operations

$$\Sigma \equiv W_1 \rightarrow W_2 \rightarrow \cdots \rightarrow W_n \equiv q,$$

where for each j, $1 \leq j \leq n - 1$, and one of the words W_j, W_{j+1} has the form $X\Sigma_i Y$, the other $X\Gamma_i Y$. (Since $\pi(T^*)$ is only a semigroup, the only permissible elementary operations in it are substitutions.) Since Σ is a special word, each W_j is also special, so that X and Y are positive[13] words in the s_b. Hence, the relations $yys_b = s_b y$ and $s_b l_i = yl_i y s_b$ imply that

$$Xl_i = L'X \quad \text{in } G$$

for some word L' in y, l_i; similarly,

$$r_i Y = YR' \quad \text{in } G$$

for some word R' in x, r_i. Therefore, in G,

$$X\Sigma_i Y = Xl_i\Gamma_i r_i Y = L'X\Gamma_i YR'.$$

It follows that for each j,

$$W_j = L_j W_{j+1} R_j,$$

where L_j is a word in y, l_i, and R_j is a word in x, r_i. If we set $L \equiv L_1 L_2 \cdots L_{n-1}$ and $R \equiv R_{n-1} \cdots R_2 R_1$, then

$$\Sigma = LqR \quad \text{in } G,$$

as we claimed.

We now prove (1). Observe that the relations of G imply that t commutes with L and k commutes with R. Thus,

---

[13] Recall that the empty word is a positive word.

$$(\Sigma^{-1}t\Sigma)k = R^{-1}q^{-1}(L^{-1}tL)q(Rk)$$
$$= R^{-1}[(q^{-1}tq)k]R$$
$$= (R^{-1}k)q^{-1}tqR$$
$$= kR^{-1}q^{-1}L^{-1}tLqR$$
$$= k(\Sigma^{-1}t\Sigma).$$

Proof of Necessity in Lemma 12.6   Throughout the proof, Σ is to be a fixed special word for which (1) holds.

Let G_1 be the group whose generators are those of G less k, and with the relations of G indicated above. Observe that G_1 is a basis of G with stable letter k:

$$G = (\_\_,k|\_\_, kr_i = r_ik, kx = xk, k(q^{-1}tq) = (q^{-1}tq)k).$$

Now (1) gives

$$k^{-1}(\Sigma^{-1}t\Sigma)k\Sigma^{-1}t^{-1}\Sigma = 1 \quad \text{in } G.$$

By Lemma 12.2, $\Sigma^{-1}t\Sigma$ belongs to the subgroup of G_1 generated by the r_i, x, and $q^{-1}tq$. Therefore, there exist $\gamma_1, \cdots, \gamma_n$ and $e_1, \cdots, e_n$ such that

(2) $$W = \Sigma^{-1}t\Sigma\gamma_1^{e_1} \cdots \gamma_n^{e_n} = 1 \quad \text{in } G_1,$$

where $n \geq 0$, each $e_j = \pm 1$, and each γ_j is one of r_i, x, or $q^{-1}tq$. We assume that n is minimal.

Let G_2 be the group whose generators are those of G less k and t, and whose defining relations are indicated above. Observe that G_1 has a basis G_2 and stable letter t:

$$G_1 = (\_\_, t|\_\_, tl_i = l_it, i \in I, ty = yt).$$

Lemma 12.2 shows that W contains a subword t^eCt^{-e} ($e = \pm 1$), such that the word C does not involve t and the group element C belongs to the subgroup of G_2 generated by y and the l_i: $C = L$ in G_2, where L is a word on y and the l_i. We shall prove that

(3) $$\Sigma = LqR \quad \text{in } G_2,$$

where R is a word in x and the r_i.

Case (i).   The letter t^e in t^eCt^{-e} is the displayed t in (2). Thus, $e = 1$ and t^{-e} occurs in some factor $\gamma_j^{e_i}$. Since C does not involve t, the word C has the form $\Sigma R'q^{-1}$, where R' is a word on x and the r_i. Equation (3) now follows.

Case (ii). t^e occurs in $\gamma_a^{e_a}$ and t^{-e} occurs in $\gamma_b^{e_b}$, $a < b$. Since C does not involve t, C is a subword of $(q^{-1}t^e q)R'(q^{-1}t^{-e}q)$, where R' is a word in x and the r_i; therefore, $C \equiv qR'q^{-1}$. Since t commutes with y and with the l_i in G_1, we have in G_1:

$$
\begin{aligned}
q^{-1}t^e q R' q^{-1} t^{-e} q &\equiv q^{-1}t^e C t^{-e} q \\
&= q^{-1}t^e L t^{-e} q \\
&= q^{-1}Lq \\
&= q^{-1}Cq \\
&= q^{-1}(qR'q^{-1})q \\
&= R'.
\end{aligned}
$$

Therefore, W has a factorization in G_1 of the form (2) with two fewer factors γ, and this contradicts the minimality of n. This establishes (3).

Let us write the defining relations $\Sigma_i = \Gamma_i$ of $\pi(T^*)$ in more detail as $F_i q_{\alpha_i} G_i \equiv H_i q_{\beta_i} K_i$, and the fixed word Σ as $Fq_\alpha G$.

Let H_2 be the free product of G_2 and the infinite cyclic group $[z]$; we have just adjoined the additional generator z, so that still $\Sigma = LqR$ in H_2. Adjoin to H_2 (superfluous) generators p_a, $a = 0, 1, \cdots, N$ and corresponding defining relations $p_a = q_a z^{-1}$. In the remaining defining relations of H_2, then, we may replace every q_a by $p_a z$. The generators q_a are now superfluous; removing them, we obtain a presentation of H_2 whose generators are z, s_b, p_a, x, y, l_i, r_i and whose defining relations are those of G_2 with the q_a replaced everywhere by $p_a z$. Now the only relations of G_2 that involve q_a are the ones of the form $\Sigma_i = l_i \Gamma_i r_i$, and these become

$$F_i p_{\alpha_i} z G_i = l_i H_i p_{\beta_i} z K_i r_i.$$

In this notation, equation (3) becomes (writing p for p_0)

(4) $$Fp_\alpha z G = LpzR \quad \text{in } H_2.$$

Let G_3 be the group whose generators are

$$s_b,\ p_a,\ x,\ y,\ l_i,\ r_i$$

and whose relations have been indicated above (the p_a are not involved in any relation of G_3). Observe that H_2 has a basis G_3 and stable letter z:

$$H_2 = (\underline{\quad}, z \mid \underline{\quad}, F_i p_{\alpha_i} z G_i = l_i H_i p_{\beta_i} z K_i r_i).$$

Returning to the notation we used when we first defined basis and stable letter, we have

$$A_i \equiv p_{\beta_i}^{-1} H_i^{-1} l_i^{-1} F_i p_{\alpha_i} \quad \text{and} \quad B_i \equiv K_i r_i G_i^{-1}.$$

Using this notation, the presentation of H_2 just given becomes

$$H_2 = (\underline{\quad}, z|\underline{\quad}, z^{-1}A_i z = B_i).$$

Now the isomorphism condition holds if the mapping $A_i \to B_i$ defines an isomorphism between the two subgroups of G_3 generated respectively by the A_i and by the B_i. Indeed, we claim that the A_i and B_i freely generate their respective subgroups. For example, let G_3^* be the group obtained from G_3 by adding the relations $s_b = p_a = x = y = r_i = 1$. There is a homomorphism $\varphi \colon G_3 \to G_3^*$, and $\varphi(A_i) = l_i$ for all i. A glance at the relations of G_3^* shows that it is free on the l_i. Suppose now that

$$A_{v_1}^{e_1} \cdots A_{v_m}^{e_m} = 1 \quad \text{in } G_3 \qquad (e_i = \pm 1),$$

i.e., there is a relation among the A_i in G_3. Applying the homomorphism φ gives a relation among the l_i, a contradiction. A similar argument shows that the B_i freely generate their subgroup.

Now equation (4) can be rewritten

$$R^{-1} z^{-1} (p^{-1} L^{-1} F p_\alpha) z G = 1 \quad \text{in } H_2,$$

so that Britton's lemma (Lemma 12.4) applies. Since the only appearance of the z is their flanking of the subword in parentheses, we conclude that $p^{-1} L^{-1} F p_\alpha$ belongs to the subgroup of G_3 generated by the A_i, $i \in I$. Therefore,

$$(5) \qquad p^{-1} L^{-1} F p_\alpha A_{v_1}^{e_1} \cdots A_{v_n}^{e_n} = 1 \quad \text{in } G_3,$$

where $v_j \in I$ and $e_j = \pm 1$. Furthermore, since $A_i = z B_i z^{-1}$, this last equation gives

$$z^{-1} (p^{-1} L^{-1} F p_\alpha) z B_{v_1}^{e_1} \cdots B_{v_n}^{e_n} = 1 \quad \text{in } H_2.$$

Therefore, using equation (4), in H_2,

$$(6) \qquad\qquad RG^{-1} B_{v_1}^{e_1} \cdots B_{v_n}^{e_n} = 1.$$

In fact, equation (6) even holds in G_3. This follows from Lemma 12.3, since the left side of (6) does not involve z.

In order to complete the proof, it suffices to prove the following lemma.

LEMMA 12.7 Let $\Sigma \equiv F q_\alpha G$ be any special word. If equations (5) and (6) hold, then Σ can be transformed into q in $\pi(T^*)$ by a sequence of at most n elementary operations.

Proof We perform an induction on n. If $n = 0$, then adding relations $x = y = l_i = r_i = 1$ to G_3 gives a group free on generators s_b, p_a; equations (5) and (6) become, in this group,

$$p^{-1} F p_\alpha = 1 \quad \text{and} \quad G^{-1} = 1.$$

Hence, $G \equiv 1$, $F \equiv 1$, and $p_\alpha = p$, i.e., $\alpha = 0$, so that we have

$$\Sigma \equiv F q_\alpha G \equiv q_0 \equiv q,$$

and the lemma is true.

For the inductive step, we assume that L is of minimal length such that (5) holds, and R is of minimal length such that (6) holds. Assume that Σ cannot be transformed into q in $\pi(T^*)$ by at most n elementary operations; we shall reach a contradiction.

We prepare for yet another application of Britton's lemma. If we add to G_3 the relations $r_i = x = 1$, we obtain the group

$$G_3^L = (s_b, p_a, y, l_i | s_b y = y y s_b, s_b l_i = y l_i y s_b),$$

and (5) holds in G_3^L. The letters l_i are stable for this group, the basis being

$$G_4^L = (s_b, p_a, y | s_b y = y y s_b).$$

In order to apply Britton's lemma, we must verify that the mapping $y^{-1} s_b \to y s_b$ defines an isomorphism between the two subgroups M_1, M_2, of G_4^L generated respectively by the $y^{-1} s_b$ and by the $y s_b$. We claim that these elements freely generate their respective subgroups. For example, a relation among the $y s_b$ gives a corresponding relation in the free group on s_b, p_a, this latter group being obtained from G_4^L by adding the relation $y = 1$. Since the isomorphism condition does hold, Britton's lemma says that

$$p^{-1} L^{-1} F p_\alpha A_{v_1}^{e_1} \cdots A_{v_n}^{e_n}$$

contains a subword $l_i^e C l_i^{-e}$, C being a word in s_b, p_a, y, and either $e = -1$ and C belongs to M_1 or $e = 1$ and C belongs to M_2.

Our proof will be complete after the consideration of three cases. Let us write $\triangle \equiv l_i^e Cl_i^{-e}$.

Case (i). $\triangle$ is a subword of $Fp_\alpha A_{v_1}^{e_1} \cdots A_{v_n}^{e_n}$.

Then l_i^e occurs in, say, $A_{v_j}^{e_j}$ and l_i^{-e} occurs in $A_{v_{j+1}}^{e_{j+1}}$ (since C involves no l_i, while each of the A does involve an l). Thus, $v_j = i = v_{j+1}$ and $e_j = -e = -e_{j+1}$, and so

$$A_{v_j}^{e_j} A_{v_{j+1}}^{e_{j+1}} = 1 \quad \text{and} \quad B_{v_j}^{e_j} B_{v_{j+1}}^{e_{j+1}} = 1.$$

By the inductive assumption, Σ can be transformed into q in $\pi(T^*)$ in at most $n - 2$ steps, contrary to our original assumption.

Case (ii). $\triangle$ is a subword of $p^{-1}L^{-1}$.

In this case, C involves only y (C involves only s_b, p_a, y, and L involves only y and the l_i). Since L^{-1} is reduced (it was chosen of minimal length), $C \equiv y^k$, where $k \neq 0$. Furthermore, the element C belongs to either M_1 or M_2. We claim that $y^k = 1$ in G_3.

Suppose $y^k \in M_1$, the other case being similar. Thus,

$$y^k = (y^{-1}s_{b_1})^{d_1} \cdots (y^{-1}s_{b_r})^{d_r} \quad \text{in } G_4^L.$$

If we set $y = 1$, then we have

$$1 = s_{b_1}^{d_1} \cdots s_{b_r}^{d_r}$$

in the free group on generators s_b, p_a. Hence, $r = 0$ or two letters cancel. It follows that $y^k = 1$ in G_4^L, and hence $y^k = 1$ in G_3. This is a contradiction, for the word L^{-1} in (5) can be replaced (by suppressing y^k) by a word L'^{-1} of the same form but of shorter length.

Case (iii). The last remaining case is when l_i^e occurs in L^{-1} and l_i^{-e} occurs in $A_{v_1}^{e_1}$.

Here, $e = e_1$ and $i = v_1$. Thus, from the definition of A_i, either

$$e_1 = 1, \quad C \equiv YFp_\alpha p_{\beta_i}^{-1} H_i^{-1}, \quad \text{and} \quad C \in M_2,$$

or

$$e_1 = -1, \quad C \equiv YFp_\alpha p_{\beta_i}^{-1} F_i^{-1}, \quad \text{and} \quad C \in M_1,$$

where Y is a word in y only.

We consider only the case $e_1 = 1$, the other case being similar. First of all,

$$(7) \qquad\qquad \alpha = \beta_{v_1} = \beta_i.$$

If we put $s_b = y = 1$, then the statement $C \in M_2$ becomes $p_\alpha p_{\beta_i}^{-1} = 1$ in the free group on generators p_a.

Therefore, there is an equation

$$(8) \qquad YFH_i^{-1}(ys_{b_1})^{d_1} \cdots (ys_{b_r})^{d_r} = 1 \quad \text{in } G_4^L,$$

where each $d_j = \pm 1$. We further assume that $r \geq 0$ is minimal.

Now G_4^L has as a basis the free group generated by p_a, y, and stable letters s_b:

$$G_4^L = (\underline{\quad}, s_b \mid s_b y = yy s_b).$$

The isomorphism condition is satisfied if the mapping $yy \to y$ generates an isomorphism between $[y^2]$ and $[y]$; this is so because y is in the basis, which is free, and so has infinite order.

We remind the reader that, in (8), F and H_i are positive words in the s_b, and Y is a word in y alone. We claim that $F \equiv UH_i$ for some word U. There do exist positive words in the s_b, W, F', H_i', such that $F \equiv F'W$ and $H_i \equiv H_i'W$; for example, let $W \equiv 1$. Suppose that W has maximal length, so that it suffices to prove that $H_i' \equiv 1$ (for then set $U \equiv F'$). Assume $H_i' \not\equiv 1$. In equation (8), replace F and H_i^{-1} by F' and $H_i'^{-1}$, respectively. Since the W cancel, we obtain a true equation in G_4^L, which we label (8'). At least one stable letter s_b occurs in (8') (since $H_i' \not\equiv 1$), so that Britton's lemma implies that the left-hand side of (8') contains a subword $J \equiv s_b^e C s_b^{-e}$, where C is a word in p_a, y. But (8') involves no letters p_a, so that C is a word in y alone. Britton's lemma further asserts that if $e = -1$, C is a word in y^2, while if $e = 1$, then C is a word in y. Now J cannot be a subword of $(ys_{b_1})^{d_1} \cdots (ys_{b_r})^{d_r}$, since r is minimal (if J were such a subword, two adjacent factors would have the same subscript s_b, and so would cancel). Also, s_b^e cannot occur in $H_i'^{-1}$: if it did, then $e = -1$ (since H_i' is positive), $d_1 = -e = 1$, and $C \equiv y$. On the other hand, we have already remarked that if $e = -1$, C must be a word in y^2. It follows, then, that s_b^e occurs in F', s_b^{-e} occurs in $H_i'^{-1}$, and C is empty. Thus, the last letter of F' is the inverse of the first letter of $H_i'^{-1}$, contradicting our choice of W as having maximal length.

Working with equation (5), we have shown that if $e_1 = 1$, then $F \equiv UH_i$. In a similar manner, working with equation (6) will yield that if $e_1 = 1$, then $G^{-1} \equiv V^{-1}K_i^{-1}$ for some word V^{-1}.

(Here is a sketch of the similar argument. If we add the relations $l_i = y = 1$ to G_3, equation (6) holds in

$$G_3^R = (s_b, p_a, x, r_i | x s_b = s_b x x, \ r_i s_b = s_b x r_i x).$$

The letters r_i are stable, the basis being

$$G_4^R = (s_b, p_a, x | x s_b = s_b x x).$$

By Britton's lemma, the left-hand side of (6) contains a subword $r_h^f C' r_h^{-f}$, where C' is a word in s_b, p_a, x, and if $f = -1$, C' belongs to the subgroup of G_4^R generated by the $s_b x$, while if $f = 1$, C' belongs to the subgroup of G_4^R generated by the $s_b x^{-1}$. The analogs of cases 1 and 2 are treated as we have done above. The remaining case leads, as above, to the desired equation $G^{-1} \equiv V^{-1} K_i^{-1}$.)

By equation (7), $\alpha = \beta_{v_1}$. If we denote v_1 by i, we have

$$\Sigma \equiv F q_\alpha G \equiv U H_i q_\alpha K_i V \equiv U H_i q_{\beta_i} K_i V.$$

Put $\Sigma^* \equiv U F_i q_{\alpha_i} G_i V$. Then, in $\pi(T^*)$, the word Σ can be transformed into Σ^* by one elementary operation (recall that the F_i and G_i were introduced solely to examine the defining relations $\Sigma_i = \Gamma_i$ of $\pi(T^*)$ in more detail). Write $F^* \equiv U F_i$ and $G^* \equiv G_i V$, so that $\Sigma^* \equiv F^* q_{\alpha_i} G^*$.

Now

$$
\begin{aligned}
p^{-1} L^{-1} F p_\alpha A_{v_1}^{e_1} &\equiv p^{-1} L^{-1} U H_i p_{\beta_i} A_i \\
&\equiv p^{-1} L^{-1} U H_i p_{\beta_i} (p_{\beta_i}^{-1} H_i^{-1} l_i^{-1} F_i p_{\alpha_i}) \\
&= p^{-1} L^{-1} U l_i^{-1} F_i p_{\alpha_i} \quad \text{in } G_3.
\end{aligned}
$$

Since U is a positive word in the s_b, the relations of G_3 allow us to "commute" l_i^{-1} past U (while amassing a few extra l and y). Therefore, there exists a word L_0 in l_i, y such that, in G_3,

$$
\begin{aligned}
p^{-1} L^{-1} U l_i^{-1} F_i p_{\alpha_i} &= p^{-1} L_0^{-1} U F_i p_{\alpha_i} \\
&\equiv p^{-1} L_0^{-1} F^* p_{\alpha_i}.
\end{aligned}
$$

Equation (5) can now be rewritten as

(5*) $$(p^{-1} L_0^{-1} F^* p_{\alpha_i}) A_{v_2}^{e_2} \cdots A_{v_n}^{e_n} = 1 \quad \text{in } G_3.$$

Similarly, in G_3,

$$
\begin{aligned}
R G^{-1} B_{v_1}^{e_1} &\equiv R V^{-1} K_i^{-1} B_i \equiv R V^{-1} K_i^{-1} K_i r_i G_i^{-1} \\
&= R V^{-1} r_i G_i^{-1} \\
&= R_0 V^{-1} G_i^{-1} \\
&= R_0 G^{*-1}
\end{aligned}
$$

for some word R_0 in r_i, x. Equation (6) can also be rewritten:

(6*) $$(R_0 G^{*-1}) B_{v_2}^{e_2} \cdots B_{v_n}^{e_n} = 1 \quad \text{in } G_3.$$

By induction, $\Sigma^* \equiv F^* q_{\alpha_i} G^*$ can be transformed into q in $\pi(T^*)$ in at most $n - 1$ steps. But Σ can be transformed into Σ^* in one step, so that Σ can be transformed into q in $\pi(T^*)$ in at most n steps. This completes the proof if $e_1 = 1$.

If $e_1 = -1$, only slight changes must be made, and these may be supplied by the reader.

This completes the proof of Lemma 12.7 and of the Novikov-Boone theorem. $\blacksquare$

We mention two other related results. Magnus (1932) has shown that a finitely presented group with exactly one defining relation always has a solvable word problem. G. Higman, *Subgroups of finitely presented groups*, Proc. Royal Soc. A, vol. 262, pp. 455–475, (1961), has an alternative proof of the word problem as a corollary of his theorem characterizing subgroups of finitely presented groups.

Appendices

Appendix I

Some Major Algebraic Systems

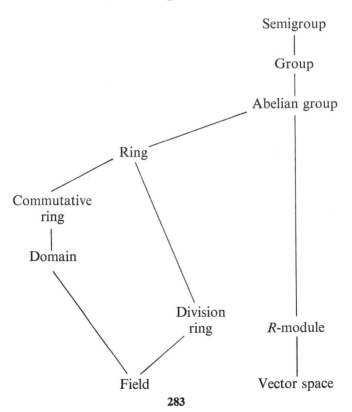

Semigroup

Group

Abelian group

Ring

Commutative ring

Domain

Division ring

R-module

Field

Vector space

A *ring* (which we always assume to contain a unit $1 \neq 0$) is a set with two binary operations: addition and multiplication. It is an abelian group under addition, a semigroup under multiplication, and the two operations are linked by the distributive laws.

A *commutative ring* is a ring in which multiplication is commutative.

A *domain* (or integral domain) is a commutative ring having no zero divisors.

A *field* is a commutative ring in which every nonzero element has a multiplicative inverse.

A *division ring* (or skew field) is a ring in which every nonzero element has a multiplicative inverse. Thus, a commutative division ring is a field, and its nonzero elements form a multiplicative abelian group.

If R is a commutative ring, an abelian group M is an *R-module* if there is a scalar multiplication defined, i.e., there is a function $R \times M \to M$ (whose value on (r,m) is denoted rm), which has the properties:

$$(rr')m = r(r'm);$$
$$r(m + m') = rm + rm';$$
$$(r + r')m = rm + r'm;$$
$$1m = m$$

for all $r, r' \in R$ and $m, m' \in M$.

A *vector space* is an R-module, where R is a field.

Appendix II

Equivalence Relations and Equivalence Classes

If X is a nonempty set, a *binary relation* on X is a subset R of $X \times X$. If $(x,y) \in X \times X$, one writes xRy instead of $(x,y) \in R$. For example, the binary relation $<$ on the reals consists of all points in the plane lying above the line $y = x$. Ordinarily, one writes $2 < 3$ instead of $(2,3) \in <$.

A binary relation $\sim$ on X is an *equivalence relation* in case, for all $x,y,z \in X$:

(i) $x \sim x$.

(ii) $x \sim y$ implies $y \sim x$.

(iii) $x \sim y$ and $y \sim z$ implies $x \sim z$.

If $x \in X$, we let $\langle x \rangle$ denote the family of all $y \in X$ such that $x \sim y$; $\langle x \rangle$ is the *equivalence class* containing x.

Let X be a nonempty set. A *partition* of X is a family of nonempty subsets $\{S_\alpha\}$ of X such that:

$$S_\alpha \cap S_\beta = \phi \qquad \text{if } \alpha \neq \beta \text{ (pairwise disjointness);}$$
$$X = \bigcup S_\alpha.$$

PROPOSITION A   If $\sim$ is an equivalence relation on X, then the family of all equivalence classes is a partition of X.

Proof   By (i), if $x \in X$, then $x \in \langle x \rangle$; thus, the equivalence classes are nonempty. Moreover,

$$X = \bigcup_{x \in X} \langle x \rangle,$$

since every $x \in X$ lies in its own equivalence class.

Suppose $\langle x \rangle \cap \langle y \rangle \neq \phi$, so that there is an element $z \in \langle x \rangle \cap \langle y \rangle$. Then $x \sim z$ and $z \sim y$; therefore, $x \sim y$, by (iii), and $\langle x \rangle = \langle y \rangle$.   ∎

PROPOSITION B   If $\{S_\alpha\}$ is a partition of X, then there is an equivalence relation on X whose equivalence classes are the S_α.

Proof   Define $x \sim y$ to mean that x and y lie in the same S_α; it is immediate that this is an equivalence relation.

Suppose that $x \in S_\alpha$; we claim that $\langle x \rangle = S_\alpha$. The definition of $\sim$ implies that $S_\alpha \subset \langle x \rangle$. The reverse inclusion follows from the fact that the S_α are pairwise disjoint.   ∎

The importance of equivalence relations is just this: Let $\sim$ be an equivalence relation on X, and let Y be the set of equivalence classes. If one treats the elements of Y merely as elements (and not as classes), then he has effectively identified equivalent elements of X.

For example, one does not wish to distinguish between the fractions $\frac{1}{2}$ and $\frac{2}{4}$, and so he decrees that two fractions a/b and c/d are "equal" if $ad = bc$. In reality, he is considering the set X of all ordered pairs of integers (a,b) for which $b \neq 0$, under the equivalence relation given by

$$(a,b) \sim (c,d) \qquad \text{if } ad = bc.$$

The rational $\frac{1}{2}$ is thus the class of $(1,2)$ and of $(2,4)$.

Appendix III

Functions

If X and Y are sets, a *relation from X to Y* is a subset of $X \times Y$. A *function f*: $X \to Y$ is a relation from X to Y such that:

(i)   For each $x \in X$, there is some $y \in Y$ with $(x,y) \in f$.
(ii) For each $x \in X$, the y above is unique.

The element $y \in Y$ is the *image* of x under f, and is ordinarily written $f(x)$. With this notation, a function f is the subset of $X \times Y$ consisting of all pairs $(x,f(x))$. In other words, a function *is* (what is usually called) its graph.

In practice, one thinks of a function as a dynamic thing; it assigns elements of Y to elements of X. Indeed, most elementary texts define a function as a "rule of correspondence." Even at a naïve level, though, this can be misleading. For example, are $(x + 1)^2$ and $x^2 + 2x + 1$ different rules? The reader may prove, using the definition above, that if f and g: $X \to Y$, then $f = g$ if and only if $f(x) = g(x)$ for each $x \in X$.

Part (ii) of the definition of function deserves a bit more comment; it says that a function is "single-valued," or, as we prefer to say, that a function is *well defined*. When attempting to define a function, one must prove that (ii) holds, lest he define only a relation.

If Y is a proper subset of X, then the function i: $Y \to X$ defined by $i(y) = y$ for all $y \in Y$ is called the *inclusion*. If Z is a third set and f: $X \to Z$ is a function, then the restriction of f to Y, denoted $f|Y$, is the composite $f \circ i$.

287

A function $f: X \to Y$ is *one-to-one* if distinct elements of X have distinct images, i.e., if $f(x) = f(x')$, then $x = x'$. This definition may profitably be compared with that of f being well defined, which is the converse: If $x = x'$, then $f(x) = f(x')$. A function $f: X \to Y$ is *onto* if each $y \in Y$ is the image of something in X, i.e., if $y \in Y$, there exists an $x \in X$ with $f(x) = y$. A function $f: X \to Y$ is a *one-to-one correspondence* if it is both one-to-one and onto; such a function always has an *inverse*, i.e., a function $g: Y \to X$ such that $f \circ g$ and $g \circ f$ are identities. One must consider both composites, for $g \circ f = $ identity implies only that g is onto and f is one-to-one.

Two sets X and Y (possibly infinite) *have the same number of elements* if there is a one-to-one correspondence $f: X \to Y$. The reader should exhibit a one-to-one correspondence between X and Y if each has three elements. On the other hand, if Z has four elements, the reader should convince himself that there is no one-to-one correspondence $g: X \to Z$. Let N be the set of positive integers; a set X is *countable* if it is finite or if it has the same number of elements as N. There exist infinite sets that are not countable, e.g., the real numbers.

If X and Y are sets, we write $|X| \leq |Y|$ in case X has the same number of elements as a subset of Y, i.e., there is a function $f: X \to Y$ that is one-to-one (but not necessarily onto). The *Cantor-Bernstein theorem* states that if $|X| \leq |Y|$ and $|Y| \leq |X|$, then $|X| = |Y|$, i.e., X and Y have the same number of elements.

Appendix IV

Zorn's Lemma

Let X be a nonempty set. A binary relation $\leq$ on X is a *partial order* in case:

$$x \leq x;$$
$$x \leq y \quad \text{and} \quad y \leq x \text{ implies } x = y;$$
$$x \leq y \quad \text{and} \quad y \leq z \text{ implies } x \leq z,$$

for all $x, y, z \in X$. The best example of a partially ordered set is a collection of subsets of a set Y, where $\leq$ means $\subset$.

A partial order is a *simple order* (or total order) if, for each $x, y \in X$, either

$$x \leq y \quad \text{or} \quad y \leq x.$$

If X is a partially ordered set, a *chain* is a simply ordered subset. For example, the rational numbers form a chain in the real numbers.

If S is a nonempty subset of X, an *upper bound* of S is an element $x_0 \in X$ (not necessarily in S) such that

$$s \leq x_0 \qquad \text{for all } s \in S.$$

Finally, a *maximal element* in X is an element y_0 which is smaller than no other element in X, i.e., if

$$y_0 \leq x, \quad \text{then } y_0 = x.$$

There are partially ordered sets having many maximal elements, and there are partially ordered sets having no maximal elements.

Zorn's Lemma   Let X be a partially ordered set in which every chain has an upper bound. Then there exists a maximal element in X.

Zorn's lemma is equivalent to a much more intuitive statement, the axiom of choice, which says that the cartesian product of nonempty sets is itself nonempty. We regard either of these statements as an axiom of mathematics, and we shall not be ashamed to use either when necessary. The reader may find a detailed discussion in P. R. Halmos, *Naive Set Theory*, Princeton, Van Nostrand, 1960.

Appendix V

Principal Ideal Domains

We shall let R denote a commutative ring with unit throughout this Appendix.

If $x_1, \cdots, x_k$ are elements of R, let $(x_1, \cdots, x_k)$ denote the set of all linear combinations of the x with coefficients in R:

$$(x_1, \cdots, x_k) = \{\sum r_i x_i : r_i \in R\}.$$

It is easy to check that $(x_1, \cdots, x_k)$ is an ideal.

If a and b are in R, one says that a *divides* b in case $ac = b$ for some $c \in R$. If $x_1, \cdots, x_k$ are in R, a *common divisor* of $x_1, \cdots, x_k$ is an element $c \in R$ that divides each x_i; a *greatest common divisor* (gcd) is a common divisor that is divisible by every common divisor.

A *principal ideal domain* (PID) is a domain in which every ideal is principal. For each ideal I in a PID R, therefore, there is an element $r_0 \in I$ with

$$I = (r_0) = \{rr_0 : r \in R\}.$$

THEOREM A   If R is a PID and if $x_1, \cdots, x_k$ are elements of R, then R contains a gcd of $x_1, \cdots, x_k$, and this gcd is a linear combination of the x.

Proof   Since R is a PID, there is an element $d \in R$ with $(x_1, \cdots, x_k) = (d)$; as any element of $(x_1, \cdots, x_k)$, d is a linear combination of the x. It follows that any common divisor of the x divides d. But d is a common divisor of the x, for each $x_i \in (d)$, so that $x_i = r_i d$ for some $r_i \in R$. Therefore, d is a gcd. ∎

A *unit* in R is an element $u \in R$ that has a multiplicative inverse in R, i.e., there is an element $v \in R$ with $uv = 1$. Two elements a and b in R are *associates* if there is a unit $u \in R$ with $a = ub$.

THEOREM B   Let R be a PID, and let $x_1, \cdots, x_k \in R$. Any two gcd of $x_1, \cdots, x_k$ are associates.

Proof   If a and b are gcd's, then each divides the other. Therefore, $a = ub$ and $b = va$, where $u, v \in R$. Hence, $a = uva$, so that $1 = uv$, since R is a domain. Therefore, u is a unit and a and b are associates. ∎

An element $p \in R$ is *irreducible* in case p is not a unit, and in every factorization $p = ab$, either a or b is a unit.

A domain R is a *unique factorization domain* (UFD) in case:

  (i) Every nonzero $a \in R$ that is not a unit is a product of irreducible elements.

  (ii) If $p_1 \cdots p_m = q_1 \cdots q_n$, where the p and q are irreducibles, then there is a one-to-one correspondence between the factors (i.e., $m = n$) such that corresponding factors are associates.

In short, R is a UFD if the fundamental theorem of arithmetic holds in R.

We wish to prove that if R is a PID, then R is a UFD; our first task is to show that every nonzero $a \in R$ that is not a unit is a product of irreducibles.

LEMMA C   If R is a PID, there is no infinite sequence of ideals

$$I_1 \subsetneq I_2 \subsetneq \cdots \subsetneq I_n \subsetneq I_{n+1} \subsetneq \cdots .$$

Proof   It is easy to check that

$$I = \bigcup_{n=1}^{\infty} I_n$$

is an ideal. Since R is a PID, $I = (d)$ for some $d \in R$. Now d got into I by being in I_n for some n. Hence,

$$I = (d) \subset I_n \underset{\neq}{\subseteq} I_{n+1} \subset I,$$

a contradiction. ∎

LEMMA D   If R is a PID and $a \in R$ is nonzero and not a unit, then a is a product of irreducibles.

Proof   If $a = bc$, where neither b nor c is a unit, then we say that b is a *proper* factor of a. It is easy to check that if b is a proper factor of a, then $(a) \underset{\neq}{\subset} (b)$.

Call a "good" if it is a product of irreducibles; otherwise, a is "bad." If b and c are good, so is their product bc. Thus, if a is bad, a has a proper bad factor. Suppose $a = a_0$ is bad. Assume inductively that there exist $a_0, a_1, \cdots, a_n$ such that each a_{i+1} is a bad, proper factor of a_i. Since a_n is bad, it has a proper, bad factor a_{n+1}. By induction, there is an infinite sequence $a_0, a_1, \cdots$, in which each a_{i+1} is a proper factor of a_i. There is thus an infinite sequence of ideals $(a_0) \underset{\neq}{\subset} (a_1) \underset{\neq}{\subset} \cdots$, and this is a contradiction. Therefore, every nonzero nonunit is good. ∎

An ideal I in R is *prime* in case $ab \in I$ implies that either a or b lies in I; an ideal I is *maximal* in R in case there is no ideal J with $I \underset{\neq}{\subset} J \underset{\neq}{\subset} R$. It is proved in Chapter 8 that every maximal ideal is a prime ideal.

LEMMA E   Let p be an irreducible element in R, where R is a PID; then (p) is a prime ideal.

Proof   Suppose J is an ideal with $(p) \underset{\neq}{\subset} J$. Since R is a PID, $J = (d)$ for some $d \in R$. Therefore $p \in (d)$ and $p = da$ for some $a \in R$. Since p is irreducible, either d or a is a unit. If a is a unit, then $d = a^{-1}p \in (p)$ so that $J = (d) \subset (p)$, a contradiction. Therefore d is a unit and $1 \in (d) = J$ so that $J = R$. It follows that (p) is a maximal ideal; a fortiori, (p) is a prime ideal. ∎

COROLLARY F (*Euclid*)   Let R be a PID and let p be an irreducible element in R. If p divides ab, then p divides a or p divides b.

Proof   If p divides ab, then $ab \in (p)$; since (p) is a prime ideal, either $a \in (p)$ or $b \in (p)$, i.e., p divides a, or p divides b. ∎

THEOREM G (*Fundamental Theorem of Arithmetic*)
If R is a PID, then R is a UFD.

Proof   By Lemma D, every nonzero $a \in R$ that is not a unit is a product of irreducibles.

If $p_1 \cdots p_m = q_1 \cdots q_n$, where the p and q are irreducibles, then p_1 divides $q_1 \cdots q_n$. By iterated applications of Corollary F, p_1 divides some q_j. Since both p_1 and q_j are irreducibles, they must be associates: $p_1 u = q_j$ for some unit u. Since R is a domain,

$$(up_2)p_3 \cdots p_m = \prod_{i \neq j} q_i,$$

and the proof is completed by an induction on $\max\{m,n\}$. ∎

Bibliography

Artin, E., *Geometric Algebra*, New York, Interscience, 1957.

———, *Galois Theory*, South Bend, Notre Dame, 1955.

Birkhoff, G., and S. MacLane, *A Survey of Modern Algebra*, New York, Macmillan, 1941.

Burnside, W., *The Theory of Groups of Finite Order*, New York, Cambridge U. Press, 1911.

Carmichael, R., *An Introduction to the Theory of Groups of Finite Order*, New York, Ginn, 1937.

Coxeter, H. S. M., and Moser, W. O., *Generators and Relations for Discrete Groups*, New York, Springer-Verlag, 1965.

Davis, M., *Computability and Unsolvability*, New York, McGraw-Hill, 1958.

Dickson, L. E., *Linear Groups*, New York, Leipzig, 1900.

Dieudonné, J., *Sur les groupes classiques*, Paris, Hermann, 1958.

Fuchs, L., *Abelian Groups*, New York, Pergamon, 1960.

Hall, Jr., M., *The Theory of Groups*, New York, Macmillan, 1959.

Jacobson, N., *Lectures in Abstract Algebra*, Vols. I and II, Princeton, Van Nostrand, 1951.

Kaplansky, I., *Infinite Abelian Groups*, Ann Arbor, U. of Michigan Press, 1953.

Kurosh, A., *The Theory of Groups*, Vols. I and II, New York, Chelsea, 1956.

Ledermann, W., *Introduction to the Theory of Finite Groups*, London, Oliver and Boyd, 1957.

MacLane, S., *Homology*, New York, Academic, 1963.

Miller, G. A., H. F., Blichfeldt, L. E., Dickson, *Theory and Applications of Finite Groups*, New York, Wiley, 1916.

Specht, W., *Gruppentheorie*, Berlin, Springer-Verlag, 1956.

Van der Waerden, B. L., *Modern Algebra*, New York, Ungar, 1948.

Zassenhaus, H., *The Theory of Groups*, New York, Chelsea, 1956.

Special Notations

I Algebra

E	identity matrix
E_{ij}	square matrix with 1 in i,j position, 0 elsewhere
$GF(q)$	finite field with q elements
K^*	when K is a field, the multiplicative group of nonzero elements of K
$K[x]$	ring of polynomials in x, coefficients in K
Z_n	ring of integers modulo n

II Elementary Group Theory

$\{a_1, \ldots, a_n\}$	set whose elements are $a_1, \ldots, a_n$
$[a_1, \ldots, a_n]$	subgroup generated by $a_1, \ldots, a_n$
ST	$\{st : s \in S \text{ and } t \in T\}$
$S \vee T$	subgroup generated by S and T
$[G:S]$	index of S in G
$|G|$	order of G
$H \lhd G$	H is a normal subgroup of G
(S,T)	subgroup generated by commutators $s^{-1}t^{-1}st$

297

III Subgroups

A. GENERAL GROUPS

G'	commutator subgroup of G
$G^{(i)}$	ith commutator subgroup of G
$Z(G)$	center of G
$Z^i(G)$	ith center of G
$C_G(x)$	centralizer of x in G
$N_G(S)$	normalizer of S in G
$\Phi(G)$	Frattini subgroup of G

B. ABELIAN GROUPS

G_p	p-primary component of G
nG	$\{nx: x \in G\}$
$G[n]$	$\{x \in G: nx = 0\}$
tG	torsion subgroup of G
dG	maximal divisible subgroup of G

IV Constructions

$\sum_{k \in K} A_k,\ \prod_{k \in K} A_k$	when K is finite, both denote the cartesian product
$\prod_{k \in K} A_k$	when K is infinite, the cartesian product
$\sum_{k \in K} A_k$	when K is infinite, the direct sum (almost all coordinates 0)
$A * B$	free product
$K \times_\theta Q$	semidirect product
$(S \mid D)$	group with generators S and relations D

V Special Groups

A_n	alternating group on n letters
A_∞	infinite alternating group

D_n	dihedral group of order $2n$
$GL(m,K)$	general linear group of $m \times m$ matrices over K
$SL(m,K)$	special linear group of $m \times m$ unimodular matrices over K
Z_0	center of $SL(m,K)$
$PSL(m,K)$	projective unimodular group $= SL/Z_0$
Q	quaternions
Q	rationals
Q_n	generalized quaternions of order 2^n
S_n	symmetric group on n letters
S_X	symmetric group on a set X
$\sigma(n)$	cyclic group of order n
$\sigma(p^\infty)$	p-primary component of rationals modulo one
T	circle group
T	nonabelian group of order 12, not A_4, not D_6
V	Klein 4-group
Z	integers

INDEX

Date Due